THE WORLD'S RAILWAYS

AND

HOW THEY WORK

Illustrated with numerous photographs
and specially drawn maps and pictures

ODHAMS PRESS LIMITED · LONG ACRE · LONDON

"Coronation Scot"; the well-known
L.M.S. streamline train at speed

CONTENTS

L.N.E.R. express crossing the Forth Bridge

CHAPTER ONE

TRIUMPHS OF RAILWAY ENGINEERING

THE story of the world's railways, like the railway itself, takes us through every possible kind of climate and country. Although it originated in Great Britain, the steam locomotive has blazed its smoky trail across whole continents.

It was the wood-burning steam engine that opened up the Golden West of America, when the prairie was no more than the haunt of buffalo and the hunting ground of the Redskin. Locomotives of the same primitive type climbed above the clouds over the mighty Andes in search of the mineral wealth of Peru.

In these new countries the railway brought civilization; it was not merely an adjunct of any established social order. But it spread with equal rapidity over the older face of Europe, and even made its way to the Far East, its fiery sparks and whirring wheels awakening a civilization that had slumbered for four thousand years.

Through India and Africa it spread to the Antipodes, the vast network of lines reaching out to become the largest single transport factor in existence. We can travel today in the same coach from Turkestan to the China Seas, or from London to the Near East. The famous Burma Road will soon become a railway; already the modern pilgrim travels by rail to visit his shrine.

Tremendous Mileage

In round figures, the route mileage of track in the world is over three-quarters of a million, more than three times the mean distance from the earth to the moon, but even this fails to give a clear picture of the enormous length of line unless it is linked up with our understanding of time.

Starting in August, and travelling at a mile a minute continuously over all the world's railways, we should journey through autumn and find ourselves celebrating

Christmas with the train still moving. The wheels would carry us on through winter to spring, and summer would find us still far from our destination. So we should travel through the seasons to yet another Christmas and beyond before completing our journey, at a mile a minute, day and night, in just over a year and five months.

This represents the length of line laid, not counting sidings or double track, but mere mileage gives no indication of the difficulties engineers have had to overcome in laying it. Across flat plains, where there are no obstructions, the task is fairly simple, but where mountain ranges or rivers have to be crossed it is one of an altogether different nature.

Gigantic Structures

Some of the structures built to carry the railway across rivers and ravines rank among the engineering triumphs of the world, and it is necessary to change our angle and consider, not the time taken to cross them, but the enormous outlay of time and material in the construction of something which the train passes, perhaps, in a flash.

When an express passes over the Forth Bridge, for example, it is crossing a colossus in which there are fifty-four thousand tons of steel. The height of the cantilevers is three hundred and sixty-one feet, and there are a hundred and fifty-seven feet of clearance under the spans for shipping at high water. Each span is nearly a third of a mile in length, and the two together form the largest pair of cantilever spans in the world.

The steel surfaces on the bridge needing paint are equivalent to one hundred and thirty-five acres, enough to make quite a sizable farm. No fewer than fifty-five tons of paint are required to give it only one coat, and a small army of over forty men is

5

employed continuously to keep it from rust and corrosion.

They scrape and paint their way across it from one side to the other, taking three years in the process, and then go back to the beginning and start all over again.

All this, in our mile-a-minute journey, would have vanished in less than two minutes, and yet it is only a beginning. The train roars on, and viaducts and bridges, cuttings and embankments, tunnels and all the other lineside structures which took years to build, become merely a blurred part of the scenery.

Speed Records

Indeed, with speeds what they are today, we should nearly double our allowance of a full mile to every minute. The time has come on British main lines, anyway, when it is possible to obtain speeds of a hundred miles an hour at will over suitable stretches of track.

These speeds, however, must not be confused with average timings, which represent the time taken from destination to destination, including all stops, speed restrictions and so on, very often given as miles an hour.

The absolute world record with steam is a hundred and twenty-six miles an hour, and was obtained by the British stream-lined locomotive Mallard, when hauling the Coronation train, on a special test run in July, 1938. It covered five miles at an average speed of a hundred and twenty miles an hour.

Another streamlined speedster is the Silver Jubilee, which has twice touched a hundred and twelve while maintaining an average of a hundred miles an hour for forty-three miles on end.

British Loading Gauge

The speeds of these British engines are all the more remarkable when it is realized how small they are compared with the giants of other nations. Their smallness is due to the small loading gauge of British railways, and has nothing to do with the width of the track.

This small loading gauge is a sad misfortune. It was one of the few mistakes of the early pioneers, who, having no conception of the way the railway was going to grow, failed to leave enough room round their tracks.

A British engine cannot be built to much more than thirteen feet above rail level without fouling the tunnels and bridges, and the width is also limited in the same way. It is these limits that are known as the loading gauge.

The space left around locomotives and rolling stock is sometimes very fine. It is the schoolboy's everlasting delight to watch how near the running boards and footplates come to the edge of a platform, and yet never quite touch it.

British engines, then, by a mere accident of fortune, have become marvels of compactness. Beneath their streamlined covering, which is only a husk hiding the sort of engine we all know, they are a mass of finely balanced working parts translating the last ounce of steam pressure into mechanical motion with the absolute minimum of friction.

Impressive American Engines

Because of their greater loading gauge, American engines are larger and, perhaps, more impressive in appearance. As a matter of fact, American engines, such as the famous Big Boy class, hold the world's record for size. So long are these mammoths that they would never negotiate curves in the track if they were not articulated, or built to " bend " in the middle.

Locomotives of this type turn the scale at the enormous weight of three hundred and forty tons. With their tenders they weigh five hundred and thirty odd tons, more than three times as much as their heaviest British rivals, and develop as much as seven thousand horse-power.

British engines, however, still hold the record, not only for speed, but for the world's longest non-stop run. This is the journey of the famous Flying Scotsman between London and Edinburgh, covering a distance of three hundred and ninety-three miles.

Locomotive building is fascinating in the extreme. Methods of construction differ slightly in different parts of the world, but the underlying principle is the same.

The foundation for the boiler and the

LARGEST STEAM LOCOMOTIVE IN THE WORLD. One of America's huge freight engines, built on a flexible frame so that it will negotiate curves. The boiler is rigid but the frame is built in two parts and hinged in the middle. There are two cylinder blocks, one in the normal position near the front of the frame, and one halfway towards the cab. The locomotive is really two engines under one boiler.

working parts consists of two main frames of steel plate, about one-and-a-quarter inches in thickness. These are set on edge and strongly braced to form a massive framework, strong enough to withstand by a considerable margin the enormous strain it has to undergo.

Fixing the Barrel

To this framework the cylinder and valve-chest castings are bolted, and the boiler is carried on it at the smoke-box and fire-box ends, with the barrel suspended between them.

It is not always realized that the boiler barrel itself is never visible in the finished locomotive. What is seen is the metal covering that goes over the lagging, a form of fire-proof wool which is first placed over the boiler to conserve heat.

The main frames are nearly always visible at the front end of the engine,

extending as two knife-edges from below the smoke-box to the buffer-beam, and portions of them are seen also at the sides, extending along the engine back to the cab. In certain countries, chiefly America, the preference is for frames of cast steel, often cast in one piece with the cylinders and valve-chests.

The construction is the same whether the locomotive is intended for standard or narrow gauge track, save that a small gauge locomotive usually has more over-hang.

The wheels are set closer together, with shorter axles, but the frames are given more width in proportion.

Narrow-Gauge Track

This is done to obtain as much carrying capacity as possible, particularly in the rolling stock, for the narrow-gauge engine is not a model, but a very real locomotive,

1 MAKING SAND MOULD FOR CYLINDERS

2 POURING METAL INTO MOULDS

CRUCIBLE

CORES

POURING BOX

FLASHES

MOULD BOXES

6 WHEEL TRUING AND QUARTERING

CRANKS

7 MAIN FRAMES MARKED FOR CENTRES

8 FRAMES SET UP INSIDE CYLINDERS FITTED

9 OUTSIDE CYLINDERS AND MOTIONS FITTED BOILER LOWERED

Progressive Stages in the
MANUFACTURE OF A STEAM LOCOMOTIVE

CYLINDER CASTING

CYLINDER

3 BORING PISTON VALVES

REAMER

BOILER WELL

5 FRAME CUTTING BY OXY-COAL GAS FLAME

NON-CONDUCTING COMPOSITION

4 HYDRAULIC RIVETER FOR BOILER PLATES

BOILER CASING

10 WHEELING

DUMMY BOGIE

11 FINAL STAGE—PAINTED AND LINED READY FOR SERVICE

ASHWELL WOOD

having certain advantages over the standard gauge engine in well defined conditions.

The chief advantage lies in the fact that narrow-gauge track is both cheaper and easier to lay, and has the additional value of being more flexible in that it can be laid to a smaller radius on the curves.

That is why there is such a preference for narrow-gauge track in mountainous country, where the line winds and twists sometimes in an almost unbelievable fashion. Serious and important railway systems, covering thousands of miles, have been laid to gauges of less than two feet.

Standard Gauge

Standard-gauge track is found in Great Britain and over most of Western Europe, except Spain, and in Canada, the United States of America and many parts of South America. On this gauge the rails are set four feet eight-and-a-half inches apart.

In South Africa and many parts of the African continent the main gauge is three feet six inches, and in India it varies from a broad gauge of five feet six inches to the extremely narrow gauge of one foot eleven-and-a-half inches. The Russian gauge is five feet exactly, it being the policy of the U.S.S.R. to build railroads of a different gauge from all those of neighbouring countries, so that in times of war it is impossible for any enemy to use his own locomotives and rolling stock on the Russian railways. The Russian loading gauge, incidentally, is the largest in the world.

One of the great disadvantages of different gauges is the obvious fact that, wherever tracks of different width happen to meet, there can be no through-running of trains. This is not so awkward as far as passengers are concerned, although it means a change of train, but there is an enormous waste of time and money in the unloading and reloading of freight.

Mixed Gauges

The most outstanding example of this is found in Australia, where the transcontinental track across the southern part of the continent is of two different gauges. This track started off as two separate railways in the days, not so long ago,

10

NARROW-GAUGE LOCOMOTIVE. J class steam engine built entirely in New Zealand to suit local conditions. An interesting point about it is that it is designed for the narrow gauge of three

when each State claimed the right to lay its railways to whatever gauge it pleased, and nobody, apparently, saw the possibility of linking the whole continent with one railway system.

Another curious example occurs in the Dutch island of Java, where the State lines are on the three-foot-six-inch gauge, and are grouped at the two ends the island, with a private line on standard gauge in between. To get over the difficulty, a

feet six inches. New Zealand engines have some steep gradients to surmount in the mountainous interior of the country, notably on the famous Rimutaka incline, where heavy freight trains sometimes need the assistance of as many as five engines. Although at first glance it looks so formidable, it is not an unusually powerful engine by modern standards and is by no means the largest of New Zealand types.

second pair of rails was laid between the standard track, so that now trains of both standard and narrow gauge can run over what is, in effect, the same track.

The main object in railway building is to keep the track as straight and level as possible, and where the terrain is really mountainous, as in Switzerland, it would seem the engineer must despair of ever achieving it.

But obstructions, to the constructive mind, are merely an incentive to further effort, and railway engineers so far have not shown themselves to be daunted at finding a mere mountain in the way. To keep the track really flat, of course, where the object is to climb to a higher level, is impossible, but some ingenious feats have been performed to keep the gradients gentle enough for ordinary working.

Most famous of these is the spiral curve, by which the engineer gains height where

there are abrupt changes of level. The spiral gives a longer track and keeps the gradient to permissible proportions.

Some such spirals in Switzerland and the Himalayas double back and forth in a bewildering manner. The train passes backwards and forwards over its own track until the ordinary passenger is hard put to it to know whether he is going or coming.

After a long climb, he finds himself crossing a bridge which a while ago he was passing under, and to add to his

bewilderment the train is now going in the opposite direction. In addition, the track may be clinging to a precarious foothold which appears to be carved out of the side of a sheer precipice.

Spiral Tunnel

More surprising still is the spiral tunnel. In places in Switzerland it is possible to see three different track levels almost one above the other. The train enters a tunnel at one level, climbs as it is following the spiral in the solid rock, and comes out well

SPIRAL CONSTRUCTION IN THE ALPS. One of the engineer's favourite tricks for gaining height without making the gradient too steep for normal working. The whole object is to lengthen the line in proportion to the height it must rise so that the rise is as gradual as possible. In the example illustrated, advantage has been taken of a natural slope in the ground that begins where the line comes under the viaduct, after which an embankment is necessary as a viaduct approach. This spiral is on the Bernina Railway line at Brusio, in Switzerland·

that the locomotive must have before it can exert any tractive effort. It is with the object of increasing this grip that driving wheels are coupled together.

Rack-and-Pinion Railways

When the gradient is too steep for adhesion alone, however, the rack-and-pinion type of railway is used. This consists in most cases of an ingenious third rail, toothed so that it will grip a cog-wheel, and laid in the centre of the ordinary track. On many sharp inclines, particularly in South America, the track is arranged so that locomotives which haul on the adhesion principle can run on to and connect with the cogwheel track.

Many ingenious systems of braking have been devised for safety on mountain railways. The most notable is a brake that acts directly on the rails like a pair of tongs, coming into operation automatically if anything goes wrong, but this is used mainly on tracks worked on the funicular principle.

Funicular railways are the steepest of all that use a normal, or nearly normal, track. In some cases the track is inclined at an angle of all but forty-five degrees, so that it has somewhat the appearance of a ladder up the mountainside. Obviously, some very special apparatus must be used on a railway of this sort, for at such an angle the coach floor has to be built in a series of steps.

Rope Haulage

Single track is usually used with a passing loop in the middle for two cars worked by rope haulage. The rope passes over a drum at the top station, and the cars balance

above the height of the entrance. Then it crosses the valley and enters yet another tunnel, repeats the performance and rises higher still.

But even these tricks fail at times. Sometimes it is either impossible practically, or unwise financially, to build such a long track as spirals require, and then the whole principle of adhesion has to be abandoned.

The adhesion method of working is simply that of allowing the weight of the engine, acting through the wheels, to supply the necessary grip on the rails

FAMOUS FIGURE-EIGHT LOOP ON DARJEELING-HIMALAYA RAILWAY. An interesting example of spiral construction. The line is laid on a narrow gauge of just under two feet, making much sharper curves possible than on standard gauge track, and on this particular section of the route trains make two complete circles. Part of the track of the lower circle can be seen on the extreme right. From here it passes right round behind the hill to the left, well outside the scope of this photograph, and

returns alongside the wall seen on the left just in front of and below the train. Here it passes under the track of the upper circle, and emerges from a short arch behind the tree in the foreground. It can be seen again to the right of the tree, now commencing the upper circle, which is completed when it crosses the bridge just ahead of the train. The mouth of the tunnel is just visible below the upper track. The sharpest curve is on the final spiral, or loop, and is known as Agony Point.

DIESEL-ELECTRIC SHUNTER. A Diesel-electric shunting engine on the Reading Railroad of the U.S.A. Because the oil engine is so easily serviced and fuelled, the Diesel-electric type of locomotive has a working day of nearly twenty-four hours' duration. It is thus one of the cheapest engines to run and is particularly suitable for use in a country where oil is the most economical type of fuel.

each other, one descending as the other slowly rises.

There is still a third method of carrying cars to high mountain fastnesses, although it does not rightly fall into the railway category, having no track at all in the usual sense of the term. It is the télépherique, or suspension line, which swings its passengers up steeply inclined cableways, in places across yawning gorges and at times with no intermediate support over distances as great as a mile.

Solving Height Problems

Cableways of this description are to be found all over the world. They solve the problem of gaining height rapidly, but are not to be recommended to anyone suffering from nerves.

The character of the railway, as it has been built up during the first hundred years, is

slowly but surely changing. For the steam engine, which has served it faithfully and well, is no longer sole monarch of the rail.

Its rival is electricity, and with the coming of electrical power some of the familiar adjuncts of steam are disappearing.

Use of Electricity

No longer are coal and soot inseparable from the iron trail. Vast hydro-electric schemes in many countries have brought into being electrical energy made by the clean power of water, and the electric locomotive has proved itself a master of swift and heavy haulage. It has the advantage over steam that its power is almost unlimited, and the control is smooth and easy no matter how vast the power.

Electric locomotives have the additional attraction of swift acceleration, and the use of electricity brings with it the possibility of innumerable advantages in signalling. The old quadrant arms of early signalling systems have vanished altogether from some lines, and all-electric automatic light signals have taken their place.

It has been proved that the light signals can be seen by day as well as by night, and that being so, the wastage of effort in the use of mechanical signalling where electricity is obtainable is inexcusable.

In modern British and American station layouts, the movement of two thumb switches and an illuminated track diagram is sufficient to line up the entire series of tracks by which any train is going to enter and leave. Thus an operation is completed in a few

seconds, which formerly would have involved a sequence of manual lever movements in several different cabins.

On the London tubes, trains even signal themselves automatically, and if any train should attempt to pass a stop signal at danger, automatic devices are in use to cut off the current, apply the brakes and bring it to a standstill.

Automatic Marshalling

Electricity is also used in marshalling yards, where the wagons are sorted for their destinations. Sorting is now automatic, for once its destination has been checked and uncoupling carried out, each wagon

AMERICAN STREAMLINING. One of the Hudson type steam locomotives of the New York Central System which pull the famous Twentieth Century Limited between New York and Chicago. These engines develop more than four thousand seven hundred horse-power at a speed of seventy-five miles an hour. Although not by any means the largest of American locomotives, they are fitted with mechanical stoking apparatus.

2 CLEARING THE SITE

LEVEL

CHAIN OFFSETS FROM ORDNANCE SURVEY

3 EXCAVATING CUTTINGS

PROPOSED SITE

SIGHTING POSTS

THEODOLITE

1 CHAIN SURVEYING

DRAINS

CONTRACTORS LINES

SECTION OF STANDARD TRACK

TWO BOLT FISH PLATE

8 TRACK LAYING

KEY

CHAIR

CHAIR SCREW

ASSEMBLED 60 FT. TRACK LENGTHS

10 SIGNAL BOXES AND GROUND FRAMES BUILT

9 FENCING

11 POINT MACHINES AND SIGNAL CIRCUITS PUT IN

BUILDING
A RAILWAY
*From Surveying to
the Finished Track*

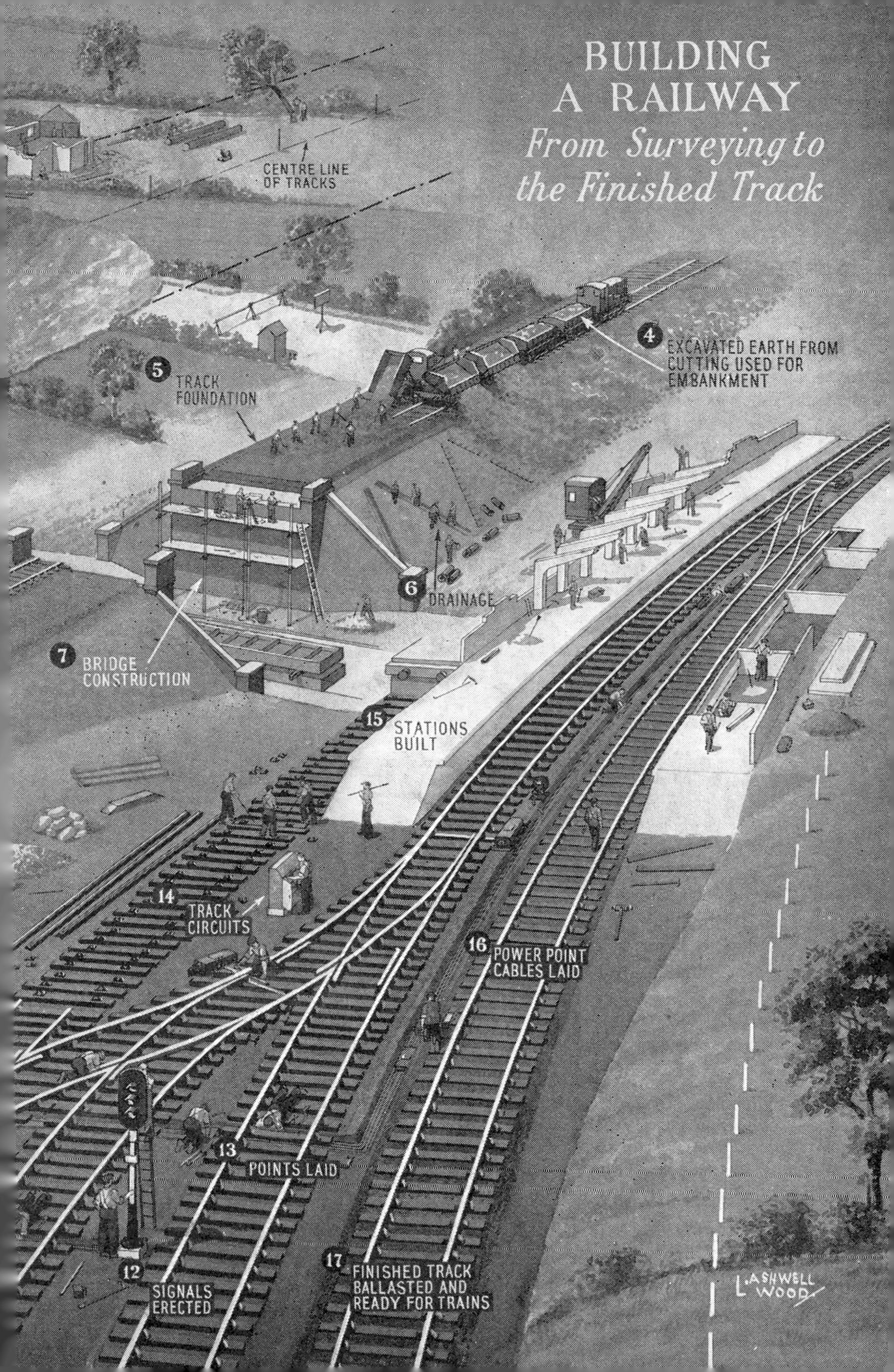

CENTRE LINE OF TRACKS

4 EXCAVATED EARTH FROM CUTTING USED FOR EMBANKMENT

5 TRACK FOUNDATION

6 DRAINAGE

7 BRIDGE CONSTRUCTION

15 STATIONS BUILT

14 TRACK CIRCUITS

16 POWER POINT CABLES LAID

13 POINTS LAID

12 SIGNALS ERECTED

17 FINISHED TRACK BALLASTED AND READY FOR TRAINS

L. ASHWELL WOOD

as it runs into its correct siding sets the switches for the next wagon behind.

With the improvement and still wider application of such automatic devices, and with radio communication from signal cabin to footplate, train to train or driver to train crew, railway operation in the future will be almost unrecognizable.

But although electricity has such advantages, there are cases where the use of a central power station is uneconomical, as, for instance, over long-distance routes, or where there is no cheap water supply. The most modern of all forms of railway transport is the Diesel-electric, in which the locomotive carries its own power station, thereby cutting out the cost of transmitting power over long distances.

The source of power is the crude-oil engine, which drives a generator, and the current so produced is used in turn to drive electric traction motors in the same manner as on an electric locomotive.

Diesel Shunting Engines

In some cases the oil engine is coupled direct to the driving wheels, as on the direct-drive shunting engines, a type of Diesel locomotive that is used in small powers.

Needing surprisingly little attention, and using very little fuel, the Diesel shunter is prepared to work uncomplainingly for twenty-four hours a day, taking fuel, perhaps, every third day, and requiring inspection only once a week or less.

But in the larger sizes, direct drive is more difficult. Like all internal combustion engines, the Diesel engine needs a clutch and gear-box if the drive is to be transmitted to the wheels mechanically, and where the power is large and the train is heavy, the shock of letting in the clutch is too great. Either the train must leap forward in response, or something will smash in the engine.

So the electric generator and motor are introduced for the sake of smooth and easy transmission, and the Diesel-electric locomotive is at once a source of immense and flexible power, capable of almost indefinite runs. Indeed, it is nothing uncommon to run the big American Diesels at very high speed for over two thousand miles without

change. Crews are changed at divisional points, but the locomotive carries on.

Sometimes a number of such engines are coupled together, becoming concentrated power stations of two, three or four units, with an output of four or six thousand horse-power. They haul trains of as many as fifteen luxury coaches at speeds up to a hundred miles an hour, or heavy freight trains of a hundred wagons at little short of a mile a minute.

Streamlined Flyers

With streamlined flyers, stainless steel coaches, lounge chairs and observation cars, sleeping, dining and light refreshment cars, not to mention such amenities as a library and radio programme, the modern long-distance express is like a moving hotel.

Gone are the days when passengers sat in dusty compartments and wearied of the journey, while the snorting steam engine dragged its weary length over vast distances, making frequent stops for fuel and water, when the travellers were glad of a chance to stretch their legs. Gone, too, is winter's penetrating cold and summer's stifling heat, at least from the interior of air-conditioned coaches.

The modern flyers travel the same routes, and they eat up the miles of gleaming track at speeds the original builders would have regarded as impossible. And, curiously enough, as journeys become shorter, so they become more comfortable.

Modern Railway Achievements

The railway of today reveals many of the greatest engineering achievements of all time. It flings its bridges across deep gorges and rivers, sometimes in face of incredible difficulties, and burrows through solid rock under whole mountains.

All over the world it is giving unceasing service in the transport of passengers and goods. Many countries in the world have contributed to its efficiency, but none more so than Great Britain, in which country, over a hundred years ago, the first steam locomotive made its appearance, startling the beholders with its fire and smoke and hissing pistons, and it is only fitting that we should learn in the following pages more of its adventures in the land of its birth.

FUNICULAR CABLE WORKED

1 in 1⅛ LIMIT

1 in 2 LIMIT

RACK AND PINION SINGLE COACH

1 in 8

RACK AND PINION – LIMIT FOR TRAINS

LIMIT OF ADHESION TRACTION

1 in 11

1 in 70

MAIN LINE WORKING

L ASHWELL WOOD

RAILWAY GRADIENTS CONTRASTED. A composite drawing showing the main limits. It is interesting to note that the least of these in appearance is a considerable slope for an ordinary locomotive. The one shown, of a gradient of one-in-seventy, is about half as steep as the steepest gradient in Britain, known as the Lickey gradient. The steepest shown above, is almost at an angle of forty-five degrees.

21

Duchess of Gloucester, a Coronation class
locomotive, backing on to an express at Euston

CHAPTER TWO

BRITAIN:
CRADLE OF THE LOCOMOTIVE

ON a pedestal at Bank Top Station, Darlington, stands what ought to be the most famous locomotive in the world. It is the historic engine Locomotion No. 1, which pulled the first train on the first railway ever opened to the general public.

It made its first run in the decade following the battle of Waterloo, two years before the celebrated adventures of the Pickwick Club began, and vied for supremacy with the stage coach and the postillion.

Those days seem very distant from the present atomic age, but they are distant only by the rapid march of events. In time, it is only just over a century since Locomotion No. 1 established the principle of lighting a fire to pull a coach along—not long in man's history of achievement.

Twelve Miles an Hour!

George Stephenson was its designer, and was himself in charge on the footplate, and the railway was that between Stockton and Darlington, in the county of Durham.

Crowds had lined the track to witness the great innovation. The primitive engine and its tender weighed only six-and-a-half tons, but it pulled a line of thirty-eight wagons behind it, filled with the privileged and more adventurous members of the community. Clanking over the rough track of the time, it is reputed to have reached a speed of twelve miles an hour, to the amazement of all beholders.

Contrast this redoubtable pioneer, with its tall chimney supported by backstays, with the streamlined Silver Jubilee engine. There could hardly be a greater difference between two types. The Silver Jubilee, with its long, sleek, streamlined covering, enormous power and speed of over a hundred miles an hour, seems to belong to another planet.

This modern mammoth made its first run a hundred and ten years to the day after that of Locomotion No. 1, pulling out of King's Cross on 27th September, 1935, and opening a non-stop service over the two hundred miles of railway line between London and Darlington.

Internal Streamlining

Many features of locomotive design have combined to make possible the high speeds of today. Curiously enough, however, the external streamlining of the engine and train are not the most important. The most vital contribution is what might be termed internal streamlining, or the provision of the smoothest possible path for the steam in order to reduce friction.

This has been done by enlarging the diameter of steam pipes and providing smooth curves in place of sharp bends.

Incidentally, it is a common fallacy that you can see steam. In actual fact, however, pure steam is invisible. It is a gas, and has all the physical properties of one. What is seen when white steam hisses into the air is steam condensate.

In spite of the vast differences between modern engines and the early locomotive, however, there are two principles of design that have survived since George Stephenson's day. One is the provision of a multi-tubular boiler, and the other is the turning of the spent steam into the chimney to make a forced draught for the fire. It is these puffs of steam in the chimney that give all steam locomotives their characteristic "chuffing" sound.

Generation of Steam

Each principle is best explained in its correct order, and it is necessary first to see how steam is generated and used to make the wheels go round.

Everybody knows the general idea, which is that the fire boils the water and

LOCOMOTION No. 1. An exact replica of the pioneer train that started it all! This full-size train, headed by the original locomotive, was arranged for the railway centenary celebrations in Britain and is shown on the original route. In spite of the complicated arrangement of vertical pistons and connecting rods, Locomotion No. 1 surprised everybody with a speed of twelve miles an hour.

generates steam, and the steam exerts a pressure on the pistons, which are connected to and turn the driving wheels. But it is not so generally appreciated that this means that it is really the heat that is producing the effect.

Boiler Details

The locomotive boiler has three divisions, fire-box, barrel and smoke-box. It is really a long barrel with a box at each end. The boxes support the barrel on the main frames, and in one of them burns the fire, while in the other the smoke and spent steam are collected and ejected through the chimney.

The fire-box, however, is really two boxes, one inside the other. Between the two there is a space for water, and the inner fire-box holds the grate, so that the fire is almost surrounded by water.

The fuel lies on a grate at the bottom of

the inner fire-box, below which is an ash-pan with dampers to control the draught. Above the grate is a curved brick arch, which makes an intensely hot chamber for combustion purposes. The hotter the fire can be kept, the more completely is the fuel burned without wasting itself as smoke.

It is in the fire-box part of the boiler that most of the steam is generated. Hundreds of staybolts keep the walls of the inner and outer fire-boxes at their correct distance apart, and resist the tendency of the enormous steam pressure to bend them out of shape.

Safety Indicator

An ever-present danger with a steam engine is that the pressure may rise and cause a boiler explosion, but pressures rise only with an increase of heat. Consequently, as long as the heat remains constant, the steam pressure will do likewise, even though no steam is being taken from the boiler.

But the temperature rises rapidly if the water level sinks below the crown of the inner fire-box, for then the crown becomes red-hot, and is in contact with steam instead of water. So the gauge glass fitted on the back of the outer fire-box, in the cab, is intended to do more than tell the driver when he has run out of water. It acts as a very definite indication of the level below which the water must not drop.

Further Precaution

As a further precaution, a plug of easily fusible metal is fitted in the crown of the inner fire-box, so that if the latter overheats, the plug melts and lets a jet of steam hiss downwards on to the fire, damping it down and eventually putting it out.

The front plate of the inner fire-box, known as the tube-plate, is pierced with a number of holes, and into these the tubes are fitted which go right through the barrel to a similar tube-plate in the smoke-box. In this way the heat of the fire is carried through the rest of the water by smoke tubes of small diameter, giving the greatest possible area of heating surface, and taking up the least amount of room.

Rapid Steaming

Without any deep calculations, it can be seen that this multi-tubular arrangement makes for rapid steaming. Not only is the heat of the fire split up and carried in small portions to every layer or particle of water, but smaller tubes can be made with thinner walls, because there is not the area for the steam to act upon, and consequently not the same strain; thus the heat in the tube penetrates more surely to the water.

So George Stephenson hit on an excellent idea right at the start, the only trouble

OVER A CENTURY AFTER. The famous L.N.E.R. streamliner Silver Jubilee, which made its trial run exactly a hundred and ten years after Locomotion No. 1, reaching a speed of a hundred miles an hour. Although it did not cause quite such a sensation as its earlier prototype, the record set up was an important milestone in railway history. This was one of the first British engines to be streamlined.

being that he needed a strong draught to make sure the gases of combustion would travel through these horizontal fire tubes. To obtain this he turned the exhaust steam, after it had been used in the cylinders, up the chimney, the strong puffs creating a suction behind them which drew fresh air through the fire. These are the two principles which were so successful that they have been used right up to the present day.

The puffs are ejected by what is known as the blast pipe, a vertical pipe in the centre of the smoke-box exactly under the chimney. The blast pipe is tapering like a nozzle, so that the exhaust steam rushes out with force and creates as strong a suction as possible.

When an engine is working hard, the suction may be strong enough to draw sparks from the fire and shoot them into the air. But such firework displays are not the best of advertisements for the efficiency of the engine, as they represent fuel being thrown away without being properly consumed.

But the steam has to do something more than draw up the fire, and before it is taken to the cylinders, it is customary to pass it through a superheater.

Superheating

This consists of a nest of small steam tubes led to and fro in larger fire tubes in the boiler, and in these it is raised to a temperature of six or seven hundred degrees Fahrenheit. This not only dries the steam out of contact with the water, but raises it to such a highly gaseous condition that it can be expanded through a greater range. The greater the expansive property of the steam, the greater the efficiency of the engine.

The superheated steam is led smoothly by a pipe of large diameter to the cylinders, and these, with their pistons, piston rods and connecting rods to the driving wheels, are the prime movers of the whole mechanism.

Just as the steam translates the heat energy of the fire into pressure, so the cylinders and pistons translate the pressure of the steam into mechanical motion.

In simple language, a cylinder is a tube with closed ends, and the piston is a plug

which slides to and fro inside it, fitting closely enough to the sides to be steam tight. Attached to the piston is a rod, which passes through a steam-tight gland at one end and is joined to the driving wheels by the connecting rod.

The entry of steam at one end of the cylinder drives the piston to the other end, thereby turning the wheels, and by a suitable arrangement of valves the steam is cut off at the right moment and exhausted into the chimney.

Cycle of Operations

Then steam is admitted at the other end of the cylinder, forcing the piston back again, and that completes one revolution of the wheels, or cycle of operations.

This means that for every revolution of the wheels on one side of the engine, in a simple two-cylinder locomotive, there are two puffs of steam, and two puffs of steam similarly for every revolution on the other side. But as the pistons are so arranged, for the sake of balance, that one is in the middle of its stroke while the other is just beginning, the two puffs become four, taken alternately from each side during one revolution of the driving wheels.

The more impulses that can be given to a wheel during one turn, the more smoothly it revolves. Besides this, there is the important factor of balancing the heavy moving parts, rotating and reciprocating, and one of the means used to achieve this end is seen in the heavy weights attached to the rims of driving wheels. The weight, revolving, acts as a counterbalance to the to-and-fro movement of the piston.

The Slide Valve

The valves used to admit and exhaust the steam can be of several types, but the one that has lasted longest, although it is not the most efficient for high pressures, is the slide valve.

This is in shape like a flat box sliding backwards and forwards in a steam chest. The open side of the box is turned downwards, so that its edges glide over a flat surface in which there are slots, known as ports, giving access to the cylinder.

The pressure of the steam in the chest keeps the box tight down on the flat surface,

ENGINEER'S EXAMINATION. An engineer testing fire-box stays with the binaural apparatus. This is very like a doctor's stethoscope. It is worn in the same way and works on the same principle, save that the "chest" is tapped with a hammer. According to the ring of the metal, so the engineer makes his diagnosis. The testing needle is held in contact with the head of the rivet during examination.

and as it slides it uncovers first one slot and then the other, admitting steam to each end of the cylinder in turn. There is a third slot in the middle, and in the same movement, as it slides, not only is fresh steam admitted at one end, but the slot at the other is connected with that in the middle, so that the used steam can get under the box and escape through the middle slot, or exhaust port, to the open air.

This simple piece of mechanism is surprisingly efficient, its chief disadvantage being that with high pressures it is forced down too tightly on the face of the steam chest, although, of course, to counteract this tendency while working, there is always the used steam underneath it, and this still has a certain amount of pressure.

Expansive Working

This brings us to the expansive property of steam, without the use of which the locomotive would be very inefficient. It was James Watt who first saw the possibility of expansive working, long before Stephenson built the locomotive, and although vast improvements have been made in the mechanical and scientific application of it, nothing new in principle has been added since his time.

Expansive working can be explained very simply in a few words. Because steam has this quality of expansion, it is unnecessary to admit it for the whole of the piston stroke. Indeed, it is inadvisable to do so, for the piston would suffer a violent jar if it came to a sudden stop with the full force of the steam behind it.

Adjustment of Cut-off

So steam is cut off considerably before the end of the stroke, and continues its work by expansion, the pressure decreasing gradually as it expands. This makes for smooth and efficient working, and the exact point of cut-off can be varied by the driver.

At starting, to overcome the inertia of the heavy train, he admits steam for as much as three-quarters of the stroke, so that there is very little expansion, and the steam, still at high pressure, is coughed out violently through the exhaust.

A few more blasts of this nature, making the fire leap and getting the train in motion,

and he notches up, or reduces the cut-off, and as the engine gathers speed he reduces it still more until the train, travelling almost under its own momentum, needs only the slightest impulses to keep it going.

At full speed, with the exhaust coming almost in a purr, steam may be admitted for less than a sixth of the piston stroke, the rapid expansion of this small amount of high-pressure steam being sufficient to keep the mammoth moving.

This is what gives efficiency, for the steam is being used fully and not wasted at high pressure, and it is in the intelligent use of the expansion gear, and in the variation of the size of the regulator opening, through which the steam passes from the boiler into the main steam pipe, that the greatest skill of the driver is called into play.

That is a description of what may be called a typical locomotive, but there is great variation in detail with different classes, in the size, number and arrangement of cylinders, types of valves and fire-boxes, and, above all, in the wheel arrangement.

Wheel Arrangements

The arrangement and size of the wheels govern the work that any particular type of locomotive is expected to do. For high speeds on fast passenger services, driving wheels with a diameter as great as seven feet are used, whereas on the hard-pulling freight engines the wheels may be well under five feet. Between the two are the mixed freight or passenger types, with a fair speed yet good tractive power.

The wheels are coupled together to increase the grip of the locomotive on the rails. Six coupled wheels, three each side, on passenger engines and eight coupled wheels on heavy freight engines are usual, although there are many six-coupled goods engines and four-coupled passenger engines still in use. But the day of the single-driver, an express engine with one large pair of driving wheels only, some of them as much as eight feet in diameter, is definitely at an end, and the only remaining examples are museum pieces.

Distinct from the driving wheels are the smaller carrying wheels used to spread the weight of the locomotive over the track.

FIRE-BOX, SMOKE-BOX AND BARREL ASSEMBLED. An advanced stage in loco-motive construction. Note the hundreds of rivets and staybolt heads on the Belpaire type fire-box, also the various valves and instruments fixed to the back-plate above the fire-doors and the firing hole. These doors are made to slide open side-ways, and the handle which controls them can be seen on the left-hand door.

Only a certain amount of weight can be allowed to fall on any particular point of the track but, conversely, an engine is limited in rigid length or it would not get round the curves.

Bogies

For this reason, carrying wheels are frequently made to swivel, and many express engines have a separate four-wheeled truck, known as a bogie, pivoted under the smoke-box, and this helps to guide it smoothly on a curve. Other types have a single pair of swivelling wheels in front, while the big Pacifics have an addi-tional pair under the cab, so that the whole length of the wheel base is as flexible as possible.

An engine is usually known by its wheel arrangement, and there is a simple system of numbers by which this can be easily described. Three numbers are used, the first for the leading wheels, the next for the driving wheels and the third for the trailing

wheels. An engine with a four-wheeled leading bogie, six coupled driving wheels and a single trailing axle would, therefore, be known as a 4-6-2; if, on the contrary, it had only the driving wheels, it would be an 0-6-0, and so on.

There is not so much variation in the types of valve and link motion, although there are three distinct valve types and two main types of gear. The gear or link motion is the mechanical means by which valves are operated.

Piston and Poppet Valves

In addition to the slide valve, there are piston and poppet valves. The piston valve, as its name suggests, is a form of piston working in a smaller cylinder alongside the driving cylinder, uncovering inlet and outlet ports in much the same simple manner as the slide valve.

Poppet valves, however, are entirely different. These lift to admit steam instead of sliding, and are supposed to be much

ASSEMBLING THE LOCOMOTIVE. Lowering the boiler and frame, complete with cylinder blocks, on to the wheels. The latter are on rails over an inspection pit so that the fitters can get at them after the main frame and boiler are in position. When the valve motion and boiler fittings are assembled, the locomotive will be practically complete. Enormous hooks support it from the overhead crane.

BOGIE CONSTRUCTION. The illustration shows the bogie of a G.W.R. King class locomotive. It is the only British type having outside bearings to the front wheels and inside bearings to the back wheels. The main weight of the locomotive is taken by the two side cup-and-ball bearings, one of which is shown separately on the ground. The bogie is held in position, however, by the central pivot.

more rapid in their action. The usual method of working them is by a camshaft, and only a few British engines, such as the Hunt class, have been fitted with them, whereas piston valves are becoming standard practice on all modern high-pressure locomotives.

Pressure is calculated as so many pounds to the square inch, and a pressure of two hundred pounds, therefore, means that every square inch of the boiler shell needs to be capable of resisting this enormous force. With every increase of pressure, the boiler must be of stronger construction, and pressures have risen today in Britain to as much as two hundred and eighty pounds. This is the working pressure of the Merchant Navy class engines, but nearly all the principal express classes work at not less than two hundred and fifty.

Most of them, too, use three or four cylinders, chiefly because the narrow limitations of the British construction gauge make it difficult to find room for two cylinders big enough to develop sufficient power.

Another kind of three-cylinder or four-cylinder propulsion is known as compounding. In compound locomotives the steam, after expanding in the first or high-pressure cylinder, is led on to a second, low-pressure cylinder, in which the same quantity of steam is allowed to expand still further, and do more useful work before being ejected through the exhaust.

Locomotives differ in many other points of working or arrangement, chiefly in the shape of the fire-box and whether they are built as tender or tank engines.

Some fire-boxes are round on top, conforming to the curve of the boiler, while others are of the Belpaire type, which has

COGWHEEL TRACK ON BRITISH MOUNTAIN RAILWAY. The famous Snowdon line in North Wales is a narrow-gauge line with special equipment for steep gradients. The two hand brakes of the small locomotive can be seen at the back of the driving cab. The coaches are open at the top, with curtains for use in bad weather, and there are doors below—a striking contrast with modern main-line comfort.

straight sides and a flat top. This is regarded as a simpler type of fire-box in which to arrange the staybolts. Bigger engines, like the Pacifics, sometimes have wide fire-boxes that spread outwards from top to bottom, and are carried across the main frames.

Engines for short distance and shunting work are frequently built without separate tenders. Their water supply is carried in flat, side tanks on each side of the boiler, and the coal is in a bunker behind the cab. These are the famous tank engines of British railways, a very sturdy and useful type in their native land, but not much used in other countries. In America, for instance, they are almost unknown.

British Tank Engines

Tank engines in Britain, however, have a wide variety of uses, as is shown by their many wheel arrangements. Here is a list of wheel arrangements and the work that the

different types are called upon to do : for suburban runs or short main line runs, 2-6-4 and 2-6-2; for general suburban lines, 0-6-2 and 2-4-2 ; for shunting, 0-6-0; for heavy freight and marshalling work, 2-8-2, 2-8-0, 0-8-4 and many others.

Types of Valve Gear

Another important difference between types lies in the gear used to operate the valves. The original valve gear, still used on some of the older engines, was designed by Stephenson, and consists of two eccentrics, or wheels offset from their centre, so that as the shaft rotates they impart a reciprocating movement to two rods attached to a sliding link. The driver has control of this link which, as it slides, both alters the cut-off and acts as a reversing gear. Needless to say, it is connected to the valve rod.

The other type of valve gear, which is coming more and more into favour, is the

Belgian Walschaerts motion, which is mounted on the outside of the engine, where its action can be clearly followed. It derives its movement from the piston rod and crank.

The locomotive is a hard-working piece of machinery, but it cannot keep working for twenty-four hours every day. Every engine, therefore, is assigned to a shed or depot, where it receives the attention necessary to keep it in good running order. It has to be cleaned, the boiler needs wash-ing out, the smoke-box and flues are swept and even minor repairs are made.

Each locomotive, too, carries its own shed number on it, as a fully qualified resident. On the L.M.S., for example, there is a small plate on the upper part of the door of the smoke-box, just below the engine number, and on this appear a number and a letter. The number indicates the district to which the engine belongs, and the letter the shed.

At the end of a hard day's work, however, it may not be possible for it to return to its

BRITISH NARROW-GAUGE LINE. The Festiniog Railway in North Wales, once a great attraction to visitors, is now used only for carrying slates from the quarries at Festiniog to Portmadoc for shipment overseas. Known as the "Toy Railway," the gauge of the track is only 1 ft. 11½ in. The locomotive in the illustration is of the Fairlie articulated type, with a double-ended boiler which carries two chimneys.

STEAM INLET

SLIDE

PORT

EXHAUST

SIMPLE SLIDE VALVE

PORT

PISTON

STEAM INLET

EXHAUST

VALVES

PORT

EXHAUST

PISTON

PORT

PISTON VALVES

STEAM INLET

EXHAUST TO BLAST PIPE

PISTON VALVES

VALVE ROCKER

REVERSING ROD

EXTENSION ROD

LINK

FORWARD ECCENTRIC

PISTON

CONNECTING ROD

BACKWARD ECCENTRIC

COUPLING ROD

ASHWELL WOOD

STEPHENSON VALVE GEAR

VALVES AND VALVE MOTIONS. There are three main types of valve, the slide valve, piston valve and poppet valve, and each has its particular advantages. First in the field was the slide valve (**top left**), which is still used widely today. For high pressures, the piston valve is superior, having less friction than the slide valve; but for efficiency of working, the poppet valve, which lifts and drops instead of sliding

34

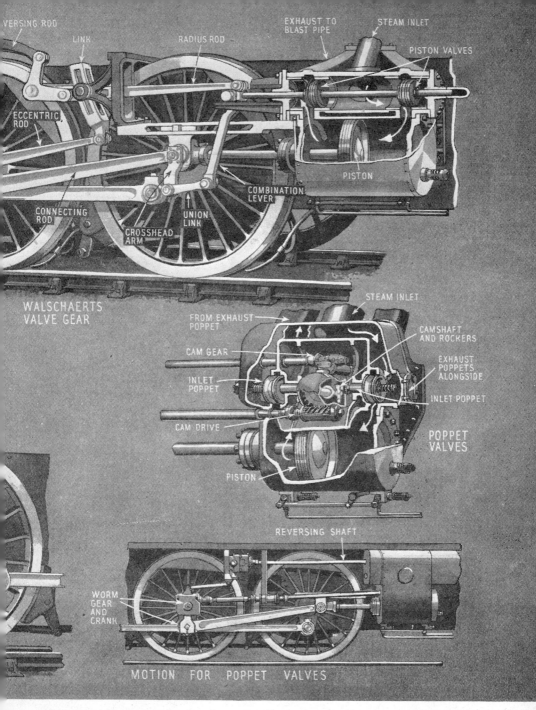

VERSING ROD

LINK

RADIUS ROD

EXHAUST TO
BLAST PIPE

STEAM INLET

PISTON VALVES

ECCENTRIC
ROD

PISTON

CONNECTING
ROD

CROSSHEAD
ARM

UNION
LINK

COMBINATION
LEVER

WALSCHAERTS
VALVE GEAR

STEAM INLET

FROM EXHAUST
POPPET

CAM GEAR

INLET
POPPET

CAM DRIVE

PISTON

CAMSHAFT
AND ROCKERS

EXHAUST
POPPETS
ALONGSIDE

INLET POPPET

POPPET
VALVES

REVERSING SHAFT

WORM
GEAR
AND
CRANK

MOTION FOR POPPET VALVES

like the others, is claimed by many to take pride of place. As far as the operation of
valves is concerned, there are again three main methods, the link motion invented
by Stephenson, that known as Walschaerts valve gear, and the conventional cam
motion for the poppet valve. In Great Britain, the Stephenson and Walschaerts
motions are both used, but the latter is the more popular in modern practice.

CROWDED QUARTERS. A view of Stratford locomotive depot. This is of the rectangular type, in which the lines are parallel, and all working has to be planned to a very strict schedule. The engines are run in and serviced in rotation, care being taken that an engine in steam is not blocked by those waiting their turn to be cleaned. Smoke cowls of the actual engine sheds can be seen on the right of the picture.

own depot, so then it has to be boarded out, and arrangements are made for it to receive attention at whatever shed may be most convenient.

These sheds are of two main types, the roundhouse and the long shed. In the round shed there is an exit and entrance track which leads to a central turntable, from which other tracks extend radially to spur lines, which are arranged in a circle. In the rectangular type of shed the tracks are parallel.

ROUNDHOUSE TYPE

The round shed requires more space, but is much easier from a working point of view, as any locomotive required can be run on to the central turntable and turned to the entrance no matter what the position of its companions. But in the parallel-track

type of shed, working has to be very carefully planned, so that locomotives required for duty are not found hiding away behind others that are under repair.

CLASSIFICATION MARKS

Not all engines are suitable for all sections of track. Certain routes can take only locomotives of limited dimensions or weight because of scanty clearances or unsuitable bridges, and this is another fact that is indicated on the engine for easy reference. On the G.W.R., for instance, there are coloured circles painted below the engine number, and these colours indicate the routes for which it is suitable. Still other tell-tale signs on an engine are those which give its power classification, showing the load it may be expected to haul.

As regards rolling stock, modern British

coaches are about sixty feet long and carried on four-wheel bogies, but some dining and sleeping cars are built slightly longer and supported on six-wheel bogies, which give somewhat smoother riding. The six-wheel bogie also has additional brake power.

SCREW COUPLING

Carriages are joined together usually by the screw coupling, which consists of two links and a screw, the latter being tightened to the point when the side buffers are just in contact. Corridor coaches on main lines, however, are sometimes fitted with the buckeye coupler, which engages automatically as the two coaches are pushed together.

With buckeye couplers, side buffers are not needed. The coaches are designed with bow-shaped ends, and this has the advantage of bringing them nearer together and shortening the gangway connexion. A greater asset is that these couplers in effect make the whole train into one articulated and continuous unit, another assistance to smooth riding. Also, because they are held more rigidly together, there is not the danger of telescoping in the event of a derailment.

ARTICULATED UNITS

There is another type of articulation which makes the train definitely a single unit, and this is to mount the ends of coaches on a single bogie. It began with mounting two coaches on three bogies, but these twins soon developed into triplets, quadruplets and even quintuplets. Most of the

QUESTION OF EXPANSION. The famous Hardwicke locomotive of the L.M.S. which travelled well over a million miles during its term of service, alongside an engine of the Royal Scot type. This photograph illustrates how, ever striving for greater power, designers have gone on increasing boiler girth at the expense of chimney height. The chimney of the Royal Scot, however, extends downwards into the smoke-box.

SUPERHEATER
ELEMENTS

SUPERHEATED STEAM PIPE
TO INSIDE CYLINDER

OUTSIDE CYLINDER
PISTON VALVES

MOTION TO INSIDE
CYLINDER PISTON VALVES

N?4468

MALLARD

OUTSIDE CYLINDER
AND PISTON

CYLINDER
DRAIN COCKS

WALSCHAERT
VALVE MOTIO

MALLARD, HOLDER OF THE WORLD'S SPEED RECORD WITH STEAM. This amazing British engine, small in size compared with some of the giants of America, reached the astonishing speed of one hundred and twenty-six miles an hour when hauling a test train in July, 1938. American and German steam locomotives have reached speeds of a mile or two an hour less, but Mallard has the record. The typical

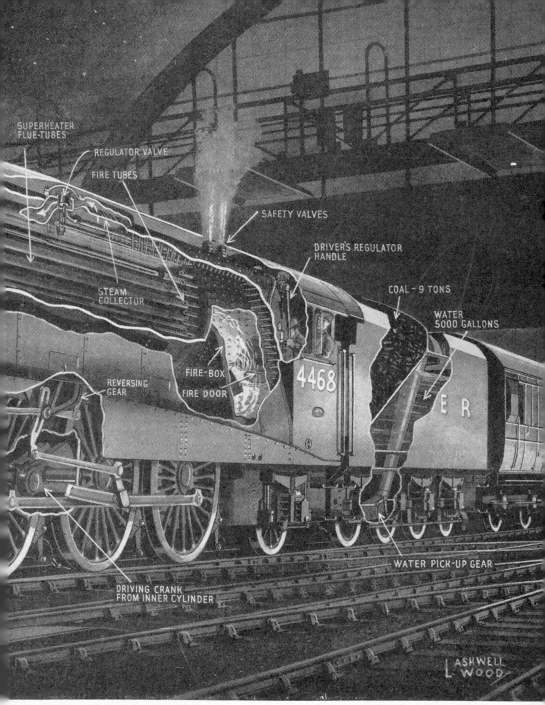

SUPERHEATER
FLUE-TUBES

REGULATOR VALVE

FIRE TUBES

SAFETY VALVES

DRIVER'S REGULATOR
HANDLE

STEAM
COLLECTOR

COAL - 9 TONS

WATER
5000 GALLONS

REVERSING
GEAR

FIRE-BOX

FIRE DOOR

4468

E R

WATER PICK-UP GEAR

DRIVING CRANK
FROM INNER CYLINDER

ASHWELL
WOOD

compactness of the working parts is well shown in the illustration. Notice the double
blast pipe below the chimney, which is elongated in consequence, and also the
smooth curve of the main steam pipe from the boiler to the cylinders. These refinements and internal streamlining have had more to do with greater economy and
higher speeds than the outer streamlined coverings so impressive in appearance.

LAUNCHING A LOCOMOTIVE. Launching trolley on heavy-duty rollers in use at the Swindon works of the G.W.R. The trolley is driven by electricity supplied by overhead wires, and travels on a number of tracks running at right angles to the rails. The new engine is run from the assembling shed sideways, thereby saving space and the necessity of clearing a whole track through the shed for its departure.

L.N.E.R. London suburban trains are made up of such sections, with eight or ten coaches carried on ten or twelve bogies respectively, instead of the sixteen or twenty bogies that would be necessary if ordinary rolling stock were used.

FOR AND AGAINST

Such articulated units have many arguments in their favour, in the way of smooth riding and light weight, the only argument against them being that if any defect develops in a particular section, even if it is no more than an overheated axle-box, the whole unit must be taken out of the train.

Other connexions between coaches consist of the air-braking and steam-heating systems, and it is now usual to provide continuous control throughout the train of the electric lighting system. A dynamo slung under the coach frame, driven by a belt from one of the axles, provides the current, which is stored in accumulators so that there may be ample reserve when the train is standing or moving slowly.

Brakes on passenger coaches in Britain are almost exclusively of the vacuum automatic type, in which the principle of action is the destruction of a partial vacuum which is maintained by the locomotive in reservoirs and in the train-pipe. From the footplate, the driver is able to apply the brakes throughout the length of the train.

SLOW BRITISH FREIGHT TRAINS

The majority of British freight trains, however, have more simple braking and coupling arrangements, and this in part explains their low speed when compared with freight trains of other countries. Couplings consist of three forged links without any screw attachment, which accounts for the spasmodic rattling noise on starting, as the locomotive pulls all the couplings taut one by one.

Similarly, as the only brake power available when the train is running is that on the

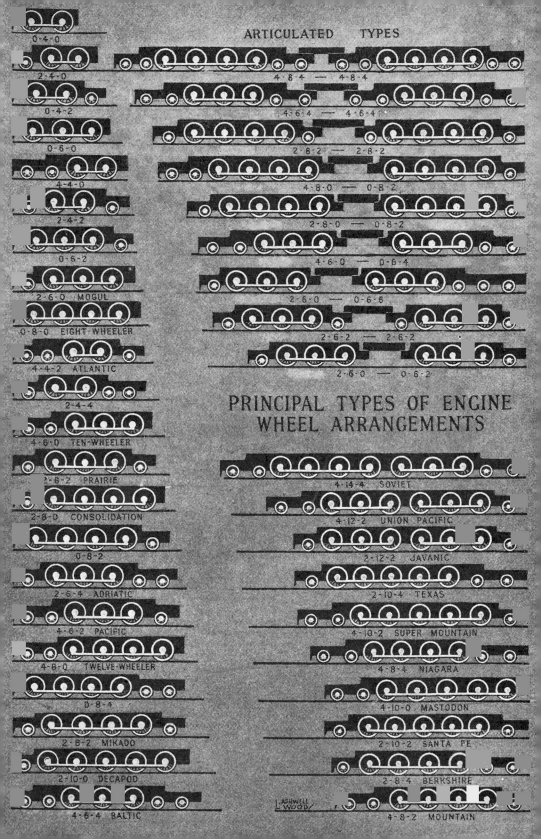

ARTICULATED TYPES

0-4-0
2-4-0
0-4-2
0-6-0
4-4-0
2-4-2
0-6-2
2-6-0 MOGUL
0-8-0 EIGHT-WHEELER
4-4-2 ATLANTIC
2-4-4
4-6-0 TEN-WHEELER
2-6-2 PRAIRIE
2-8-0 CONSOLIDATION
0-8-2
2-6-4 ADRIATIC
4-6-2 PACIFIC
4-8-0 TWELVE-WHEELER
0-8-4
2-8-2 MIKADO
2-10-0 DECAPOD
4-6-4 BALTIC

4-8-4 — 4-8-4
4-6-4 — 4-6-4
2-8-2 — 2-8-2
4-8-0 — 0-8-2
2-8-0 — 0-8-2
4-6-0 — 0-6-4
2-6-0 — 0-6-6
2-6-2 — 2-6-2
2-6-0 — 0-6-2

PRINCIPAL TYPES OF ENGINE
WHEEL ARRANGEMENTS

4-14-4 SOVIET
4-12-2 UNION PACIFIC
2-12-2 JAVANIC
2-10-4 TEXAS
4-10-2 SUPER MOUNTAIN
4-8-4 NIAGARA
4-10-0 MASTODON
2-10-2 SANTA FE
2-8-4 BERKSHIRE
4-8-2 MOUNTAIN

L. ASHWELL WOOD

MECHANICAL
COAL PUSHER

SAFETY VALVES
AND WHISTLE

FIREBOX
STAYS

WATER
LEVEL

STEAM REGULATOR
AND VALVE

FEED-WATER
VALVES

OUTER FIREBOX

INNER
FIREBOX

STEAM PIPE
TO SUPERHEATER

WATER
4,000 GALLONS

COAL-
10 TONS

FIRE
DOOR

BRICK
ARCH

SUPERHEATED
ELEMENTS IN FLUES

FIRE TUBES

SAND-BOX
FILLERS

MECHANICAL
LUBRICATORS

BOILER
CASING

WALSCHAERTS
VALVE GEAR

TOTAL WEIGHT
ON TURNTABLE
164½ TONS

PISTON

OUTSIDE
CYLINDER

FIREMAN
WORKING
TURNTABLE
CONTROLS

LOCKING
LEVER

TURNTABLE
RUNNERS

ASHWELL
WOOD

L.M.S. STREAMLINED
PACIFIC
Duchess Class

SUPERHEATER
HEADER

SUPERHEATED STEAM PIPE
TO CYLINDERS

SMOKE
BOX

STREAMLINED
OUTER CASING

SUPERHEATER
TUBES

DOUBLE
BLAST
PIPE

EXHAUSTS TO
BLAST PIPE

MAIN
FRAME

INSIDE
CYLINDERS

VACUUM CONNEXION
FROM TRAIN PIPE
OPERATES TURNTABLE

SOUTHERN RAILWAY ELECTRIC LOCOMOTIVE. Type used for heavy freight haulage. The electric locomotive is not often seen in Great Britain, where electrical working is confined more or less to the running of suburban passenger trains, with the motor units built as part of the coach. The separate locomotive shown above is in use on the Southern Railway and is pictured pulling a heavily laden goods train.

engine and tender and the guard's brake at the rear, there is another terrific clatter when the engine brakes are applied and the buffers of the trucks hit up against one another as the long line gradually comes to a standstill.

There are, however, a certain number of freight trains run in which the wagons are equipped with screw couplings and the continuous vacuum brake, and these can be operated at far higher speeds. Also, it is nowadays the practice to marshal half a dozen such wagons behind the engine in trains which are otherwise made up of loose-coupled wagons, in order to add to the engine brake-power.

BRITISH ELECTRIC RAILWAYS

But if Britain is a trifle behind the times in freight rolling stock, there are other matters in which she is definitely ahead, and one of these, in certain respects, is electrification. The Southern Railway owns what is easily the largest and most ramified suburban electric railway in the world.

There are certain conditions necessary

before it can pay to electrify a railway system, and the most obvious is a line that carries a dense suburban traffic. The great asset of electricity is that it makes possible quicker acceleration from rest than steam, and this makes it possible both to speed up schedules and also to put a greater number of trains on the line, thereby doubly improving the service.

UTILIZING WATER POWER

That is why so much electrification has taken place around large cities, but it is, of course, not the only reason for electrification.

Steep gradients and tunnels also provide a good incentive, and wherever there is a good water supply for the generation of cheap current, electrification follows as a matter of course.

On electric railways in Great Britain, with very few exceptions, current is picked up from conductor rails laid at the side of the track. These are rolled from a type of steel known as conductivity steel, which is practically pure iron, and so opposes the

COAL 3½ TONS

ROSS POP SAFETY VALVES

STEAM DOME

CLEAR VIEW
BEHIND

TOP CLACK VALVE
BOILER FEED

FEED-WATER TRAY

FIRE-BOX

STEAM PIPE
TO SUPERHEATER

SUPERHEATER TUBES

4-WHEEL
BOGIE

TANK CAPACITY
2000 GALLONS

TANK CONNECTING
DUCT

WALSCHAERTS
GEAR

MECHANICAL
LUBRICATOR

SPARK
ARRESTED

5 FT. 9 IN. DRIVING
WHEELS

EXHAUST
BLAST PIPE

SUPERHEATED STEAM
PIPE TO CYLINDER

2-CYLINDERS
19⅝ × 26 IN.

CYLINDER DRAIN COCKS

PONY TRUCK WHEELS 3 FT. 3 IN.

L.M.S. TANK LOCOMOTIVE. This is a three-cylinder engine with a taper boiler in which the barrel increases in diameter towards the fire-box end. The wheel arrangement is 2-6-4 and there is a totally enclosed cab which affords cover for the enginemen in bad weather. The engine weighs ninety-two and a half tons in working order. The tank principle of locomotive design originated in Britain and its use is particularly characteristic of British railway practice, but in many countries it is unknown.

ENGINES YOU CAN SEE
ON BRITISH RAILWAYS
Reproduced to scale to show comparative sizes

Streamlined Pacific Plymouth for mixed traffic service

3-Cylinder tank for fast, suburban work

Heavy tank locomotive for coal trains

2-Cylinder tank with electric headlights

Sir Francis Drake - 4-cylinder express type

Latest Pacific for mixed traffic

Heaviest British Pacific type - Duchess of Atholl

New high-pressure express engine

least possible resistance to the flow of current.

In some cases the current is returned through the running rails of the track, but in others a fourth rail, also made of conductivity steel, is laid in the centre for the return of the current.

CONDUCTOR SHOES

With third-rail and fourth-rail electrification, complicated bonding and insulation are necessary through the switches and crossings at junctions and elsewhere, and it is also necessary for locomotives or motor-coaches to carry more than one set of conductor shoes, spaced well apart, to bridge gaps in the continuity of the conductors.

Direct-current supply is usual with this type of electrification, and in Britain is used at a pressure of six hundred volts. Direct-current motors are the simplest and most effective for railway work, and they are generally arranged in pairs to give two normal running speeds, half-speed when they are connected in series, and full speed when in parallel.

They are also very compact, and this makes it possible to mount them in the coach, so that a separate locomotive is not required.

With this method of working, suburban trains are assembled in units, generally of three or four coaches, of which the end ones are motor-coaches with all the motors under the control of the motorman in the driving compartment at the front end.

This is known as multiple-unit working, and its value lies in the simple fact that the motor power available is proportioned to the whole length of the train. If additional accommodation is required in the rush hours, a second unit is coupled to the first, often with a couple of trailer coaches between them. On the long-distance services between London and the south coast, many of the multiple-unit trains are composed of three four-coach units coupled together, making twelve coaches in all.

ELECTRIC LOCOMOTIVES

Contrasting with this system is the method of working with independent electric locomotives. With these, overhead electrification is usual, and with higher voltages, even up to fifteen hundred volts. But as direct-current voltage increases, there is an increase in the weight and cost of the

UTILITY LOCOMOTIVE. Extraordinary war-time product of the Southern Railway in Britain, shorn of all possible trimmings. The main frames are visible and the boiler looks like a series of surrealistic patterns. Nothing approaching this utilitarian design is likely to be seen again. Apart from its peculiar appearance, however, it is an ordinary locomotive of the Q 1 class, shown hauling a trainload of war material.

PRINCIPAL RAILWAYS OF THE
BRITISH ISLES

0   MILES   100

SHETLAND
ISLANDS

ORKNEY
ISLANDS

Cape Wrath   Thurso   Duncansby Head
HEBRIDES   Wick
                    Helmsdale
                Lossiemouth Banff Fraserburgh
        Tain Dingwall   Elgin   Peterhead
SKYE   INVERNESS
    Kyle of Lochalsh   Fort Augustus   ABERDEEN
    Mallaig   Ballater   Stonehaven
    Fort William
MULL   SCOTLAND   Montrose
        PERTH   Arbroath
        STIRLING   DUNDEE
        Dunfermline
ISLAY   Dunbar
    GLASGOW EDINBURGH
        Berwick
    Ayr   Girvan
    Dumfries   Morpeth
Malin Head   NEWCASTLE Tynemouth
Burtonport Letterkenny LONDONDERRY Larne Kirkcudbright CARLISLE SUNDERLAND
Killybegs   NORTHERN Stranraer Workington DURHAM W.Hartlepool
Donegal IRELAND BELFAST Whitehaven Keswick Darlington MIDDLESBROUGH
Ballina Sligo Enniskillen Downpatrick Ramsey   Scarborough
Westport   ISLE OF Flamborough Head
        Dundalk MAN Bridlington
    Carrick on Kingscourt Douglas Barrow LANCASTER YORK HULL
    Shannon Oldcastle Drogheda   Withernsea
Galway Athlone Navan Mullingar IRISH Blackpool PRESTON Grimsby
    Athenry   SEA Southport MANCHESTER DONCASTER Skegness
    EIRE   DUBLIN Holyhead LIVERPOOL SHEFFIELD Cromer
Kilkee   Bray ANGLESEY Rhyl CHESTER ENGLAND LINCOLN
    LIMERICK Wicklow   CREWE Derby Nottingham YARMOUTH
    Arklow Barmouth Stafford LEICESTER NORWICH
Dingle Tralee Kilkenny Cardigan Shrewsbury Bury St.Edmunds
    WATERFORD Bay Aberystwyth BIRMINGHAM PETERBOROUGH Cambridge IPSWICH
    WEXFORD Cardigan WALES Worcester NORTHAMPTON Colchester Harwich
    Rosslare Fishguard GLOUCESTER Southend
CORK Youghal Pembroke   BRISTOL READING LONDON
    Fishguard   CARDIFF Bath Basingstoke Guildford Margate
Queenstown Bristol Channel Salisbury Canterbury Dover
Schull Clonakilty Ilfracombe Bideford Barnstaple SOUTHAMPTON BRIGHTON Folkestone Calais
        Bude Tiverton Bournemouth Portsmouth Eastbourne Boulogne
        EXETER Weymouth ISLE OF Hastings
    Padstow   WIGHT
    Newquay Plymouth Torquay Lyme Regis
    Penzance Truro
SCILLY ISLES Falmouth PLYMOUTH   Dieppe

NORTH
SEA

ATLANTIC
OCEAN

ENGLISH CHANNEL

Cherbourg Havre Rouen

CHANNEL
ISLANDS

St.Malo

FRANCE

S.J.TURNER, F.R.G.S.

OIL-ENGINES FOR THE RAIL. Three examples of direct-drive, low-power shunting locomotives in use on the L.M.S. Each one weighs thirty tons, develops two hundred horse-power and can pull a load of seven hundred tons. The heavy-duty oil engine is located under the car-type bonnet, which takes the place of the boiler of a steam engine. Diesel engines have been used in Britain so far for shunting work only.

motors and the complexity of the control equipment, and the voltage, therefore, is kept as low as possible. There is no such limit with alternating current, but this has not found favour in Great Britain.

ADVANTAGES OF ELECTRICITY

One of the advantages of electrification is that the electric locomotive or motor-coach can be almost continuously at work, whereas the steam engine needs definite intervals of rest in its working day for attention to the fire-box and other details.

Another advantage is that it is possible to control the speed of acceleration automatically. As the driver moves the handle of the master-controller to the first running position, the motors accelerate at a fixed rate, each pair being in series, so that each motor receives half the line voltage. Resistances are inserted in series with each motor, and are cut out step by step as the speed increases to the maximum possible at half the line voltage.

Then the resistances are reinserted, and each pair of motors is changed over from series to parallel working, after which the resistances are again cut out step by step until full speed is obtained. The control is entirely automatic, and makes possible the precision of acceleration and train working that is so important on lines carrying a dense and rapid traffic.

Automatic control is possble with electricity in a variety of ways. There are, for example, the remarkable central control rooms on the Southern Railway, where the working of a large number of sub-stations is under constant observation on a large control panel by means of lights and other visible indications, whereas the sub-stations themselves require no attendance until, as the control panel instantly reveals, something is out of order.

DIESEL-ELECTRIC WORKING

There is one other form of motive power used on railways today without mention of which no description of the locomotive and its development would be complete. This is the oil engine as evidenced in the Diesel motor, usually coupled with a dynamo and known as the Diesel-electric locomotive.

The extraordinary advances made in the use of this type of power in other countries argue well for its general adoption all over the world, providing, of course, the newer atomic steam engine does not in some fashion eclipse all others in one bright burst of meteoric brilliance.

The Diesel-electric principle, however, itself cuts out the use of coal, and this fact has somewhat retarded its growth in Great Britain. The Great Western Railway has a number of Diesel-driven rail-cars, with a direct mechanical drive, but there are limits to the power which can be transmitted in this way. A much more flexible drive is obtained when the Diesel engine is used to drive a dynamo, so producing current which propels the locomotive by means of electric motors.

The principle is thus one requiring a complete power station on wheels, but in spite of its seeming complexity it has all the advantages of ordinary electric haulage with none of its disadvantages.

The Diesel engine is easily refuelled, and is always ready for work. It can make runs of almost indefinite duration, and it can be coupled to others of its kind to produce powers almost as indefinite. It has been used in Great Britain, so far, however, only for shunting purposes.

The view advanced hitherto is that it is preferable, if possible, to use steam produced from the country's native coal, rather than to rely on a power for which dependence is placed on imported fuel. But the advantages of the Diesel-electric locomotive, especially for high-speed long-distance work, are so great that a more favourable attitude towards it is possible in the future despite the high initial outlay.

CAB OF A DIESEL SHUNTING ENGINE. Direct-drive type. The locomotive is built for standard-gauge track, and develops one hundred and sixty horse-power. It is only in small powers such as this that the principle of a clutch and gear-box can be used with the oil engine for locomotive work. The cab shown below is arranged for both right- and left-hand drive so that the driver is in full control from either window.

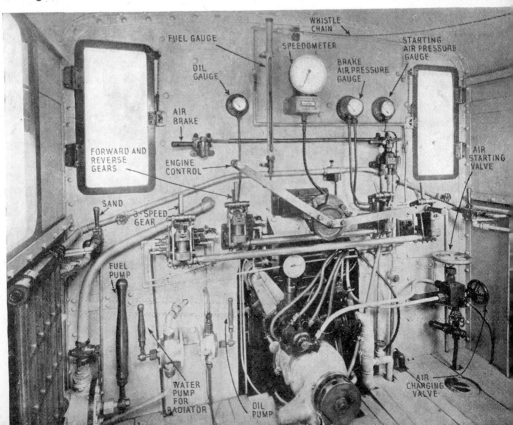

Night shift work in the L.N.E.R. locomotive sheds at Doncaster

CHAPTER THREE

HOW THE RAILWAY WORKS

THE work of the railway engineer is a battle with Nature to secure a track sufficiently level for railway operation. The steepness of gradients and the sharpness of curves govern both maximum loads and average speeds over any given route. For operating purposes, the ideal track is one that is straight and level, as, for example, the main line of the London & North Eastern Railway over the great Plain of York, between York and Darlington, but Nature does not often permit such a line to be laid.

In undulating or mountainous country, the engineer's task is to plan a route in which the best possible compromise is reached between gradients and curves, on the one hand, and heavy constructional costs in cuttings and embankments, tunnels and viaducts, on the other. The greater the importance of the line, the more the expense that will be justified on construction, in order to flatten gradients or to shorten the route.

On some of the engineering works, such as the Forth Bridge or the Severn Tunnel, millions have been spent in order to save minutes; but in course of time the economies in operation thus made possible, or the new traffic created, have thoroughly justified the expenditure.

KEEPING DOWN GRADIENTS

The general aim in planning main lines is to keep gradients down to a maximum steepness of one in two hundred or so. For example, this is the ruling gradient over most of the L.N.E.R. main line between London and Darlington. But the flattest main line in Britain is that laid by Brunel for the Great Western Railway between Paddington and Bristol, which, apart from two short downgrades at one in a hundred between Swindon and Bath, is all but level for the entire 118 miles.

As gradients steepen, so the demand on locomotive power increases. The one in seventy-five ascent on the L.M.S. from Euston up to Camden makes it necessary for trains to be "assisted" by an engine pushing from behind. Such long climbs as those from Oxenholme to Shap Summit (nine hundred and eighteen feet) in Westmorland, and from Beattock to Beattock Summit (one thousand and fourteen feet) in Scotland, with continuous lengths of gradient as steep in parts as one in seventy-five and one in seventy, require the provision of a number of locomotives, constantly in steam, to give assistance to freight and heavy passenger trains.

HIGHEST IN BRITAIN

The highest main-line summit in Great Britain is Druimuachdar, on the Highland main line of the L.M.S. between Perth and Inverness, and this is nearly fifteen hundred feet above the level of the sea.

The steepest main-line gradient in any part of the British Isles is probably the Lickey, a shade steeper than one in thirty-eight, for two miles continuously; it is situated on the L.M.S. West of England line from Bristol to Birmingham, immediately north of Bromsgrove, and two tank engines in the rear help most northbound trains from here up to Blackwell. The G.W.R. has some very severe gradients west of Newton Abbot, in Devonshire; a short length of one in thirty-six, then the drop to the Dart Valley at Totnes, after that another steep ascent to Brent. But the G.W.R. prefers to attach its assisting locomotives as pilots in front, and practically every train in each direction between Newton Abbot and Plymouth is double-headed.

REDUCING CURVES

Acceleration of train services, during the last decade before the Second World War, and particularly the introduction of high-speed streamline trains, has made it necessary to pay much more careful attention than before to curves. On fast running main lines, the general aim is to keep curvature down to a sharpness not exceeding about one mile radius, but this is not always possible and as curve radii

1 FROM MAIN TO COALING TOWER

FIREMAN PHONES "ON SHED"

LOCO COAL SIDINGS

2 TURNTABLE

11 FIREMAN PHONES "OFF SHED" ROAD TO MAIN LINE

CANTEEN AND REST ROOM

ASH HOPPERS TO DISCHARGE PLANT

10 EXIT SHED VACUUM TESTED ETC.

FOREMAN AND CLERKS

LOCO SUPERINTENDENT'S OFFICE

DRIVERS' NOTICE BOARD

RUNNING REPAIR SHOPS

WHEEL DROPPING

L ASHWELL WOOD

LOCOMOTIVE SERVICING DEPOT. The main shed is of the rectangular type with the tracks running parallel, a design that takes up less space than the roundhouse type, but demands greater accuracy in the working rota. In these sheds the loco-motive receives every attention necessary to keep it in running order, and it is this regular and expert service that is responsible, in great measure, for the in-

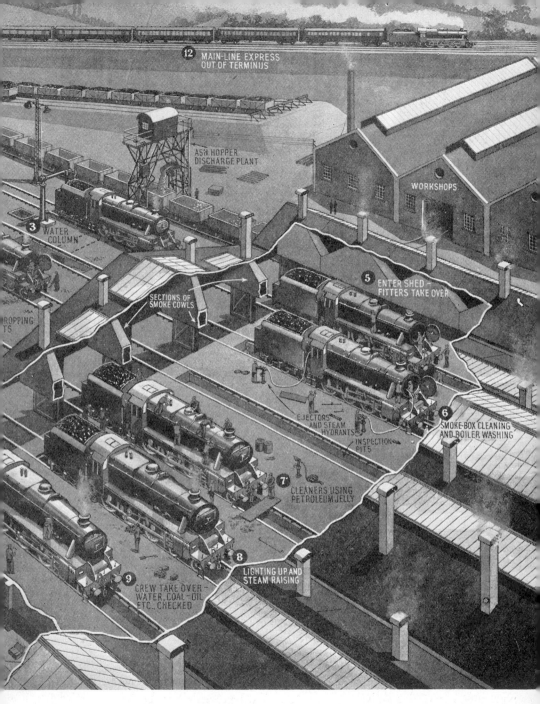

12 MAIN-LINE EXPRESS
OUT OF TERMINUS

ASH HOPPER
DISCHARGE PLANT

WORKSHOPS

3 WATER
COLUMN

5 ENTER SHED —
FITTERS TAKE OVER

SECTIONS OF
SMOKE COWLS

ROPPING
TS

EJECTORS
AND STEAM
HYDRANTS

6 SMOKE-BOX CLEANING
AND BOILER WASHING

INSPECTION
PITS

7 CLEANERS USING
PETROLEUM JELLY

8 LIGHTING UP AND
STEAM RAISING

9 CREW TAKE OVER —
WATER, COAL — OIL
ETC., CHECKED

frequency of mechanical breakdowns on the railway in normal times. The numbered stages show the series of operations from start to finish. It is by keeping to a routine that the engines are passed systematically through the various servicing processes and turned out ready for duty at the required moment. Without careful planning, one engine, out of action, might easily be found blocking the way of another in steam.

THE MODERN IDEA. Lawns in place of ashpits! A scheme for improving the general appearance of the railway in operation on the L.N.E.R. Railway station gardens, particularly in outlying districts, have been popular for many years, but it is only recently that the clearing of the spaces between the tracks at junctions and elsewhere, and the sowing of grass and small shrubs, has become the authorized procedure.

diminish to less than half a mile, it becomes essential to impose speed restrictions.

To counteract the tendency of a train to overturn when rounding a curve at speed, the track is super-elevated or banked, so that the outer rail is higher than the inner. This banking is worked out very carefully. The amount of banking is really a compromise between the demands of the fastest passenger trains and the restraint of the slower-moving traffic. Actually, many curves in tracks nowadays are not simple bends, but are introduced by spirals which lead to the full curvatures, during which the banking is worked up gradually. This plan adds greatly to the smoothness of running at high speeds.

BULL-HEAD RAILS

British railway track differs from that of all other countries in its use of the bull-head rail, in section rather like a dumb-bell, except that the foot is smaller than the head. Elsewhere, the flat-bottom rail, with a similar head but a flat foot, is standard.

The bull-head rail is carried in cast-iron "chairs," in which it is firmly held, tilted inwards at an angle of one in twenty, by wooden or steel keys. Each chair is secured by three chair screws to the sleeper, which serves both to tie the track to gauge (in fact, in North America a sleeper is known as a tie) and also to distribute the weight of the moving trains over as large an area of the ballast as possible.

The rails are secured together by pairs of fish-plates, which are now much shorter than formerly, with only one bolt through each rail-end instead of the previous two, in order that the joint sleepers may be brought close together, and the joint better supported.

In earlier days, the flat-bottom rail became popular because it could be spiked down direct to the sleepers. Therefore, the carriage of heavy tonnages of chairs to the site, when new lines were being laid, was avoided. But in modern practice, in order to preserve the timber of the sleepers, the flat-bottom rail is laid on steel or cast-

ENTERING THE CITY. The viaduct method. One of the greatest difficulties the modern permanent-way engineer has to face is that of getting the trains into and out of the cities that they serve. Underground schemes for main-line travel are in operation in countries where there is electrical haulage, but the arch and the viaduct are still common in Britain, as here at London Bridge Southern Railway station.

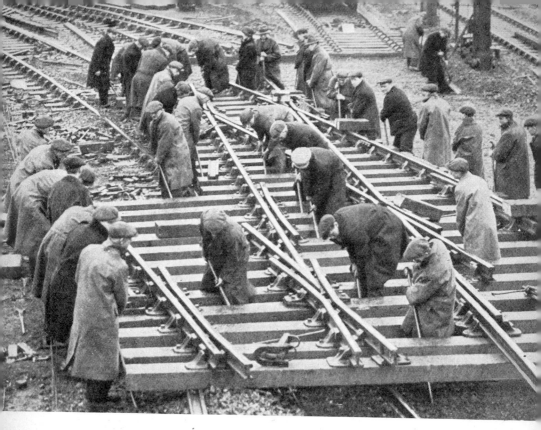

iron sole-plates, and has more elaborate fastenings than the old dog spike; consequently, flat-bottom track is as expensive to lay as bull-head, if not more so.

The advantage of the flat-bottom rail is that its greater depth and its wide foot make it stiffer than the bull-head rail, and, for this reason, flat-bottom track is easier to maintain in good line than bull-head. At the present time British railways are experimenting with flat-bottom rails on their main lines. Already, a considerable mileage has been laid, and it is quite possible that this type of rail may become the future standard for use on British railways.

STANDARD RAIL WEIGHTS

The standard weight of bull-head rail in Great Britain is ninety-five pounds per yard, but the flat-bottom rails just referred to are of one hundred and ten and one hundred and thirty-one pounds per yard sections. Some American railways, like the Pennsylvania, go even as far as a one hundred and fifty-two pounds per yard section to carry their heavy rolling stock. In length, British railways have standardized on sixty feet rails, though the L.N.E.R. has used a considerable tonnage of ninety feet, and the L.N.E.R. and L.M.S. have obtained lengths as long as one hundred and twenty feet from the rolling mills.

WELDED RAILS

Even longer lengths have been obtained by welding, especially on the tube lines of London Transport. Provided the rails are held tightly enough, expansion and contraction give no trouble, either in tunnels or in the open. It has been proved by experiment that the tendency to expand or contract, with variations in temperature, can be confined within the rail as an unrelieved stress which is less than the elastic limit of the steel, so that the rail does not move, even on the hottest days. In America, rails have been welded in continuous lengths up to a mile in the open, and longer lengths still in tunnels.

British railways together purchase some

COMPLETE TRACK LAYOUT. Made-up section being manhandled into position by means of crowbars. It was actually drawn to the site by a locomotive, over a slipway built for the purpose. Below is a drawing showing the two main types of rail in use, the bull-head type being that most favoured in Britain, while the flat-bottom rail, standard in almost all other countries, is now being tried extensively in Britain also. At one time, the flat-bottom rail was far easier to lay than the bull-head, being merely spiked down as the track progressed, but today, owing to a number of refinements, it is quite as complicated as the bull-head type. Spring keys are sometimes used today in place of the wooden wedge in laying the latter. Notice the modern fish-plate, which has only two bolts instead of the former four. The flat-bottom rail is sometimes fastened down with hook bolts on to a base plate which is held in position by a type of coach screw in the same manner as the bull-head chair. Rails of special alloy steel are used at junctions and wherever there is exceptionally heavy traffic.

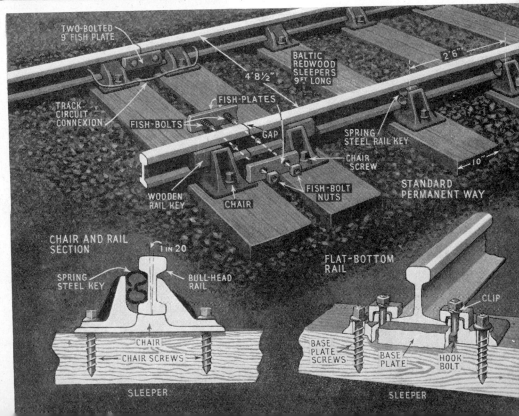

TWO-BOLTED 9" FISH PLATE

BALTIC REDWOOD SLEEPERS 9FT LONG

2'6"

4'8½"

TRACK CIRCUIT CONNEXION

FISH-PLATES

FISH-BOLTS

GAP

SPRING STEEL RAIL KEY

CHAIR SCREW

10"

WOODEN RAIL KEY

CHAIR

FISH-BOLT NUTS

STANDARD PERMANENT WAY

CHAIR AND RAIL SECTION

1 IN 20

FLAT-BOTTOM RAIL

SPRING STEEL KEY

BULL-HEAD RAIL

CLIP

CHAIR

CHAIR SCREWS

BASE PLATE SCREWS

BASE PLATE

HOOK BOLT

SLEEPER

SLEEPER

ROBOT TRACK-LAYER IN BRITAIN. A method of laying rails at the rate of two hundred yards an hour. The track-layer does not even interfere with traffic on the next line. It is shown here on a section of L.N.E.R. line in Northumberland. The track-layer lifts the old sections of line and lays the new in their place in the short space of a few minutes. In America, mechanical tracklayers are used extensively.

250,000 tons of rails annually to replace rails which have worn down under traffic. A rail, in the course of its life, the duration of which varies between wide limits, according to the traffic passing over it, may lose up to half an inch from its head by wear, and replacement is then essential.

MANGANESE STEEL RAILS

To obtain better wear, a medium manganese type of rail steel is now in general use, and rails for hard-wearing locations are heat-treated, in what are known as sorbitic plants, to increase the combined hardness and toughness of the running surface.

For exceptionally severe running conditions, an alloy steel containing twelve to fourteen per cent of manganese is favoured but this is so expensive that its use is strictly limited.

Sometimes, as in the well-known layout at the east end of Newcastle Central Station, L.N.E.R., the crossings are cast solid in this manganese steel instead of being built up from rolled rails.

For maintenance, railways are divided into lengths, each under the charge of a

ganger with platelayers or undermen. Between them, they walk the whole of the length daily, to see that everything is in safe running order, and to do any necessary work in keeping the line in good repair. Relaying or renewal of track is carried out by special gangs, which move from place to place for the purpose, with all necessary equipment for handling the rails and other components and for expediting the work.

RENEWING THE TRACK

As far as possible, the actual renewal is carried out on a Sunday, with complete possession of the track concerned; for a week or so afterwards, while the new track is being packed up on the ballast to a perfectly level surface, the speed of trains over it is restricted. Temporary speed restrictions of this description are indicated to drivers by two signs exhibited at the lineside, a "C" at the beginning of the restriction, for "Commences," and a "T" at the end, for "Terminates." Half-a-mile before the "C" sign there is an horizontal green board, showing a green and a white light at night, to give advance warning, so

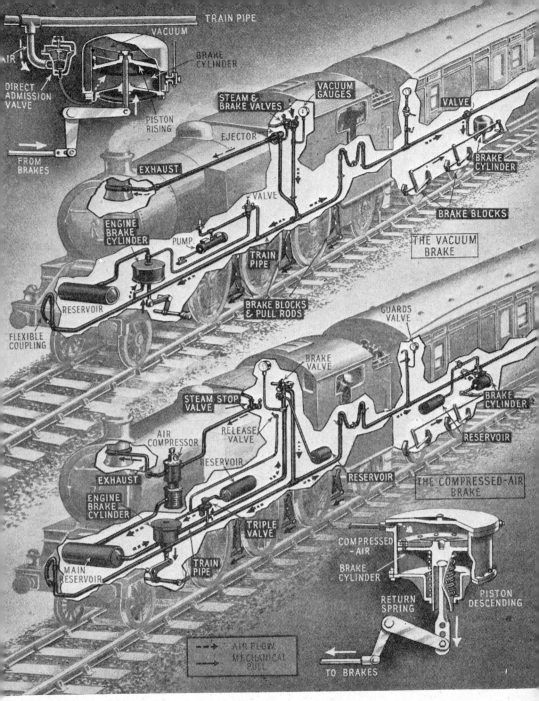

TRAIN PIPE

VACUUM

BRAKE CYLINDER

DIRECT ADMISSION VALVE

PISTON RISING

FROM BRAKES

EXHAUST

STEAM & BRAKE VALVES

VACUUM GAUGES

VALVE

EJECTOR

VALVE

BRAKE CYLINDER

ENGINE BRAKE CYLINDER

PUMP

TRAIN PIPE

BRAKE BLOCKS

THE VACUUM BRAKE

RESERVOIR

BRAKE BLOCKS & PULL RODS

GUARDS VALVE

FLEXIBLE COUPLING

BRAKE VALVE

STEAM STOP VALVE

AIR COMPRESSOR

RELEASE VALVE

BRAKE CYLINDER

RESERVOIR

EXHAUST

RESERVOIR

RESERVOIR

THE COMPRESSED-AIR BRAKE

ENGINE BRAKE CYLINDER

TRIPLE VALVE

COMPRESSED -AIR

MAIN RESERVOIR

TRAIN PIPE

BRAKE CYLINDER

RETURN SPRING

PISTON DESCENDING

AIR FLOW
MECHANICAL PULL

TO BRAKES

BRAKING SYSTEMS. Vacuum and compressed-air types. In the compressed-air type of brake it is the air pressure, above that of the atmosphere, which forces the brake blocks into contact with the wheels, whereas the reverse operation takes place in the vacuum type. In this, it is the creation of a vacuum that causes the brake piston to rise. Both systems are employed extensively throughout the world.

WATERLOO. Largest railway station in Britain. Built in the early days on a site formerly occupied by cow yards, this station even then had the unusual number of four separate tracks. Today, it has no fewer than twenty-one platform lines and two other tracks besides. In normal working times, it deals daily with well over fifteen hundred trains and not less than one hundred and twenty thousand passengers.

that speed may be reduced in good time.

In the United States, considerable use is made of mechanical tracklaying equipment, but although a plant of this description has been tried in Great Britain, on the L.N.E.R., the narrow limitations imposed on the plant by the restricted British loading gauge have militated against complete success.

NEW MATERIALS FOR SLEEPERS

Attention has been directed recently to the use of substitutes for timber sleepers. One of the most obvious of these might appear to be concrete, but although it has advantages, concrete is by no means ideal. Concrete sleepers are extremely heavy and generally more costly than timber.

Another alternative is the steel sleeper,

but there are objections also to the use of this in Great Britain. One objection is the British climate, which is liable to cause excessive corrosion, and the other is the difficulty of devising a sleeper which will hold a bull-head rail securely. Steel sleepers for flat-bottom rails are a simpler matter altogether, and in tropical countries, especially where the fondness of ants for a diet of timber may cause the wooden sleeper to have a very short life, steel sleepers have been extensively used. They are made from thin steel plate, pressed while hot into a trough shape, which when inverted beds firmly in the ballast. Clips are pressed out of the upper surface to hold the feet of the rails.

As befits the country which was the cradle

of railway transport, Great Britain boasts some notable examples of railway engineering work. The earlier of these are the more remarkable in that they were designed when little experience was available in regard to structures of such magnitude, and when there could have been little idea of the future weight and speed of railway traffic. Moreover, these early structures were built before Bessemer improved the making of steel, and the only materials at the designers' command were wrought-iron and masonry.

Yet some of the first of these great bridges built are still in use. For example, the Royal Border Bridge at Berwick, a masonry viaduct of twenty-eight arches, each spanning sixty-one feet six inches, and carrying the rails over one hundred feet above the waters of the River Tweed, was designed by Robert Stephenson and opened in 1850. Welwyn Viaduct, in Hertfordshire, with its forty arches of a maximum height of eighty-nine feet, came into use in the same year.

Today, nearly a century later, with no more attention in the intervening years than the renewal from time to time of parts of their masonry, they are carrying the express trains of the L.N.E.R., heavier and faster than their designers could have dreamed possible.

REMARKABLE TUBULAR BRIDGE

When Robert Stephenson had carried his North Wales main line of the then London & North Western Railway along the coast from Chester through Conway to Bangor, the Menai Straits barred his access to the island of Anglesey and to Holyhead. To overcome this obstacle, Stephenson designed the Britannia Tubular Bridge, a remarkable structure consisting of two parallel wrought-iron tubes or box girders, rectangular in section and set up on edge, one housing the down line and the other the up line.

Each tube, fifteen hundred feet in length and nearly five thousand tons in weight, is continuous across the bridge, and is supported at three points intermediately on masonry towers. With the use of steel, and our modern knowledge, we should not design a similar structure today, but

HOW A DERIVED MOTION WORKS. Ingenious arrangement, invented by the late Sir Nigel Gresley, designed to enable the piston-valve spindles of the two outside cylinders to give the necessary motion to the piston-valve spindle of the middle cylinder, so that two sets of valve-motion only, instead of three, are required.

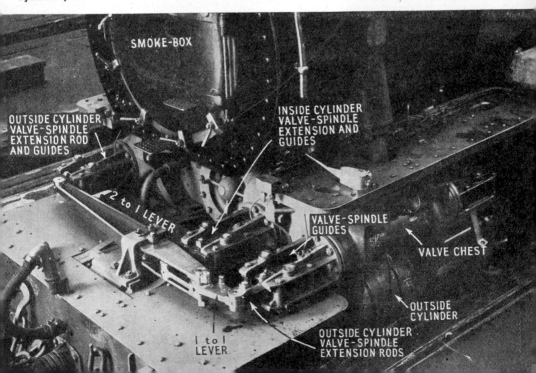

ONE METHOD OF CARRYING TRAINS OVER WATER. Royal Albert Bridge, on the Great Western Railway, was designed by Brunel, and opened to traffic nearly a hundred years ago. Its unique feature is the pair of curved elliptical iron tubes from which the floor is suspended. Although built before modern weights and speeds were dreamed of, it is still used to carry all but the heaviest main-line passenger traffic.

this most original conception, also opened for traffic in 1850, still stands as a monument to the genius of a notable railway pioneer.

The same may be said of Brunel's famous bridge, the Royal Albert, which carries the G.W.R. main line from Devon across the Tamar into Cornwall at Saltash. The deep waterway has been cleared by two four-hundred-and-fifty-one feet spans of unique design, each deriving its strength from a curved wrought-iron tube, elliptical in section and with a major diameter of sixteen feet nine inches, from which the floor of the bridge is suspended by vertical ties. Opened in 1859, the old bridge is still carrying G.W.R. main line traffic, and only the heaviest passenger locomotives are barred from crossing it.

But the advent of steel, with its combination of ductility and strength greatly exceeding that of wrought iron, has altered the technique of bridge design com-

pletely. One British steel bridge still takes a prominent place among the engineering wonders of the world, even though it was completed as far back as 1891. This is the bridge carrying the L.N.E.R. main line to Aberdeen across the Firth of Forth north of Edinburgh, which incorporates the biggest pair of cantilever spans in the world, each of them 1,710 ft. across.

Many years ago it was obvious that there could be no effective railway route up the east coast of Scotland until both the Firth of Forth and the Firth of Tay had been bridged. The latter was the easier proposition of the two, as the Tay is comparatively shallow; thus it was possible to find foundations for bridge piers at comparatively short intervals, and to build a lattice-girder viaduct with spans of relatively moderate length.

Unfortunately, the first Tay Bridge design made insufficient allowance for the possible effects of wind pressure, and in a furious gale one winter's night in December, 1879, while the night mail was crossing, the central portion of the bridge was torn from its foundations and overturned into the Firth, after having been in service for little over a year. The present Tay Bridge, of considerably more massive construction, was opened in 1887, and with its length of just over two miles, made up of eighty-five spans, is the longest in Britain.

The designer of the first Tay Bridge had also designed an immense two-span suspension bridge to carry the railway across the Firth of Forth, and building had already begun, when it was brought to a sudden stop by the Tay Bridge disaster. The plans were scrapped, and two eminent engineers —Sir John Fowler and Sir Benjamin Baker— were called in to prepare a new design. They decided on a bridge of the cantilever type, far exceeding in size anything that had been built previously.

The principle of the cantilever is one of balance, which makes possible economies in the weight of steel required to bridge any given gap. In the Forth Bridge, symmetrically-shaped cantilevers of diamond pattern, balanced about the centre, are used; they are three in number, broadened at their bases to stand foursquare on massive pillars of masonry. For the centre cantilever, the island of Inchgarvie was available as a solid base; indeed, the site of the bridge was chosen because of the advantages offered by Inchgarvie in simplifying the foundation problem. But it was necessary to sink foundations, by the caisson method, deep below the waters of the Firth for the two side cantilevers.

The stability of the cantilevers is sufficient to enable them to support, between each pair, a 346-ft. lattice-girder span, weighing 846 tons, by which the length of each main span is proportionately increased. The two main 1,710 ft. spans, with the two end 690-ft. spans, and the space occupied by the bases of the cantilevers, together make

ANOTHER WAY OF CROSSING. Harwich-Zeebrugge train ferry. By means of ferry steamers, through passenger and freight coaches are run across many wide waterways where bridges are out of the question. The ferry steamer is run by means of a connecting bridge into a dock where the water level can be regulated, so that the rails on its deck can be adjusted to the height of those on shore.

TRAIN FERRY Nº 3   LONDON.

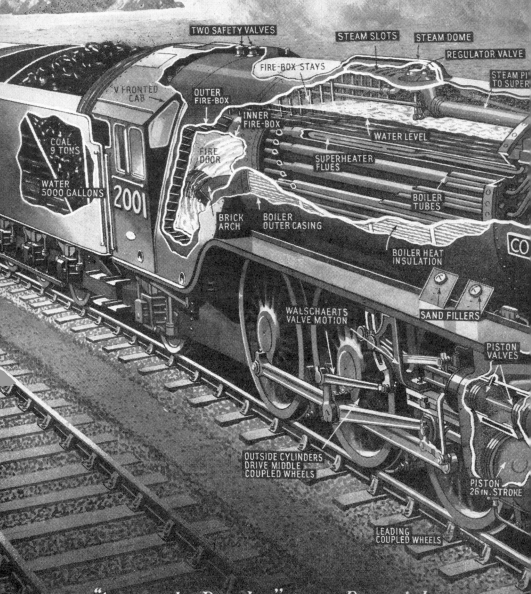

TWO SAFETY VALVES
STEAM SLOTS
STEAM DOME
REGULATOR VALVE
FIRE-BOX STAYS
STEAM PI'
TO SUPER
STEAM PI'
TO SUPER
V FRONTED CAB
OUTER FIRE-BOX
INNER FIRE-BOX
WATER LEVEL
COAL 9 TONS
FIRE DOOR
SUPERHEATER FLUES
WATER 5000 GALLONS
2001
BOILER TUBES
CO
BRICK ARCH
BOILER OUTER CASING
BOILER HEAT INSULATION
WALSCHAERTS VALVE MOTION
SAND FILLERS
PISTON VALVES
OUTSIDE CYLINDERS DRIVE MIDDLE COUPLED WHEELS
PISTON 26 IN. STROKE
LEADING COUPLED WHEELS

"Across the Border" near Berwick
THE NEW "COCK O' THE NORTH" LOCOMOTIVE
Rebuilt - 3-cylinder Pacific

DOUBLE CHIMNEY

SMOKE
DEFLECTORS

SUPERHEATER HEADER
AND PIPES

SUPERHEATED
STEAM PIPE TO
INSIDE CYLINDER

SMOKE-BOX
DOOR

E NORTH

EXHAUST
BLAST PIPES

SMOKE-BOX
CASING

SADDLE

MAIN FRAMES

XHAUST FROM
UTSIDE CYLINDER

EXHAUST FROM
INSIDE CYLINDER

INSIDE CYLINDER
DRIVING LEADING
COUPLED WHEELS

Nº 2001

ACROSS
THE
BORDER

SCOTLAND X LNER + ENGLAND

ASHWELL
WOOD

up a total length of over a mile. With the approach viaducts, the Forth Bridge is well over a mile and a half in length.

Each span derives its strength mainly from two great curved steel tubes, each twelve feet in diameter and large enough to take a tube train. They are arched from one cantilever to the next. The superstructure of the bridge, with its maze of steel bracings, has been built on them and has withstood the fiercest of gales for more than half a century without giving a moment's anxiety to those responsible for its maintenance. The cantilevers tower 361 ft. above the water-line, and the spans give shipping a headroom of 157 ft. above high water mark.

Another Cantilever Type

There is only one other true cantilever bridge in Great Britain, and that is situated in the west of Scotland; it carries the Ballachulish branch of the L.M.S. across

Loch Etive at Connel Ferry, near Oban. This is of rather a different design; the two cantilevers are inclined inwards, and between them support a single five-hundred-foot span. A single line of railway runs across the bridge.

Across the Tyne

Among other notable British bridges are the two which carry the L.N.E.R. across the deep gorge of the River Tyne at Newcastle. The older High Level Bridge, as it is called, was an engineering wonder when it was built, for it was opened as far back as 1849. It has six 125-ft. spans, of cast-iron arch construction, and is a double-deck structure, with three railway tracks on the upper deck and a roadway below.

In 1906, however, the more modern King Edward bridge was opened, half a mile upstream from the High Level Bridge, and for the first time permitted through running.

This great structure has two three-hundred-feet steel lattice-girder spans in the centre and carries four tracks.

The most famous of British tunnels is the Severn, by which the Great Western Railway main line to South Wales passes under the estuary of the River Severn. It is four and a quarter miles in length. Brunel's original main line to Cardiff and beyond, unable to cross this wide stretch of water, was taken circuitously round the head of the estuary by way of Gloucester. The opening of the Severn Tunnel diverted this traffic through Bristol instead, and with the help of the later cut-off built from Wootton Bassett, west of Swindon, to Patchway, near the eastern end of the tunnel, has reduced the journey from Paddington to South Wales by twenty-five miles.

Battle Against Water

Difficulties caused by irruptions of water into the workings were so severe that it was eleven years from the beginning of the work before the Severn Tunnel was finished.

Water broke in from the river-bed, and also from the ends, the latter due to the tidal wave, or bore, which sweeps up the estuary at regular intervals, as well as from a powerful underground source known as the Great Spring. Even since the opening of the tunnel it has been necessary to maintain pumping machinery, with a capacity of twenty million gallons of water daily, in order to keep this spring from flooding the line. The Severn Tunnel cost two million pounds sterling.

Through the Pennines

Elsewhere, the principal British tunnels are those which have been bored through the "backbone" of England, the Pennine range, to open up communication between Yorkshire and Lancashire. Totley is the longest. It is three and a half miles in length and is on the L.M.S. line between Sheffield and Manchester. The L.N.E.R. line between the same two cities passes through the two single-line Woodhead Tunnels, and the L.M.S. line from Leeds to Manchester

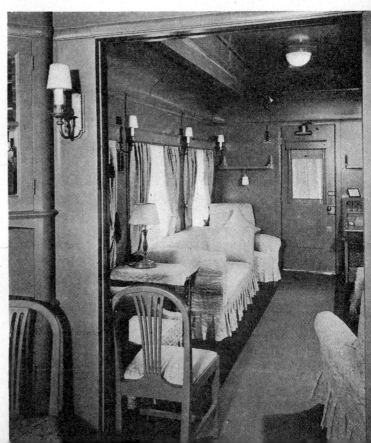

ROYAL TRAIN OF TO-DAY. Sitting-room of the Royal train which is provided for the King and Queen when they visit Canada. The photograph gives some idea of the progress of comfort in a little over a hundred years. No such elaborate interior was dreamed of in the days of the Lion, shown on the opposite page. The carriages were little more than stage coaches of the road adapted for rail travel and the refinements of interior furnishings, separate from the coach itself, were something beyond the imagination of the builders. Nowadays the travelling suite can be as comfortable as any hotel. A wooden box seat, with a cushion on top, was considered the acme of comfort in the days of the Lion.

through three parallel tunnels at Standedge; all of these are a few yards over three miles in length.

Actually, it is possible, in one through tube journey under London, to remain in a tunnel continuously for seventeen and a quarter miles. This is on the Northern line between East Finchley and Morden via the Bank. But the boring of single-line tube tunnels, a little less than twelve feet in diameter, through London clay or similar types of soil, differs totally from the laborious work needed in blasting a path through solid rock, deep under mountains.

Non-stop Runs

British railways have always taken a lead in running express trains over great distances without stopping. Notwithstanding the limitations of the island in which they are made, some of these non-stop runs easily hold the world-record for length. The longest of them is the summer journey of the L.N.E.R. Flying Scotsman, over the 393 miles between London and Edinburgh, covered in seven hours at an average speed of fifty-six point one miles an hour.

Next in order are the L.M.S. runs between Euston and Carlisle, varying in length between two hundred and ninety-eight and three hundred and one miles according to whether the train concerned is stopping at Carlisle passenger station, or outside the station for change of crew and train examination only. This non-stop run is made three times daily and five times each day during the summer. Except in the height of the summer season, when the L.N.E.R. non-stop Flying Scotsman timing is in force, the L.M.S. holds the world's non-stop record.

On the G.W.R., the longest journey without a stop is over the two hundred and twenty-five miles between Paddington and Plymouth. The Southern has nothing longer than the one hundred and eight miles between Waterloo and Bournemouth. No less than one hundred and twenty non-stop runs over one hundred miles in length are operated daily by British railways.

Slip Coaches

One method which is used by the G.W.R. to increase the length of run has been by slip coaches, which have made it possible to set down passengers at inter-

G.W.R. Cornish Riviera Limited on the sea coast at Dawlish

DINING CAR OF THE CORONATION SCOT. Another example of modern comfort. Progress in recent years has been in the direction of light and an air of spaciousness, with brightness introduced into the scheme by carefully contrasted colouring. The dining car shown is part of the train which, just before the Second World War, toured Canada and the U.S.A., afterwards being shown at the New York World Fair.

mediate stations without stopping the main train for the purpose. Severance of the train is effected from a guard's compartment at the front end of the slip portion, which has special equipment for the purpose. The front coupling hook of this coach is hinged; the coupling from the rear coach on the main train lies in the curve of the hook, with the hinged end of the hook held securely in the closed position by a sliding wedge. The latter is controlled by a lever in the guard's compartment.

Brake-pipe Connexion

A special type of coupling is also used to connect the brake hose-pipe on the slip with that on the back of the main train, and it is so designed that when the two pipes are forcibly pulled apart on the severance of the train, they come asunder without damage. This appliance is carried forward on the back of the main train, and automatically seals the vacuum in the train-pipe; otherwise the train itself would be brought to a sudden stop. The guard must seal the vacuum in the brake-pipe in the slip portion before he attempts to divide the train, and this is his first operation as the train approaches the slipping station.

Then, at the appropriate distance, varying according to the gradient, the speed of the train, and other factors, he pulls back his lever.

This action withdraws the wedge, allowing the front of the coupling hook to fall over, and the coupling of the coach ahead to fall out. The train is now in two halves, and the slip guard, by light pressure of his hand-brake, causes the slipped carriage to draw well behind the express. Finally, by suitable use of the vacuum brake, the guard brings the slipped coaches to rest at the station platform, with the express by now well on its way.

Another development which has played its part in increasing the length of runs has been the automatic exchange of mails. A train such as the L.M.S. West Coast Postal, needs only to stop at the principal junctions between London and Aberdeen, where the volume of mail matter exchanged is beyond the capacity of the automatic apparatus; elsewhere, all picking up and delivery of mails take place while the train is travelling at full speed.

Delivering the Mail

As the train nears a station at which a mail delivery is to be made, the mailbags for that place are strapped up tightly in stout leather pouches. These are attached by catches to traductor arms, which normally stand upright against the van side, but when required are pulled by the weight of the pouches, against the tension of a spring, into an horizontal position, so that the pouches are hanging well clear of the train. At the same time, a door at the side of the van is rolled back, and this movement opens out a large net, which lies folded in a recess when it is out of action. The mouth of the net, also well out from the van side, points forward in the direction of travel.

Meantime, a postal official of the town concerned has come to the fixed apparatus at the side of the line. He mounts the lineside standard, after strapping up his mailbags in pouches, attaches the latter to catches similar to those on the traductor arms, and turns them out towards the line. The mouth of the large ground net gapes wide open to receive the pouches off the train. The approach of the express is signalled by a bell in the postman's cabin.

Rapid Exchange

The exchange is over in a flash. A leather-bound rope above the mouth of the train net snatches the pouches off the ground standard, and drops them into the net, which is so shaped that the pouches are hurled through the van door and fall neatly on a mat in the centre of the van floor. Similarly, the pouches hanging at the side

of the train are "collared" by the ground net, and the traductor arms on the train swing back to the vertical. The van door is rolled to, closing the train net, and the exchange is complete.

Much of the correspondence put on to the train requires sorting, and the sorters and other postal officials carried on board total over forty men.

The special coaches used are capacious vans, with sorting counters along one side, and racks containing hundreds of pigeon-holes above them; along the other side are the rows of pegs on which the bags of letters are hung.

At times a heavy delivery is made by the West Coast Postal and the traductor arms along three or four sorting coaches may be in use simultaneously. It has also been quite a common practice on this train to do some of the sorting for the Irish Mail, on which the postal accommodation is limited to one or two vans, and to transfer the sorted letters from one express to the other without stopping either. This is done by dropping the Irish letters from the West Coast Postal into the ground net at Nuneaton; here the pouches are promptly taken and hung up on the ground standard, from which they are collected by the Irish Mail as it passes a quarter of an hour later.

Mail is also carried on passenger trains, for these in general run faster and adhere to rigid schedules.

Traffic Controls

It is not possible to work all freight traffic on hard-and-fast schedules owing to the fluctuations which occur in it from day to day.

Therefore, the main-line railways are divided up into areas, each with a control office which is in telephonic communication with every goods and marshalling yard and every signal-box in the area. The wall of the control office is mainly occupied by large track diagrams showing all the lines and sidings in the area.

Indicators hung on these diagrams at the appropriate points, show each train that is moving or standing in the area, and information as to its locomotive, the number of wagons, the crew and when they came on duty, and other details. Movements of the

Postal express pouch collecting mail at sixty miles an hour

trains are reported by telephone from the signal-boxes, and the position of the indicators on the control board is altered accordingly. The control office is thus able to arrange the working of engines and crews in such a way that the best use is made of each engine in steam.

Marshalling Yards

One particularly interesting feature in the control of freight-train working is the marshalling of trains in the great freight yards. At these concentration points, trains converge from all directions, and the wagons of which they are composed require to be sorted according to their destinations. In this sorting, gravity is often made to play a part. The wagons of each incoming train are uncoupled, and the trains are then pushed slowly over an artificial hump, on the far side of which there is a steep slope. This causes each wagon, after clearing the hump, to draw rapidly away from the rest of the train, and gives time for the switches giving access to the gridiron of sorting sidings to be moved, between wagon and wagon, in order that each wagon may run, according to its ultimate destination, into the correct track.

By the latest equipment, the work of marshalling has been completely mechanized. Before a train is pushed over the hump, the wagons are uncoupled in the usual way, and a list of their destinations, compiled by a shunter, is posted by pneumatic tube to the control tower.

Automatic Working

From these particulars, the entire movements of the wagons of the complete train are set up on a control machine which operates the switches leading to the gridiron. As each wagon runs down the hump, the switches are automatically reset behind it for the next wagon following. The switches beyond these are moved by power from the control tower.

To speed up working, the gradient off the hump is steepened: but in order that wagons may not suffer damage by running too fast into the gridiron tracks, and colliding with wagons already there, railbrakes are located in the tracks between the master-switches and the gridiron

switches, gripping the wheel-flanges as the wagons pass through them, so slowing the wagons down. The action of the rail-brakes is also controlled from the tower, and is intensified or reduced according to whether the track into which the wagon is running is full or empty.

The working day of the railway lasts for twenty-four hours. Some trains may stop running for an hour or so after midnight, but the servicing of locomotives, constant attention to all forms of apparatus and the maintenance of the track, create the necessity for shift working as a normal routine.

Even the ordinary working day, from before daylight till midnight, would be impossible without changing shifts. Very few railway workers have what is understood by the average person as a normal day, and these are usually only to be found in the offices.

The engine-driver and the signalman, the staffs of the locomotive sheds, platelayers and line engineers, and all those connected with the actual working of the traffic, have to get used to changing hours. Otherwise continuous service would be impossible.

Training an Engine Driver

The staff at an engine shed includes fitters and others concerned with locomotive maintenance, as well as cleaners, firemen and drivers.

Cleaning is the first rung of the ladder which leads ultimately to driving. The driver-to-be, during his work of cleaning the engines, inside and outside, is learning how they are designed and built. He is next passed as a fireman, and during his years of firing, by watching his driver at work, he learns the management of a locomotive. At the same time, he is becoming acquainted by degrees with the characteristics of the lines over which he works. He learns the signals and gradients, and railway rules for working trains.

Working up slowly from shunting engine to passenger and express passenger engine, the fireman is next passed as a driver, and the same process of working up from shunting engine to express passenger engine puts him at length into the top link at his shed, to which all the most responsible

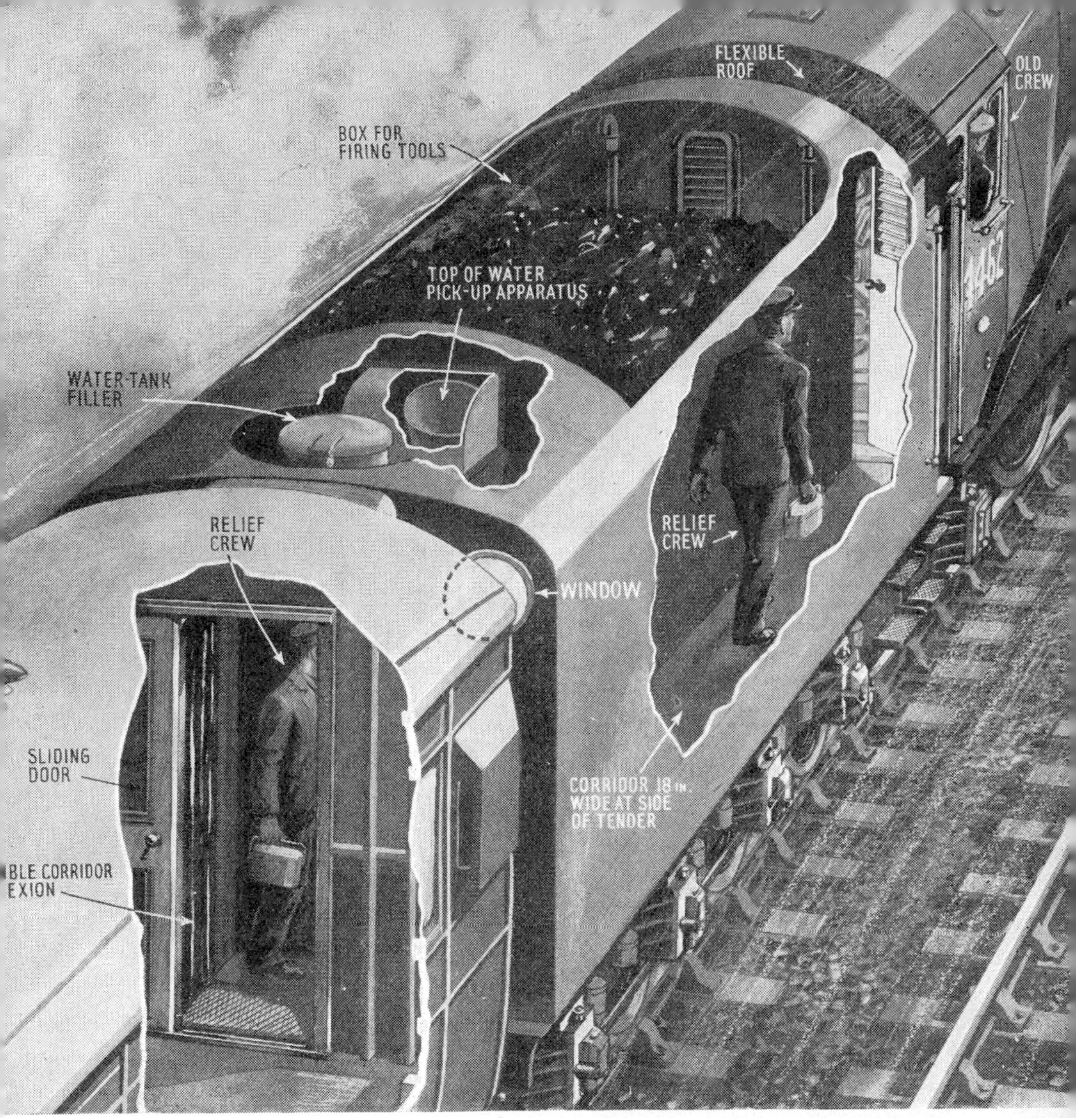
FLEXIBLE ROOF
OLD CREW
BOX FOR FIRING TOOLS
TOP OF WATER PICK-UP APPARATUS
WATER-TANK FILLER
RELIEF CREW
RELIEF CREW
WINDOW
SLIDING DOOR
BLE CORRIDOR EXION
CORRIDOR 18 IN. WIDE AT SIDE OF TENDER

CORRIDOR TENDER specially built to enable train crews to be changed on the non-stop journey of the Flying Scotsman. The L.N.E.R. is the only railway company in the world that has produced tenders of this type. They are so arranged that a narrow passage-way, just wide enough for a man to pass through, connects the corridor of the first coach in the train with the foot-plate of the locomotive. These tenders carry five thousand gallons of water.

and lucrative workings from the shed are entrusted. This is a long road, and it knows no short cuts.

Drivers and crews of long-distance expresses are frequently away all night, and the arranging of the working rota and the schedules, in conformity with duty and off-duty periods, is a task in itself. Similar careful planning is necessary with regard to the locomotives themselves, so that engines in steam are not left standing idle for long periods. In addition, their times of coaling and taking on water have to be planned, and it is on points of this nature that accurate schedules and high-speed timings depend.

A locomotive tender, for example, should have sufficient coal capacity for the longest

CUT RUNS AWAY DOWN
1 IN 18 FOR 50 YARDS

130 YARDS AT 1 IN 75

OUT TO
MARSHALLING
SIDINGS —

HUMP
SUMMIT

3 MILES AN HOUR UP FROM
RECEPTION SIDINGS
GRADIENT 1 IN 80

KING
POINTS

QUEEN
POINTS

CUT GOING THROUGH
RAIL BRAKES

FLOOD LIGHTS
AND LOUDSPEAKERS

RAIL
BRAKES

QUEEN
POINTS

KING
POINTS

CONTROL
CABIN

HUMP

HYDRAULIC
ACCUMULATOR

HYDRAULIC
POWER

HUMP
SUMMIT

UP SLOW   UP FAST   MAIN   LINE   DOWN FAST   DOWN SLOW

**HUMP MARSHALLING YARD. Where freight wagons are sorted out according to
their destinations. The hump is a rising section of track over which the shunting
engine pushes a line of uncoupled wagons. The sorter in the reception sidings
has previously made a note of their destinations and this information has been**

SORTING SIDINGS WITH EMPTY FISH VANS, OIL TANKS, INSULATED VANS, CONTAINERS AND FLATS, OPEN WAGONS, COVERED VANS, CATTLE VANS AND GUARDS BRAKES

WAGON REPAIR SHOPS

TRAIN BEING ASSEMBLED

COMPLETED TRAIN PULLING OUT TO PICK UP GUARD'S VAN

ENGINE BY-PASS ROADS

RAIL BRAKES IN ACTION

BRAKE RAILS GRIP WHEEL TYRES

WHEELS LIFTED CLEAR OF RUNNING RAILS

LIFTING BEAM

HYDRAULIC JACK

passed to the control cabin where it is fed to the point-setting mechanism in a sequence corresponding to the position of each wagon in the line. As the cuts break away and run down the slope, the switches are set ready for them, each wagon or group of wagons altering the points for the one immediately behind.

77

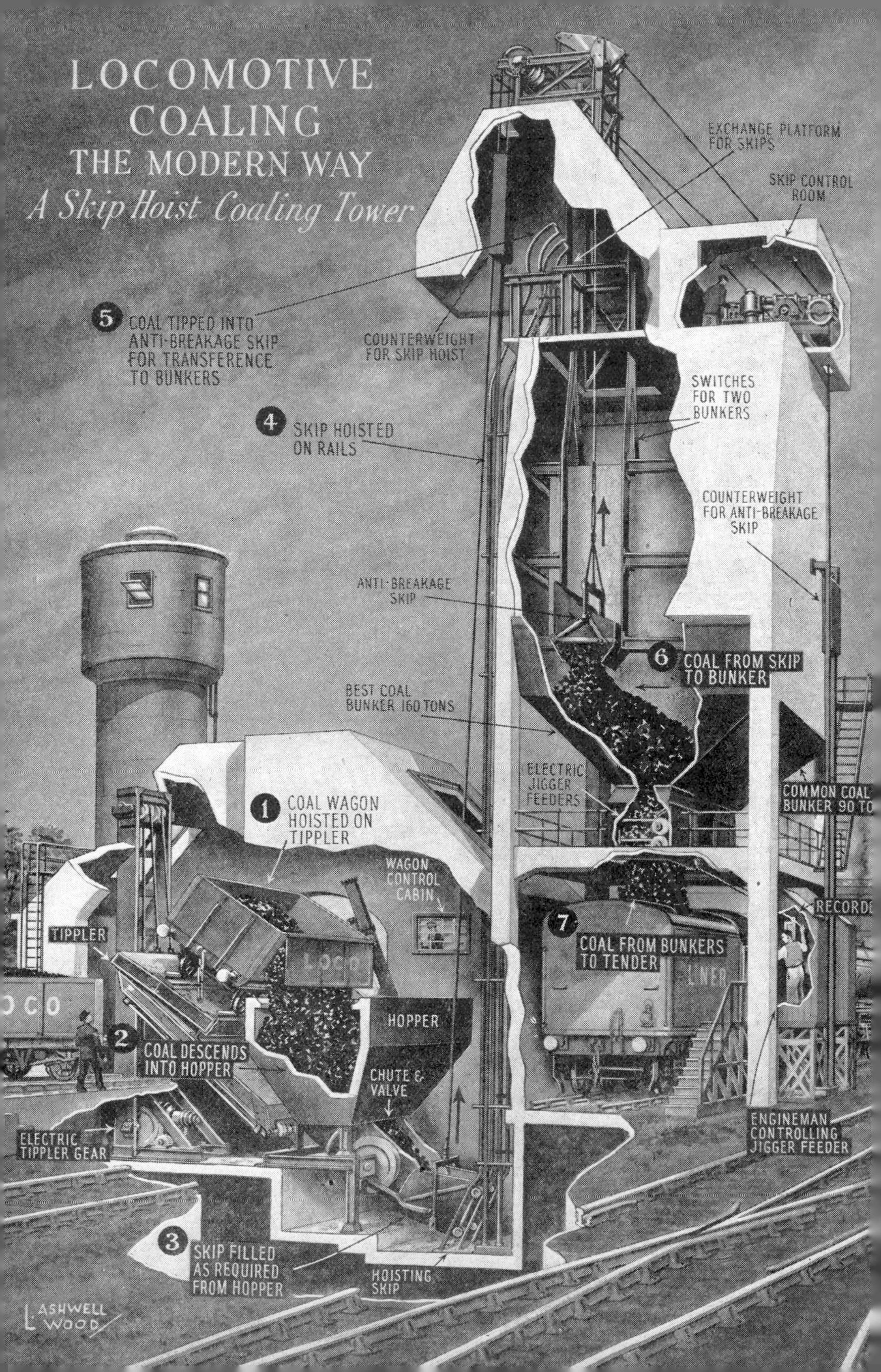

LOCOMOTIVE COALING
THE MODERN WAY
A Skip Hoist Coaling Tower

EXCHANGE PLATFORM
FOR SKIPS

SKIP CONTROL
ROOM

5 COAL TIPPED INTO
ANTI-BREAKAGE SKIP
FOR TRANSFERENCE
TO BUNKERS

COUNTERWEIGHT
FOR SKIP HOIST

SWITCHES
FOR TWO
BUNKERS

4 SKIP HOISTED
ON RAILS

COUNTERWEIGHT
FOR ANTI-BREAKAGE
SKIP

ANTI-BREAKAGE
SKIP

6 COAL FROM SKIP
TO BUNKER

BEST COAL
BUNKER 160 TONS

1 COAL WAGON
HOISTED ON
TIPPLER

ELECTRIC
JIGGER
FEEDERS

COMMON COAL
BUNKER 90 TO

WAGON
CONTROL
CABIN

RECORD

TIPPLER

7 COAL FROM BUNKERS
TO TENDER

LOCO

HOPPER

2 COAL DESCENDS
INTO HOPPER

CHUTE &
VALVE

OCO

ELECTRIC
TIPPLER GEAR

ENGINEMAN
CONTROLLING
JIGGER FEEDER

3 SKIP FILLED
AS REQUIRED
FROM HOPPER

HOISTING
SKIP

L ASHWELL
WOOD

COALING BY MACHINERY. There are several methods in use on British railways. In the skip coaling tower, illustrated on the opposite page, the coal is tipped from the truck at rail-level, and falls into a hopper from which it is led by a chute to the skip or bucket. This is raised on steadying rails and tipped by means of a curve in the rails into a bucket inside the tower. In the bucket it is lowered and shot into one or other of the two storage bunkers, according to grade or quality, from either of which it can be fed as required to the locomotives standing below. In the second type of coaling tower, shown on the right, the coal wagon is raised bodily on a lifting section of the rails, and the coal is tipped direct into the bunkers. In both types the principle is the same and consists in storing the coal above the level of the tender for easy feeding by gravity.

runs that it may be called upon to make, so that it need not re-fuel during its working day, and it would be a sad misfortune if, say, a tank engine of small coal capacity were to be the only one available for a long freight run at any particular time when an additional train was required.

Modern Coaling Methods

Many improvements have been made in coaling engines, particularly as regards the speed with which it is done. A modern skip coaling tower delivers coal to a locomotive tender from bunkers built over the track, coal of the necessary grade pouring through a wedge-shaped chute until the tender is full.

The bunkers are loaded by skips which travel up rails outside the coaling tower,

and tip their contents automatically into a descending container, which in turn fills the bunkers. The skips themselves are filled from a hopper when on the ground level, or just below ground level, and the hopper gets its supply from coal wagons drawn up on a feeder track close by. These wagons are tilted so that they shoot their contents into the hopper in one go, thereby effecting an enormous saving in time over the former manual methods. The coal passes from the wagon to the tender, by means of the coaling tower, without once being touched by hand.

Another system of coaling has been devised in which the coal wagon itself is used as a form of skip. In this method, instead of tilting the wagon at ground level, and passing the coal through hopper and skip to the overhead bunkers, the wagon itself is lifted bodily up the side of the coaling tower, not tilting its load until it reaches a chute leading directly to the bunkers.

Coal for Long Runs

The biggest British tenders, such as those attached to the Pacific type locomotive, will carry nine to ten tons of coal, which is sufficient for runs of four hundred miles or so.

This is enough, in other words, for the world's longest non-stop run, that of the Flying Scotsman, which does just under four hundred miles on its famous trip between London and Edinburgh.

This run is so long that it is necessary to change engine crews on the way, and to make this possible there has to be a connexion between the footplate and the train, in which the relay crew await their turn for duty.

Connexion is by means of a corridor tender, the only corridor type in existence in the world. It has a passageway actually alongside the coal and water supplies and through this the crews reach the footplate of the locomotive.

The corridor, only eighteen inches wide and five feet high, is carried along the right side of the tender to the rear, where it bends sharply and gives access to a door in the centre of the back of the tender; there a gangway connexion provides for coupling to the gangway of the leading coach. A compartment is reserved in the latter for the engine crews, who change places at the midway point on the run, just north of York. These eight-wheel tenders are the heaviest on British railways. When fully loaded, they weigh sixty-four tons, or as much as two full-length corridor coaches.

Taking Up Water

Although they carry enough coal for a day's working, however, even the largest British tenders do not carry more than five thousand gallons of water, enough in one sense, but not nearly enough for the longest runs. Fortunately, water is much more easily taken on board, even while the train is in motion. The usual method is to scoop it up from troughs laid between the rails, and it is possible to lift as much as

80

WATER SCOOP. Water is scooped up from a long narrow trough between the rails by force of engine speed alone. As the train approaches a water-trough,

two thousand gallons at speed at a time.

Each trough has to be laid on a perfectly level stretch of line, and is just over a quarter of a mile in length. Under the tender of the engine is a hinged scoop, the end of which is shaped like a large kitchen shovel.

The scoop is lowered as the train approaches the trough, and a slight down gradient in the track automatically dips it into the water. By the speed of the train alone, water is forced up under tremendous pressure, and travels through a vertical

DOME

ORDINARY TANK FILLER

AIR-DISPLACEMENT VENT

TANK SPACE

COAL SPACE

RISER PIPE

SUPPORT BRACKET

COUNTERWEIGHT

SCOOP LIFTING LINK

ECONOMIZER LIFTING LINKS

HINGE

SCOOP LOWERED

ONOMIZER GUIDING ATER INTO SCOOP

the scoop is lowered and then a slight down-grade of the rails causes it to dip into the trough. The lowest speed at which water can be lifted is about twenty miles an hour, but in America there are scoops which lift over seven thousand gallons of water from a single trough at a speed of seventy-five miles an hour.

delivery pipe and mushroom head into the water tank in the tender.

There is a gauge on the tender front, visible in the cab, which indicates when the tank is full, and it is then the fireman's duty to lift the scoop clear of the trough, a job for which suitable mechanism is provided. But, travelling at speed, this could not be left entirely to human fallibility, so there is a further gradient at the other end which lifts the scoop clear before it reaches the end of the trough.

Troughs such as these are located on all

main express routes at suitable points, not merely on straight and level track, but also where there is a good supply of water. In some cases, however, the water is hard and unsuitable for use in a steam engine, so then a water-softener plant is installed.

From a large lineside tank, controlled by a sensitive ball-valve arrangement, water is fed to the trough at a number of different points, so that it may fill rapidly for the next train after an express has taken its supply.

Many such arrangements make for the efficiency of the railway, not the least of

EIGHTY MILES AN HOUR WITHOUT MOVING. In the G.W.R. Works at Swindon. A locomotive on the test rollers. These rollers are movable, and can be adjusted so that the centre of each driving wheel is exactly above the centre of each roller. High speeds can be worked up while the engine remains stationary, and a braking arrangement on the rollers tests the pulling power of the engine at various speeds.

which is the testing of locomotives under load, both in actual service conditions and on plants built specially for the accurate observation of their performance.

One such plant exists at the Swindon works of the Great Western. In principle it is similar to many others throughout the world, all of which consist of huge rollers on which the engine is mounted for the test.

These rollers can be adjusted in such a way that the centre-line of each coupled axle on the locomotive is exactly over the centre-line of each roller. On the regulator being opened, at the beginning of the test, the driving wheels begin to revolve, driving the rollers while the engine itself remains stationary.

In this way, the locomotive can be worked up to what are, in effect, tremendous speeds and by ingenious braking devices the

rollers take up and keep a continuous measurement of the power that is being developed. Above all, even speeds can be maintained in unvarying conditions, as compared with road tests on the line, which are subject to variations of weather, gradient and other conditons.

Other methods have been devised to make tests under actual working conditions, and of these the dynamometer car is a good example. The locomotive pulls this special car by a coupling connected to a spring balance, and, by an ingenious arrangement of further springs, drums and balance weights, records are made of all the necessary facts of the engine's abilities.

The Hallade track recorder is another ingenious piece of mechanism, in this case for the purpose of testing the condition of the track. As the rails wear, and rain and

OSCILLATING BUCKETS

HARD-WATER SUPPLY PIPE

REAGENT MIXING TANK

INTAKE TANK

SOFT-WATER PIPE

ENGINE PICKING UP FROM TROUGHS

WOOD-FIBRE FILTER

PUMP HOUSE

SOFT WATER RISING

PICK-UP TROUGH

TROUGH SUPPLY TANK

CHEMICAL REAGENT SUPPLY TANK

PRECIPITATE SETTLING TANK

SLUDGE VALVE

WATER-SOFTENING TOWER. Necessary, but probably seldom recognized piece of apparatus, used wherever the water requires treatment for boiler use. Water can be unsuitable for steam-raising for a variety of reasons, chief of which is the lime content, which causes an excessive amount of fur or scale on the inside of the boiler. The storage tank for the pick-up troughs is shown on the right.

INTERIOR OF DYNAMOMETER CAR. Used to test the capabilities of a locomotive under actual running conditions. In the foreground is the moving paper roll on which the recording pens give a continuous record of the pull of the locomotive, through the medium of the lever in front of the table, which is connected with the draw-bar. Many other valuable data are recorded. The car shown belongs to the L.N.E.R.

frost make their insidious encroachments on ballast and embankments, many inequalities arise in the permanent way which might not be noticed until, perhaps, they had gone too far. These are all recorded by the apparatus, whose principle of working is simple in the extreme.

A clockwork mechanism drives a drum by means of a small chain, and a roll of paper unwinds at an even speed. Above this are a number of pens which mark the paper as it moves beneath them. If the whole apparatus is perfectly steady, the pens merely draw a straight line, but, placed on the floor of an ordinary coach, travelling over any section of line for which data are needed, they draw a series of waves in accordance with the vibrations received, and from these the engineers can tell the state of the track.

The pens are connected to pendulums, which swing with the jolting of the coach, one for sideways movement, one for movement in the direction the train is travelling, and the third for vertical movement, or bumps. A pneumatic tube and press-button used by the operator marks on the roll the mile posts or other lineside structures passed.

For the use of railway staff, in connexion with the running of trains, working time-tables are prepared which give not only the times of the various passenger trains, but all movements of freight and coal trains, rolling stock, light engines and a mass of

HALLADE TRACK RECORDER. Ingenious piece of mechanism for making a record of the state of the track while the train is in motion. The recorder is placed on the floor of the coach and the record appears in the form of a continuous graph on the paper roll, which is fed to the pens by clockwork.

detail necessary for the smooth working of schedules.

In preparing time-tables, the modern practice is to plot the entire train service over each route on large sheets of squared paper, in the form of a graph. The stations are given as the vertical ordinate, and the hours of the day as the horizontal ordinate. Each train, therefore, appears as a diagonal line, steeper or flatter according to its speed. A horizontal break in any line indicates a stop. Different kinds of line are used to indicate different types of train.

Automatic electric block
signal installation on the
Canadian Pacific Railway

CHAPTER FOUR

MODERN METHODS OF SIGNALLING

O F all the factors that make for safety in the control of trains, none is more important than signalling. Modern methods are becoming more and more automatic, until the trains on some lines not only signal themselves, but even come to a standstill without any movement on the part of the driver, if they happen to reach a stop signal at danger.

In the early days of railway operation, safe running was attempted merely by keeping a time interval between the trains, and it is a curious fact that, if strict timetable observance were possible, no further safety precautions might be needed.

But it was soon realized that many factors might upset such strict observance, and that some means must be found of separating trains by a space interval rather than by an interval of time.

Block Signalling

Such was the origin of the British block system of signalling; and how important this space interval is, may be better understood when it is realized that some main line junctions and termini handle hundreds of trains in one working day.

Clapham Junction is the world's busiest junction, with two thousand five hundred trains passing through it daily. London Bridge, partly junction and partly a terminus, handles over two thousand trains daily. Of the London termini, Waterloo is the busiest, with nearly fourteen hundred trains a day, although Liverpool Street tackles eleven hundred, all steam-operated.

To make this enormous volume of traffic possible, the trains themselves must be spaced as closely as one every two minutes or less, at the busiest rush hours. On the London tube lines, the spacing is even closer, as many as forty trains to the hour passing over the same track, with a record on one line of forty-three to the hour.

The block system is simple in theory. A railway line is controlled by a series of signal-boxes, each of which is responsible for working a group of signals in its own vicinity. Between the area of control of each pair of boxes, there is a block section, and the general principle is that not more than one train or engine shall be in motion at the same time, on the same line of rails, in any one block. The block sections thus ensure that the necessary space interval shall be maintained between the trains.

Semaphore Type

Before we go into the signal-box, however, and see how it is worked, it is necessary to have some acquaintance with the various types of signal.

In the older type of semaphore signal, the arm is lowered to an angle of forty-five degrees when pulled off, but the newer type, standard on nearly all lines today, is the upper-quadrant signal, with the arm inclined upwards at forty-five degrees when in the off position. In both cases, the signal is on when the arm is horizontal, and semaphore signals of either upper or lower quadrant type always point to the left of the track which they control.

Automatic Safety Device

It is essential that if any part of the operating connexion to the arm should break, the arm should return automatically to the horizontal position. In the lower-quadrant type, this is assured by the provision of a heavy spectacle casting for the coloured glasses for night use, which balances the arm, but the upper-quadrant arm would fall to danger by its own weight, this being one of the advantages which has caused the change from the lower to the upper-quadrant type. Balance weights are used at the foot of the post to take up the slack in the wire from the signal box.

The coloured light indications which take the place of the arm at night, are exhibited by the two glasses in the spectacle frame moving up and down in front of a white lamp. At the back of the lamp, on the opposite side to the colour signals, a small white light is shown, which is obscured when the arm is pulled off by what is known as a back-light blinder. This is to show the signalman, when he can see only the back of the signal, that the arm has responded to the pull of his lever. If the signal is out of sight of the box, an electric repeater, worked by the movement of the arm, is provided in the box for the same purpose.

Stop Signals

Running signals, those controlling running lines as distinct from sidings, have two main divisions, stop and distant signals. Stop signals have arms with square ends, and are painted red; distant signals have ends like fish-tails, and are painted yellow.

A stop signal in the horizontal position is at danger, and compels any train approaching it to stop; a distant signal in the horizontal position is at caution, and may be passed in that position, but at reduced speed and with the driver prepared to bring his train to a halt at the next stop signal.

At night, stop signals show a red light for danger, and distant signals show an orange light for caution. When pulled off, both show a green light.

Distant Signals

As a train approaches the end of a block section, the first signal to be sighted is the distant, usually from a half to three-quarters of a mile away from the box that controls it. Immediately before the box there is a stop signal, known as the home, and a little more than a train's length beyond the box there is another stop signal, known as the starter.

A mechanical locking-table under the signal-box floor prevents the signalman from pulling off the distant signal until the home and the starter are also in the off position. This assures the driver, when he sees a distant signal in the clear position, that all the stop signals of the next box applying to the track on which he is running are also in the clear position. Conversely, when the distant signal is at caution, he knows that all stop signals ahead are at

TOKEN SIGNALLING. This system is sometimes used on a single track to prevent two trains entering the line from opposite ends. No train is allowed to proceed unless the driver carries a token. Electrically-controlled instruments at both ends of the line contain the tokens, and it is impossible to release a token until the last one withdrawn has been fed back into one of the instruments.

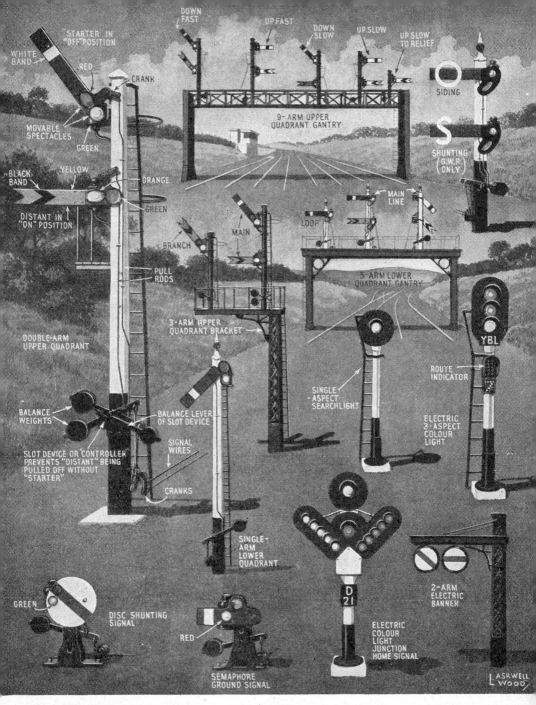

STARTER IN "OFF" POSITION

WHITE BAND

RED

CRANK

DOWN FAST

UP FAST

DOWN SLOW

UP SLOW

UP SLOW TO RELIEF

SIDING

MOVABLE SPECTACLES

GREEN

BLACK BAND

YELLOW

ORANGE

9-ARM UPPER QUADRANT GANTRY

S

SHUNTING (G.W.R.) ONLY

GREEN

DISTANT IN "ON" POSITION

MAIN

BRANCH

PULL RODS

LOOP

MAIN LINE

5-ARM LOWER QUADRANT GANTRY

DOUBLE-ARM UPPER QUADRANT

3-ARM UPPER QUADRANT BRACKET

ROUTE INDICATOR

YBL

BALANCE WEIGHTS

BALANCE LEVER OF SLOT DEVICE

SINGLE-ASPECT SEARCHLIGHT

ELECTRIC 3-ASPECT COLOUR LIGHT

SIGNAL WIRES

SLOT DEVICE OR CONTROLLER PREVENTS "DISTANT" BEING PULLED OFF WITHOUT "STARTER"

CRANKS

SINGLE-ARM LOWER QUADRANT

GREEN

DISC SHUNTING SIGNAL

RED

D 21

2-ARM ELECTRIC BANNER

ELECTRIC COLOUR LIGHT JUNCTION HOME SIGNAL

SEMAPHORE GROUND SIGNAL

L ASHWELL WOOD

TYPES OF SIGNALS. In the upper-quadrant type, which is gradually replacing the lower-quadrant type, the arm is raised when the signal is pulled off. In the event of any breakage of a connexion, the arm would drop to danger or caution by reason of its own weight. In the lower-quadrant signals, the spectacle casting holding the glasses was sufficiently weighty to balance the arm.

GROUND SIGNALS. Standard type of Southern Railway ground signal, here seen in use at Ashford, Kent. Ground signals control the movement of trains on sidings and loops and are made as distinct as possible, in shape and appearance, from those of the running track. They are also used for shunting and marshalling. Ground signals are of various types, and sometimes resemble miniature signal arms.

danger, and thus has time and space in which to pull up. The faster the train, therefore, the more important is the function of the distant signal.

At junction boxes, or boxes controlling sidings, there may be additional signals. An advanced starter, ahead of the starter proper, is a common addition when a siding track comes out on to the main line ahead of the starter.

Junction Protection

Similarly, for the protection of a junction, there may be an outer home, farther out from the box than the home signal. If the outer home were not provided, it would be necessary to keep the train at the previous box, if the junction were blocked by a train from another direction. But the double protection of both outer home and home allows the train to come through the block section as far as the former, even when the junction is blocked, and so helps in the all-

important business of keeping the traffic moving.

Where block sections are short, the starting signal of one box is often mounted above the distant signal of the next, on the same post. In such cases, a mechanical contrivance, called a slot, is provided at the base of the post to ensure that the distant signal, even when its balance-weight has been pulled off, shall not move to the off position until the starter also is off. The slot returns the distant signal to caution automatically, as soon as the stop signal returns to danger.

Splitting Home Signals

At the approach to a junction, splitting home signals are installed, one semaphore, usually the tallest, controlling the main line ahead, and the others controlling divergencies of track to left or right of it.

In earlier days, the approaches to terminal stations were often controlled by

RED

MAIN STARTING SIGNAL

INSULATORS

Nº 2 TRACK CIRCUIT

ELECTRIC MOTOR

MAINS SUPPLY

POINT THROW BAR

GEARING

TO SIGNAL-BOX

NOTCHED STRETCHER BLADE

POINT LOCK

POINT LOCK BAR

SIGNAL DETECTORS

TO MAIN & BRANCH HOME SIGNALS

SIGNAL CIRCUIT

Nº 1 TRACK CIRCUIT

TO SIGNAL-BOX "C"

POINT MACHINE

DETECTOR

POINTS LOCKED FOR BRANCH

ENLARGED VIEW OF POWER POINT LAYOUT

TRACK RECORDER

SIGNAL REPEATERS

LEVERS

ELECTRIC INTERLOCKING FRAME

BRANCH HOME

WHITE

JUNCTION HOME SIGNAL

GREEN

SIGNAL CIRCUITS

INSULATORS

TRAIN ENTERING SECTION "B"

POINTS CIRCUIT

SIGNAL-BOX "B"

APPROACH TRACK CIRCUIT

BATTERIES & RELAYS

SIGNAL CIRCUIT

TRACK CIRCUIT RELAYS & BATTERY

TO SIGNAL-BOX "A"

2682

3 ASPECT COLOUR LIGHT SIGNAL SET AT DANGER BEHIND TRAIN BY APPROACH TRACK CIRCUIT

MAIN DISTANT SIGNAL

ASHWELL WOOD

ELECTRIC COLOUR LIGHT SIGNALLING
Simplified Track Layout and Circuits

complicated and spectacular gantries of signals, with many posts and arms, but to-day, when the main aim is to simplify signal indications, these are disappearing. It is now the practice to install for each running line a single stop arm above a frame in which appears a letter or number, the number indicating to which line or platform the track is set.

Use of Dwarf Signals

For controlling sidings, it is customary to use dwarf semaphore signals, or ground signals, of a type as distinct as possible from the running signals. Small draw-ahead semaphore signals are also used to permit restricted movement past stop signals when the block section ahead is not clear. These allow a driver to draw past a stop signal at danger, but only so far as will permit him, say, to run to a platform which is already

partly occupied, or to shunt back to another track or siding.

All-electric light signals, which dispense with arms, throw a beam of such brilliance as to be visible from considerable distances in broad daylight. They duplicate the semaphore indications and use red for danger, orange or yellow for caution, and green for clear. On busy routes, four-light signals are used, giving red, yellow, double yellow and green. Single yellow shows that one section ahead is clear; double yellow, two sections; and green, at least three sections. The purpose is to enable drivers, where trains are running on very short headway, so to control the speed of their trains that unnecessary acceleration or braking is avoided.

Electric colour-light signalling is often completely automatic in its action. Automatic action is achieved by means of track

much of the London underground network.

Track circuits are also used extensively at stations and elsewhere to prevent a signalman from admitting a second train to a section that is already occupied. The usual method of application in such cases is an electro-mechanical lock on the lever concerned, together with a visual reminder in the shape of a track circuit indicator.

The block system is worked under very carefully defined rules. In the signal-box the electric block instruments stand on a shelf above the levers, immediately in front of the signalman. Movement of a train from the box in the rear to the one in advance is authorized by a code of bell signals on single-stroke bells, and is confirmed by indicator needles on the dials of the block instruments.

In a Main-line Box

Let us imagine ourselves in a main-line signal-box at a time when an express train is expected. It is the middle box in a sequence of three—A, B and C. First, our signalman B hears a single stroke on the bell operated by A. This is known as the call-attention beat, and signalman B acknowledges it by sounding a similar single beat back to A.

Next come four beats from A in equal succession, which, according to the code, mean "Is line clear for express passenger train?" Signalman B again repeats the signal back to A, sounding four beats on the A-B circuit, and then, provided the line is clear, he sets the needle of his A-B block instrument from its previous line-blocked

circuits, whereby the two rails of one track are made to carry a weak current, but are insulated from each other. When a train is standing or running on a track-circuited section, a short circuit is created through the wheels and axles, and this is used to break down a relay which, in its turn, keeps the next stop signal behind the train at danger until the track-circuited section has been cleared. All the London tube lines are signalled in this way.

Combined Methods

Sometimes automatic signalling is combined with semaphore signals, as over the Southern Railway between Woking and Basingstoke, but the operating principle is the same. On this particular stretch of line, the actual movement of the signal arms is by pneumatic power, and electro-pneumatic signalling is similarly in use over

MANUAL SIGNAL-BOX. Type of signal-box from which the signals are moved and controlled by heavy manual-levers. A lever is connected by wire with the signal or by rodding with the pair of points it controls, and quite an effort may be required to pull over a pair of points or move a locking-bar. Except at busy junctions and termini, the majority of boxes in use are of this type.

position to line-clear. The electrical circuit causes a similar needle on A's A-B block instrument to take the line-clear position, and A can then pull off his signals.

Signalman B has next to obtain line-clear from signalman C, in the box ahead, so he rings call-attention on the B-C bell circuit and, after hearing its acknowledgment, follows it with the four beats in succession. Watching the B-C block instrument, he sees the needle jump to line-clear and then lowers his signals, starter first, home next and the distant last. Nothing may now foul the track until the express has passed.

Next, our signalman B hears two beats on the A-B bell, and adjusts the needle of the A-B instrument to train-on-line. The co-acting needle in A's box similarly moves to train-on-line, and both instruments thus indicate that the block section between A and B boxes is occupied by a train. This bell signal is generally known as train-

94

entering-section, and is given by A at the moment when the express roars past him.

Soon the rumbling sound of the train is heard approaching box B, in which we are standing. As it flashes past the box, our signalman B rings two beats—train-entering-section—on the B-C circuit to signalman C, and watches the needle of the B-C instrument move to train-on-line.

Signalman B now has to advise signalman A that the train has passed. First he puts his signals back to danger, and then he rings two-beats-pause-one-beat back to A, and adjusts the needle of the A-B instrument from train-on-line to line-blocked, the needle of the A-B circuit in A's box showing a corresponding movement. Not until this has been done is signalman A permitted to offer the next succeeding train to our signalman B.

Last of all comes signalman C's two-pause-one ring back to signalman B, who

LOCKS 5. RELEASES 3

LOCKS I. RELEASES 3.5

RELEASED BY 1.2

LOCKS I.2 RELEASES 6

RELEASED BY 2 LOCKS I. RELEASES 6

RELEASED BY 4.5

TRACK DIAGRAM

TRACK CIRCUIT INDICATOR SHEWING "OCCUPIED" or "CLEAR"

BLOCK INSTRUMENTS FROM "A"

BLOCK INSTRUMENTS TO "C"

TELEGRAPH TO SIGNAL BOX "C"

4 DOWN MAIN STARTING

ELECTRIC REPEATER FOR DISTANT

BATTERY

RELAY

POSITION OF SIGNAL BOX "B"

TRACK CIRCUIT

INSULATORS

LOCKING FRAME

TELEGRAPH FROM SIGNAL BOX "A"

5 DOWN MAIN HOME

SIGNAL DETECTOR

3 DOWN MAIN TO BRANCH "OFF"

1 FACING POINTS

2 FACING POINT LOCK

RODDING FROM SIGNAL BOX

1000 YARDS (Approx)

TRACK CIRCUIT

DOWN MAIN

NOTCHES IN STREICHER BLADE

6 DOWN MAIN DISTANT AT "CAUTION"

SIGNAL DETECTOR SLIDES

INSULATORS

INSULATORS

WIRE TO SIGNAL 5 LOCKED

WIRE TO SIGNAL 3 FREE

FACING POINT LOCK BOLT

ELECTRIC REPEATER WIRE FOR DISTANT

TRAIN LEAVING SECTION AND ENTERING STATION LIMITS

ENLARGED VIEW OF POINT MECHANISM

BLOCK SIGNALLING. Box B as described in the text. The section of line it controls would be much longer in practice than that shown between the signals, caution, home and starter, and the box has been enlarged to show the locking sequence of the levers. Also enlarged is the mechanism of the facing points, showing the position they would be in for this setting of the signals.

AMAZING BURROWING JUNCTIONS
CHALK FARM-PRIMROSE HILL TUNNELS
L.M.S. MAIN LINE LONDON

DOWN FAST TRAIN FROM EUSTON

FROM ENGINE SHED

DOWN ELECTRIC TRAIN FROM EUSTON TO WATFORD

DOWN SLOW

EUSTON LINES

UP SLOW

GOODS LINES

ENGINE LINE

UP FAST LINE TO EUSTON

7100

DOWN ELECTRIC LINE FROM BROAD ST. TO WATFORD

FROM GOODS YARDS

BROAD ST. LINES

PRIMROSE HILL TUNNELS

UP FAST

DOWN SLOW

UP SLOW

DOWN

UP

ELECTRIC LINES

ENGINE LINE FROM SHEDS TO GOODS YARD

DOWN ELECTRIC LINES

UP ELECTRIC TO EUSTON

SKEW BRIDGE

RETAINING WALL

NORTH LONDON LINES

DOWN

UP

UP EMPTY CARRIAGES TO EUSTON

UP STOP SIGNAL NORTH LONDON LINE

UP ELECTRIC TRAIN TO BROAD ST.

ELECTRIC SIGNALS

THIS LINE GOES UNDER ALL TRACKS TO FAR SIDE OF DOWN FAST LINE

L. ASHWELL WOOD

watches the needle of the B-C instrument return to line-blocked. The sequence of signalling the express past box B is thus completed. There are variations of the "Is line clear?" code for each type of train; a stopping passenger train, for example, is indicated by three-beats-pause-one-beat and so on.

Bell-Signal Code

The code of bell signals hangs in a prominent position in every signal-box. Besides the normal code bells, it has a great many variations covering every conceivable happening, both normal and abnormal, in the movement of the trains. In any box, the block instruments controlling a double line are four in number, one to the box in front and one to the box in rear for each track.

On some lines, the up and down indications for each direction are combined in a single instrument with two dials. At junction signal-boxes, the array of instruments is astonishing, and it takes the ear of an expert to distinguish the various tones of the many bells and gongs that are in use.

Below the instrument shelf in a manually-worked box is the row of levers, the shafts coloured in accordance with the signal they work.

Levers of stop signals have red shafts, those of distant signals are yellow, locking-bars are blue, and those not actually in use but reserved for possible future extensions are painted white. Each lever carries a number on a brass plate, and these numbers correspond with the numbers shown on a large diagram of the layout controlled by the box, hung above the instrument shelf, on which every signal and switch is clearly and distinctly indicated.

Switch Locking-Bars

Locking-bars are used to ensure that a switch shall not be moved while a train is actually passing over it. Such movement has caused many accidents in the past, and is easily possible in the long gap between the two bogies of a modern coach. The bars

ELECTRICAL TRACK DIAGRAMS such as this are an important factor in the safe movement of traffic at high average speeds over congested routes. They indicate clearly to the controller the state of the signals and positions of the trains at any moment throughout the twenty-four hours. The panel which is shown in the photograph is on the East Coast main line of the L.N.E.R. at Northallerton, Yorkshire.

10 FACING SINGLE LEAD

ALL ELECTRIC SIGNAL BOX

8 DOUBLE JUNCTION

9 RUNNING CROSSOVER

F

F

7 SCISSORS CROSSOVERS

6 TRAILING CROSSOVER

C
F

F

5 DIAMOND WITH DOUBLE SLIP

UP AND DOWN FAST

F

F

4 DIAMOND WITH SINGLE SLIP

B

UP AND DOWN SLOW

F

CHECK RAILS

F

RELIEF LINES

3 TRAILING JUNCTION

A

GROUND SIGNAL FOR POINTS

1 SWITCH DIAMOND

F

2 FACING CROSSOVER WITH DIAMOND CROSSING (Very Rare)

TRAILING POINTS

A
B
C

ELECTRIC POINT MACHINE

FACING POINTS

F DENOTES FACING POINT LOCKS

F

FACING POINT LOCK

L. ASHWELL WOOD

TYPES OF SWITCHES, showing all practical layouts. Trailing crossovers are much safe than facing crossovers. With the former, a train must shunt to change from one line to the other; with the latter, it can run straight on to the other track. All facing points, whether for crossovers or junctions, have locks for this reason.

99

SIGNALLING INSTRUCTION MODEL. Although signalling is becoming more and more automatic, a great measure of safety still depends on the signalman and his training, and models such as this are used a great deal to impart the necessary knowledge of track layout. Years of practical experience must, however, elapse before a signalman is permitted to take over even the smallest section on his own.

are used in conjunction with the more important switches, chiefly those to and from running lines.

At the switch, alongside the rail, there is a bar of reversed-L or T section some forty feet long, carried on rocker arms and normally lying clear of the wheel flanges. If the locking-bar lever is pulled over in the box, the bar swings on its rockers, but cannot do so if a train is standing or moving over a switch, as in that event the bar would foul the flanges.

The movement of the bar is connected with the movement of a switch-lock. Before the switch can be moved, it must be un-locked with a simultaneous movement of the locking-bar, and after it has been moved, it must be re-locked before the appropriate signal can be pulled off.

Locking Table

Under the floor of the signal-box is the locking-table, a complicated arrangement of slides and studs which prevents the signalman giving conflicting signals that

might result in a collision. Junctions are interlocked in this way, so that trains shall not be allowed to cross one another's paths. Also, the interlocking ensures that only the signals corresponding to the line that has been set can be pulled off. It is the locking-table, too, that prevents a signalman from pulling off the distant signal until all the stop signals on the same portion of the track are also in the clear position.

Electric Signal-Boxes

The equipment of many modern junction signal-boxes is entirely electric. The heavy manual levers have been replaced by a row of short levers which can be flicked over with a touch of the thumb and finger. This not only considerably reduces the manual work involved, but with electricity it is possible to make one small lever line up an entire track at one movement.

The wiring in such all-electric signal-boxes is extremely complicated and the equipment is elaborate and highly expensive, but there is no question of the ultimate

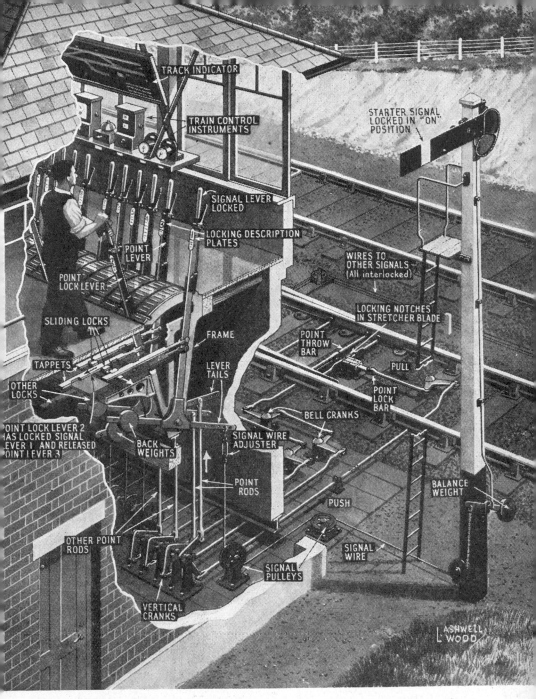

TRACK INDICATOR

TRAIN CONTROL INSTRUMENTS

STARTER SIGNAL LOCKED IN "ON" POSITION

SIGNAL LEVER LOCKED

LOCKING DESCRIPTION PLATES

POINT LEVER

POINT LOCK LEVER

WIRES TO OTHER SIGNALS (All interlocked)

SLIDING LOCKS

FRAME

LOCKING NOTCHES IN STRETCHER BLADE

TAPPETS

LEVER TAILS

POINT THROW BAR

PULL

OTHER LOCKS

POINT LOCK LEVER 2 HAS LOCKED SIGNAL LEVER 1 AND RELEASED POINT LEVER 3

BACK WEIGHTS

SIGNAL WIRE ADJUSTER

BELL CRANKS

POINT LOCK BAR

POINT RODS

PUSH

BALANCE WEIGHT

OTHER POINT RODS

SIGNAL PULLEYS

SIGNAL WIRE

VERTICAL CRANKS

ASHWELL WOOD

SIGNAL LOCKING FRAME—Safety device that makes it impossible for the signal-man to set any points or switches unless all signals correspond. The frame is located under the floor of the signal-box and consists of a number of locks sliding on a bar. These are moved by the tappets, or keys, connected to the signal levers.

101

economy. At London Bridge station, for example, a single all-electric box with three hundred and eleven levers has replaced four manual signal-boxes, and the earlier staff of fifty signalmen and twelve boys has come down to sixteen men and eight boys, of whom, at the busiest hours of the day, six men are needed to work the signal frame, and four boys to record the movement of the trains.

Remote Control

Some of the all-electric signal-boxes control the approaches to a station from a considerable distance. Many wayside signal-boxes, indeed, have been abolished by erecting intermediate signals and working them electrically from the nearest adjacent box. All future development of railway signalling is likely to be in the direction of electrical operation.

On electric lines, too, it is a relatively simple matter to install interceptors at the side of the track, which, in the event of a driver attempting to pass a stop signal at danger, strike a trip-lever on the motor coach. This cuts off the current and automatically applies the brakes, in some cases being capable of pulling up a train in its own length.

Similar equipment for steam-operated services is not so easy to devise. The Great Western Railway, however, has gone some way towards it by installing audible cab signalling, as a supplement to the visual signalling, over the whole of its main lines.

A ramp is fixed in the middle of the track at the approach to a distant signal, and if the signal arm is at caution the ramp is dead, but if it is in the clear position the ramp is electrified. Under each locomotive there is a contact arm, and if this strikes the ramp when it is dead, a loud horn sounds in the cab and a partial application of the brakes is made automatically. But if the line is clear and the ramp is electrified, the sound of the horn is replaced by that of a small bell, and the locomotive continues on its way unchecked. The value of such an appliance in foggy weather will be easily appreciated.

AUTOMATIC CAB-SIGNALLING by means of electrified ramp. An engineer testing the mechanism. The ramp can be seen in the centre of the track. If the line is clear ahead the ramp is electrified and a bell rings in the engine cab, thus providing an audible signal for the information of the engine driver. But if the signal is at "caution," the ramp is dead, a siren blows and brakes are automatically applied.

NATIONAL CODE OF ENGINE HEADLAMPS
Also Carriage Tail Lamps

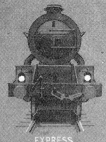

EXPRESS PASSENGER TRAIN

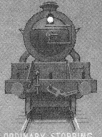

ORDINARY STOPPING PASSENGER TRAIN

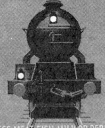

EXPRESS MEAT, FISH, MILK OR PERISHABLE TRAIN WITH OVER ⅓ OF WAGONS FITTED WITH CONTINUOUS BRAKES: OR TRAIN OF EMPTY PASSENGER STOCK

EXPRESS FREIGHT OR BALLAST TRAIN LESS THAN ⅓ OF WAGONS WITH CONTINUOUS BRAKES

THROUGH FREIGHT OR BALLAST TRAIN

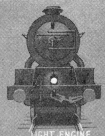

LIGHT ENGINE OR ENGINES

PARCELS, NEWSPAPERS, FISH, MILK, MEAT, HORSE OR PERISHABLE TRAIN COMPOSED OF COACHING STOCK

THROUGH MINERAL OR EMPTY WAGON TRAIN

ORDINARY FREIGHT TRAIN CALLING AT INTERMEDIATE STATIONS

PRINCIPAL SOUTHERN RAILWAY ROUTE INDICATING CODES (WHITE DISCS IN DAYTIME AND LIGHTS AT NIGHT — THE NUMBERS ARE OF THE ENGINE DUTY ROSTERS)

WATERLOO-EXETER-PLYMOUTH

WATERLOO-SOUTHAMPTON-BOURNEMOUTH

VICTORIA-FOLKESTONE-DOVER

PASSENGER TRAIN TAIL LAMP

G.W.R. SLIP COACH TAIL LAMPS

END OF THREE SLIP PORTIONS

END OF TWO SLIP PORTIONS

END OF ONE SLIP PORTION

MOSCOW METRO, the first railway of its kind to be built in Soviet Russia. It connects the centre of the city with the suburbs. The coaches used are of the usual square, bulky type common to Russian railways. Many of the underground sections, lying near the surface, were built by the cut-and-cover method described in these pages.

CHAPTER FIVE

UNDERGROUND RAILWAYS

IT is the present-day congestion of large cities that has forced the railway to go underground. Long ago, in London, it was realized that suburban railways could provide a valuable service to the centre of the city if only they could find room to move.

The same difficulty has applied to all other cities as they have grown, and attempts have been made to find the necessary space for the tracks. In New York, for many years, there was an elevated system which overcame the difficulty in part by carrying the track overhead, along the sides of streets and houses, providing a terrific roar and rattle and a continuous nightmare for all those who lived near it. It was no uncommon experience in some upper-storey flats to have the trains tearing past the windows.

The elevated principle has been tried in other parts of the world, but sooner or later it gives place to the subway. Only by carrying the trains underground, instead of above it, can a service be provided in built-up areas in a really satisfactory and quiet manner.

London's Famous Underground

The London Underground, which holds pride of place among all underground railways, was started some time before electric traction had advanced sufficiently for the trains to be driven electrically, and some really heroic efforts were made to get rid of the smoke and soot from steam locomotives. The large brick vents that carried the smoke to the surface can still be seen on some stations, but it can hardly be said that this method was satisfactory, or earned the unqualified approval of passengers. Taking a journey then, on the first of the underground railways, was like travelling in a fog.

This, of course, was on the subway underground, not the tube railway as it is known today. When electric traction had become properly established, and en-gineers realized that the chief objection to railway laying in a tunnel had been overcome, they soon turned themselves into moles and commenced the deep-burrowing of the amazing network of lines which is the envy of other cities and towns.

Boring the Tunnels

They were fortunate in having a subsoil of clay, which was easy to get through, but precautions had to be taken against subsidence and the seeping of water into the tunnels. The tunnels were made completely circular, of a diameter of roughly twelve feet, reinforced with steel and the sides at the stations were afterwards bricked in. The rails were set just above the floor of the cylindrical tunnels, and the coaches were made specially low for the purpose. Spaces for stations were also cylindrical, but of a larger diameter.

Much of the boring could be done mechanically, by implements like the Price Rotary Excavator, which drives a circular shield ahead of it under hydraulic pressure and cuts away the clay in the process.

The problem of getting down to these deep-level railways was originally overcome by means of lifts, with spiral stairs for use in an emergency. The lifts soon became automatic in operation, and have now been replaced at all the more modern stations by escalators, or moving flights of stairs, a much more efficient method in that it reduces congestion and enables passengers to keep moving to and from the trains.

Moving Staircases

These ever-moving flights of stairs are kept in motion by a revolving drum, in much the same way as a factory conveyor belt is driven, save that the stairs have the added complexity that they are mounting or descending a slope, and must travel on the flat for a few paces at top and bottom, and still remain individually level, while going up or down.

Each stair is separate, but linked to its

neighbour in such a way that it can rise or fall the necessary distance from the flat to become a proper stair with rise and tread. It travels on rails at each side on small rollers, two rails each side, and one above the other. These rails are close together on the slope, but open out top and bottom so that the stair tread remains level.

Sub-surface Lines

Not all the world's underground railways, however, are at such a deep level as the London tube. The Paris Metro is merely a sub-surface line, as is the New York subway. Indeed, in places where the ground is of hard, or comparatively hard rock, tunnels have not been bored at all. Channels or cuttings have first been made of the required depth, and then bridged over and filled in.

The method used in building the Moscow underground railway is sometimes known

as the cut-and-cover method. Where the lines went deeper, the subsoil of Moscow, a treacherous carboniferous mixture impregnated with water, gave the engineers a great deal of trouble. Scarcity of steel also made it necessary to use concrete instead for lining the tunnels.

Only through the middle section, where the ground level is higher, was true tunnelling employed. Here, conditions were easier, for the subsoil was mainly sand.

Moscow's Large Coaches

The Moscow underground uses large coaches, and tunnels of fifteen feet diameter were driven to accommodate them. The platforms at the stations are nearly five hundred feet in length, and can thus accept trains of eight cars. Each car seats fifty passengers and has standing room for one hundred and fifty more.

It is intended to have eight lines

UNDERGROUND RAILWAYS IN PARIS AND BERLIN.

None of the underground railways of Europe is on the deep levels of the London tubes. The Paris underground is, for most of its length, only just below street level. So near the surface is it, that in many cases tunnels were not bored at all. Channels were cut down from the roadway and were then roofed over and covered with concrete, a system known as the cut-and-cover method, which was also used in the construction of London's Inner Circle and District line. The photograph (left) shows the Richelieu-Drouot station. A feature of the French Metro is its simplicity of design. The Berlin tube has both high and low level lines, but is still not deep by comparison with the London Underground. Berlin had, however, the largest underground railway station in Europe, that of Potsdamer Platz, shown in the illustration. Ordinary stairs gave access to the high level platforms and escalators to the deep level trains. With the opening of this station, Berliners were able to go straight through by train between the southern and northern districts, and Berlin prided itself on the possession of one of the most up-to-date underground railway systems on the Continent.

ESCALATOR TO DEEP LEVEL

TRAIN ON HIGH LEVEL

Labels in illustration:
SLIDING DOORS

RUBBER EDGES

PLEASE KEEP CLEAR OF THE DOORS

40-SEAT CAR

ALL WIRING AND MECHANISM BELOW FLOOR LEVEL

RECESS FOR SLIDING DOOR

MOTOR LEADS →

138 H.P MOTOR

SEAT

REDUCTION GEARS

DOOR EXTENSION

AIR SUPPLY FOR CLOSING DOOR

CENTRE RAIL SHOE

THROW OF ARM FOR OPENING DOOR

PISTON

BRAKE SHOES

RACK AND PINION

FLEXIBLE BRAKE-PIPE CONNEXION

COMPRESSED-AIR BRAKE CYLINDER

AIR SUPPLY FOR OPENING DOOR

DOOR ENGINE

NSPORT

SAFETY ON THE LONDON TUBE. This drawing shows clearly two of the main safety devices installed on the London Underground. On the left is the mechanism which controls the sliding doors. This is electro-pneumatic in action and is so arranged that the train cannot start until all doors are closed. Signalling also is automatic, arranged so that the train stops when the signals are at danger. The first train, by

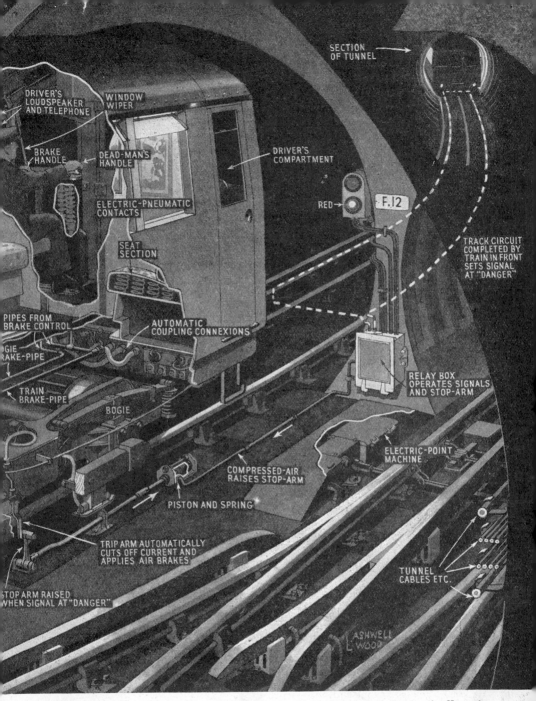

SECTION OF TUNNEL

DRIVER'S LOUDSPEAKER AND TELEPHONE

WINDOW WIPER

BRAKE HANDLE

DEAD-MAN'S HANDLE

DRIVER'S COMPARTMENT

ELECTRIC-PNEUMATIC CONTACTS

RED

F.12

SEAT SECTION

TRACK CIRCUIT COMPLETED BY TRAIN IN FRONT SETS SIGNAL AT "DANGER"

PIPES FROM BRAKE CONTROL

BOGIE BRAKE-PIPE

TRAIN BRAKE-PIPE

BOGIE

AUTOMATIC COUPLING CONNEXIONS

RELAY BOX OPERATES SIGNALS AND STOP-ARM

ELECTRIC-POINT MACHINE

COMPRESSED-AIR RAISES STOP-ARM

PISTON AND SPRING

TRIP ARM AUTOMATICALLY CUTS OFF CURRENT AND APPLIES AIR BRAKES

TUNNEL CABLES ETC.

STOP ARM RAISED WHEN SIGNAL AT "DANGER"

ASHWELL WOOD

completing an electric circuit, shown by a white dotted line, also automatically sets the signal behind it and raises a stop-arm alongside the running rail. If the next train following attempted to pass before the section ahead was clear, the arm would engage with the trip-arm at the side of the motor coach, which would cut off the current and apply the air brakes on the train, at once bringing it to a standstill.

TRAINS WITHOUT DRIVERS. Station on the London post office tube railway. Used for the carriage of bags of letters and light parcels, this narrow-gauge tube railway underneath London is automatic in action. The trains travel on their own from station to station, the men being required only for loading and unloading the mail-bags.

eventually radiating from the centre of the city, giving a total of thirty-two miles altogether, and linking all the terminals of the main line railways.

Notable features of this Metro are the stations, with their coloured marbles surrounding the pillars that support the station roofs, their brightly tiled walls, great spaciousness and brilliant lighting.

Upwards by Underground

More remarkable, however, is the underground railway of Oslo, capital of Norway, which begins in the centre of the city at the National Theatre Station, and ends on top of the Holmenkollen ridge, fifteen hundred feet above the sea. The national ski-ing contests are held on these slopes, and at such times the tube is very busy, bringing sightseers and others from under the city

110

to the summit of a mountain amid the snows.

In the early days of the tube, the engineers took advantage of the fact that they could bore at any level to give a slight down gradient to the track from each end of each of the stations. The idea was to make gravity assist braking and acceleration, but this method has been completely discountenanced by the metadyne system of working, which, apart from doing away with a great deal of complicated equipment, introduces a current-saving principle known as regenerative braking.

Reversing the Motor

The retarding effort necessary to bring a train to a stop is supplied by reversing the action of the motors, so that from being motors receiving electric current and turning it into mechanical motion, they temporarily become generators producing current and feeding it back to the rails.

In other words, when it is necessary to pull up a train, instead of providing all the retardation needed with the brakes and merely wearing out brake shoes, the train's momentum is made to drive the generator and produce current to take the place, in part, of that which has been used.

Post-Office Tube

Tube systems have also been used for some railways that are not of the public or passenger-carrying type, as in the tube railway of the London post office. Built on lines similar to the passenger tube, only of smaller diameter, it is completely automatic in its action, small trains carrying the mail rapidly from point to point, controlled only from the stations.

Automatic working is the keynote of the safety for which the London Underground is famous. The London Passenger Transport Board, over its whole system of lines, carries millions of passengers annually, yet has been able to say that for a whole year there was not a single accident due to any mishap to the trains.

One of the safety devices in use is the electro-pneumatic brake governor, which makes it impossible to pass current to the motor unless the air pressure of the brake system is at full pressure.

Compressed-Air Brakes

This needs a little explanation. All tube trains are fitted with the Westinghouse system of braking, which varies from other pneumatic control in that the brakes are applied by air pressure instead of a vacuum. The pipe that connects all coaches is filled with air at a pressure equivalent to fifty pounds to the square inch, and the brakes will go on fully, or can be applied with full force, only when this air is at the correct pressure.

But it might so happen that a leakage occurred unnoticed, and when the brakes were required, their effect would be either very feeble or non-existent. The electro-pneumatic governor takes good care of this by seeing that if the air is not up to the requisite pressure, no current can reach the motors. So if the brakes are not acting, the train cannot even start. The actual brake is of the clasp type, which acts on both sides of the wheel.

A further safety device is the familiar "dead man's handle," which forms a part of the controller in the driver's cabin. Only the driver, or motorman, is needed in the cab of an electric train, and in the event of any sudden personal accident or illness, there is no fireman to take charge.

Safety is assured, however, by this handle, which is in reality a knob acting against a spring so weak that it can be kept continually depressed by the palm of the hand, without effort. Current is permitted to pass only as long as it is depressed, and if for any reason the driver's hand leaves the knob, the current is automatically cut off and the brakes are applied, thereby bringing the train to a standstill.

Other safety devices are connected with signalling, which is completely automatic in its action, each train signalling itself and setting the signals for the next one behind. In addition, the train itself applies the brakes if the driver should fail to notice that a signal is against him.

Train Describer

Behind all this automatic working, however, there must be a mind in control. Safety devices do their work as long as they are looked after, and trains signal themselves once their routes and times have been planned.

Signalmen are employed only at junctions, but station staffs all along the route need to know what sort of trains are coming, their destination, stops and so on, and this is given by what is known as the electrical train describer.

A master-describer is located at the starting point and contains a continuous paper ribbon, which is perforated to correspond with the destination and intermediate stops of each train. The perforating is done by electrical impulses, negative impulses leaving the ribbon untouched, but positive impulses producing a puncture.

To describe a train, the signalman at the starting station sets pointers on the destination and non-stop dials at the appropriate positions, so causing a magnet to drive

ODD SORT OF TUBE RAILWAY, built solely for the use of American senators. This unusual railway runs under the streets of Washington, the Federal capital of the United States of America, and facilitates the movement of senators between different government offices. Private citizens are not allowed to use it. The armchair coaches are driven by electric motors and current is supplied through an overhead track.

round a ratchet wheel and contact arm, step by step, until the description of the train is complete.

This information is transmitted electrically all along the line, the receiving apparatus being similar in principle. A long loop of the ribbon, therefore, in both receivers and transmitter, stores the descriptions from the time they are first fed into the transmitter. As the train passes intermediate stations it automatically cancels its own description.

Latest Automatic Instruments

The latest describers provide for as many as twelve different destinations, and fifteen variations in the number of intermediate stops. Train describers are used in the signal-boxes of other busy suburban

lines, but on the tubes they also work the platform indicators which show passengers where the next train is going.

Automatic instruments of this nature can be made to perform a variety of duties. As an example, the describing apparatus at Wood Green station, on the Piccadilly line, also operates the switches.

Working the Switches

If a train is described as being for Wood Green, and therefore needs to reverse at that station, the train describer, on receipt of this information, automatically throws the switch from the northbound track to the siding, and also clears the signal controlling it. After the train has arrived and come to a stand on the siding, the mechanism restores the switch to the through line and alters the signals accordingly.

But this is not all. When the time comes for the train now in the siding to leave again and return on the southbound track, the signalman at the adjacent station of Arnos Grove simply feeds the description of the train into the apparatus in correct sequence, and the train describer causes all the proper switch and signal movements to be made at Wood Green.

Constant Service

Not only do these devices make for safety, but they so assist smooth running as to be one of the main factors in the surprising frequency at which tube trains follow each other, roughly at over forty to the hour. A very close watch is kept on the smoothness of the running, and what is known as a headway chart in clock form is used on all underground services.

At a certain selected point on each route,

an electrical contact is fixed, and is operated as each train passes over it. The circuit so completed causes a small inked hammer to strike the margin of a circular sheet of paper, which revolves and makes one complete revolution every twenty-four hours. This is the chart.

What the Charts Show

If the service on the line concerned is functioning normally, the marks on the outer edge of the chart will be spaced evenly, but any gap in the sequence of marks indicates an interruption in the flow of traffic, and steps can be taken to have the trouble rectified. These charts were designed first of all to assist the traffic controllers, but they have now been placed on public view in the Piccadilly and St. James's Park booking halls, where six dials give a daily demonstration of the remarkable efficiency of London tube operation.

In addition, headway clocks are mounted

JAPANESE UNDERGROUND. It is usual to think of Japan as a land of shrines and tea-gardens, but Tokyo is as overcrowded as New York, and Japanese railways are among the most efficient in existence. Here is the interior of a coach on the Tokyo underground railway, with waitresses in traditional costume selling refreshments.

at the tunnel entrances of various tube stations, and work on the fly-back action of a stop-watch. Each train, as it passes the clock, resets it to zero, and the hand then begins to move round the dial. In this way the driver of a train can see clearly how many seconds have elapsed since the train ahead left the station, and, by judging the interval between that and his own, is able to regulate his speed in such a way as to be as economical of current as possible.

Dense Passenger Traffic

Without swift running, the London tubes would be quite unable to carry their enormous volume of traffic. Mere figures make hard reading, but they are necessary to show the difference between tube traffic and the traffic customarily carried on other lines.

Whereas, in a normal working year, the four main-line companies of Britain carry an average of some forty-four thousand passengers over each route mile of line, the corresponding figure for the tube railways is nearly one and a quarter million.

Add to this the fact that the main volume of the traffic is not only carried in a small and congested area, but arrives in bulk during rush-hour periods, and some idea will be gained of the necessity for smooth and swift running of trains.

To speed up the tube services, a number and variety of devices have been adopted on the tubes to hurry the passengers along. In addition to the escalators, which in themselves admit of no dallying, there are the batteries of automatic ticket machines, which issue both tickets and change. In the booking offices, also, there are automatic ticket-printing machines, which go on printing tickets as long as there are passengers asking for them.

Facilitating Movement

The coaches are designed to facilitate movement in the swiftest possible way. Each coach has three wide pairs of double doors, sliding into the coach walls on roller bearings, with ample space round them for standing, and plenty of seats for slack periods. In addition, the doors are pneumatically-operated, which gives a chance

for yet another safety device. Not until all doors in the train are properly closed can the guard give the electric bell-signal to the driver to start the train.

Another item making for safety is the telephone system installed throughout the tunnels, by which the driver can always get into touch with a station or control. All he has to do is to stop the train and connect the portable instrument he carries to the two wires running along the side of the tunnel.

Such are some of the devices which, with the interlocking of all signalling and point operation, make for safe running at speed. The speed of the trains in the tube, with their extremely short distances between stations, is not often greater than thirty-five to forty miles an hour, but their slickness of operation is unequalled anywhere in the world.

Direct-current electricity at six hundred volts is used for driving the trains. For dense train services, maximum reliability and minimum cost of maintenance, it has advantages over alternating current. However, high-voltage alternating current is generated at the power station, this being more economical to distribute over distances. It is transformed into low-voltage direct current at a number of sub-stations for feeding the line conductors.

Conductor Rails

The conductors are extra steel rails laid beside the running rails. It is possible, of course, to use just one extra rail as the positive, or supply line, and the running rails as the negative, or return lines. The London tube, however, has what is known as fourth-rail electrification, in which the positive rail is laid beside the track, with another high conductivity rail laid in the middle for the return of the current.

The reason for this is that both conductor rails can then be of high-conductivity steel, which offers much less resistance to the passage of current than ordinary running track, thereby in the long run effecting a saving, although it is more expensive in the beginning. The greater the cross-section, or thickness of the conductor rails, the lower the resistance, so such rails are made as heavy as possible, even up to a hundred and fifty pounds in weight for a

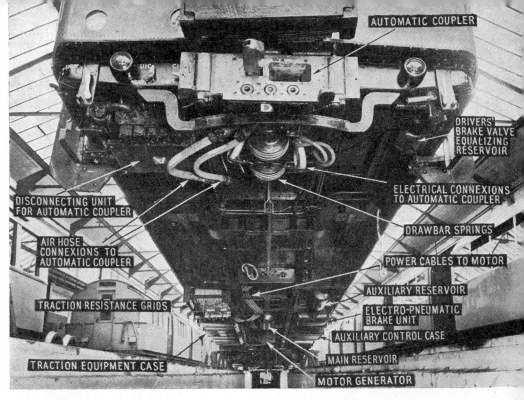

AUTOMATIC COUPLER

DRIVERS' BRAKE VALVE EQUALIZING RESERVOIR

DISCONNECTING UNIT FOR AUTOMATIC COUPLER

ELECTRICAL CONNEXIONS TO AUTOMATIC COUPLER

DRAWBAR SPRINGS

AIR HOSE CONNEXIONS TO AUTOMATIC COUPLER

POWER CABLES TO MOTOR

AUXILIARY RESERVOIR

TRACTION RESISTANCE GRIDS

ELECTRO-PNEUMATIC BRAKE UNIT

AUXILIARY CONTROL CASE

TRACTION EQUIPMENT CASE

MAIN RESERVOIR

MOTOR GENERATOR

UNDERNEATH A TUBE MOTOR COACH, showing the compact arrangement of the mechanisms. A modern motor coach carries its working parts under the floor, leaving the full length of the coach, except the small space occupied by the driver's compartment, available for passengers. The automatic coupler at the end is electro-pneumatic in action. It is used in conjunction with the central spring buffer just above.

yard of rail, heavier than the running rails themselves.

The sub-stations feed the current (when it has been converted from high-voltage alternating to low-voltage direct current) to the conductors in sections. In each section the conductors are always at line voltage, when the power station and sub-stations are working, but current is not actually flowing until a train enters the section and completes the circuit through its controllers and motors.

At any moment, however, a number of trains can be in motion on the same section, taking power from the conductors in parallel, just like electric lamps off a main supply in a house.

Only certain of the many types of electric motor are suitable for railway working, and series-wound direct current motors meet the necessary requirements in the simplest and most effective way. They

exert the maximum effort on starting, but they do not maintain a constant speed, or endeavour to do so as the load imposed upon them increases. For example, they do not overload themselves by trying to take a train at the same speed uphill as on the level without any regulation adjustment being made by the driver.

Remarkable Compactness

Modern electric motors are very compact in construction, and for this reason it has been possible to build all the latest tube trains with the entire electric equipment under the floors of the cars, so that the whole body of the motor coach, apart from a small driving compartment at one end, is available for passengers. The underneath of a motor coach is such a mass of gear it seems impossible ever to trace all its connexions or make out what all the different parts and contacts mean.

115

PRINCIPAL RAILWAYS OF
EUROPE

ICELAND

0   MILES   500

A R C T I C

FAROES

ATLANTIC

OCEAN

SHETLAND IS.

ORKNEY IS.
Wick

Narvik

Namsos

Andalsnes
Trondhjem

Otta
Sarna

Bergen

BRITISH
ISLES

Mallaig
Oban
Aberdeen

Kristiansand
Skagen

Gefle

OSLO

STOCKHOL

*NORTH
SEA*

Burtonport
Glasgow Edinburgh
Belfast
Galway Carlisle Newcastle
Dublin Liverpool Scarborough
Holyhead Hull
Bantry Cork Fishguard Birmingham Grimsby

DENMARK
Esbjerg Kiel
Cuxhaven
Bremerhaven
Emden Hamburg
Bremen Hanover BERLIN

Grenaa
COPENHAGEN

BALTIC
Rostock
Sassnitz
Kolberg Danzig
Stettin
Bromberg
Posen

Königsb

SEA

Yarmouth
Amsterdam
Padstow LONDON Harwich
Bristol Ostend
Penzance Dover HOLLAND
Southampton Boulogne
Cherbourg Havre BELGIUM Brussel
St Malo Lille Cologne
Brest Rouen Amiens LUXEMBURG Frankfurt
PARIS Metz
Le Mans Orleans Strasbourg Nürnberg
Tours Nantes Munich

Magdeburg
Leipzig Dresden
PRAGUE
CZECHOS
Pilsen
Stuttgart
Linz
VIENNA
AUSTRIA

Breslau
Lod

*BAY OF
BISCAY*

FRANCE
Limoges
Lyons
SWITZERLAND
Udine

BUDAPEST
HUNGAR

Coruna Gijon Santander
Oporto Valladolid
Bordeaux
Bayonne
Salamanca Saragossa
PORTUGAL MADRID
LISBON SPAIN
Valencia
Seville Barcelona
Granada
Cadiz Alicante
Algeciras Malaga Almeria Cartagena
GIBRALTAR

Toulouse Nimes
Marseilles
Nice
Turin Milan
Genoa Bologna
Leghorn Florence
ITALY
Ancona
Venice Fiume Zagreb
Split

BELGRA
YUGOSL

*ADRIATIC
SEA*

CORSICA
Ajaccio
PortoTorres Aranci
SARDINIA
Iortoli
Portoscuso Cagliari

ROME
Naples
Brindisi
Reggio Taranto

Durazzo
Elba

SPANISH MOROCCO
Algiers Oran
Rabat Fez

MEDITERRANEAN
BALEARIC ISLANDS

Trapani Palermo
Messina
Catania SICILY

MOROCCO ALGERIA
AFRICA TUNIS MALTA SEA

J.TURNER,F.R.G.S.

ZEPPELIN RAIL-CAR, the fastest car on rails so far invented. Maximum speed on trial was a hundred and forty-three miles an hour. This German car was the fore-runner of the Flying Hamburger, in the sense that it was a self-contained unit built solely for speed, but aero-dynamic propulsion did not prove a practical proposition and Diesel-electric propulsion was used for the famous Flying Hamburger.

CHAPTER SIX

THE FASTEST TRAINS IN EUROPE

THE extraordinary vehicle on the opposite page, half airship and half rail-car, with a propeller for what is sometimes known as aero-dynamic propulsion, holds the world's record for speed on rails. It can hardly be called a locomotive, for its pulling power at the head of a line of ordinary railway coaches would be relatively small, but it achieved the object for which it was designed, and that was high speed.

The Kruckenburg car, as it was named, appeared in 1931, and was of German design and construction. On test, it reached a speed of one hundred and forty-three miles an hour, thereby beating the previous record of a hundred and thirty, which also was held by Germany.

Air-driven Rail-Car

The Germans have always had a flair for producing something more startling than has been seen before, and this rail-plane, although it was never actually put into service, certainly showed the trend of their experiments. The car was ninety-five feet in length, of especially light construction so that it could be carried on only four wheels, and streamlined to reduce its resistance to swift passage through the air. The motive power was an ordinary aeroplane motor, which drove the four-bladed propeller at the rear.

The Kruckenburg car progressed by means of the stream of air directed rearwards by the propeller, in the same manner as an aeroplane. What would have happened if it had appeared in regular service, causing a minor hurricane on leaving a platform, is impossible to say.

The previous record of a hundred and thirty miles an hour had been gained by an electrically driven locomotive, in the year 1903. This was in the days of hansom cabs and "horseless carriages," before the first "flying machine" had succeeded in leaving the ground. What is more, the car that travelled at such a speed, unheard of at the time, was streamlined and capable of seating fifty passengers.

A still earlier electric car had reached a hundred miles an hour in 1901, but it did so much damage to the track that the test had to be abandoned.

Before high speeds can be attempted, the track must be suitable, which is why, in spite of the great speeds possible today, speeds on many sections of line are still comparatively moderate.

Unsuitable Tracks

A track can be unsuitable for various reasons. There may be sharp curves in it, or it may be laid over bridges on which there are speed restrictions, or speed restrictions may be in force owing to level crossings and so on. So it is sometimes not much good building a powerful locomotive without practically rebuilding the track, which is what happened in Germany and other European countries just before the Second World War.

High record speeds, however, must not be confused with high average timings. The average timing is the time taken by a train between any two points given as miles an hour, and including all stops. To gain, say, an average timing of eighty miles an hour, the locomotive must be capable of far higher speeds intermediately. The line must be cleared for it, and any slight delay may mean travelling at a much higher speed between stops to maintain the average timing.

Speed and Weight

Speed must be judged in conjunction with the weight carried. Rail speeds seem low beside those of the aeroplane and the racing car, but the weight of the average train is out of all proportion to the weight of cars and aeroplanes. Some modern passenger expresses, travelling at a hundred miles an hour, weigh as much as a thousand tons. Even freight trains in some parts of the world travel at over sixty miles

MAILS

TURBO-BLOWER

VERTICAL FANS

BAGGAGE

1,300 H.P. DIESEL

AUXILIARY GENERATOR

AIR-COMPRESSOR DUCTS

CABLE DUCT

FUEL TANKS

MAIN GENERATOR

OIL COOLER

150 H.P. AUXILIARY DIESEL

GENERATOR

DRIVER'S CABIN

CONTROLS

LEADING BOGIE & TRACTION MOTORS

STREAMLINED CASING

ASHWELL WOOD

DIESEL-ELECTRIC TRAIN. Power unit, which in recent years has begun to challenge steam on an extensive scale in the haulage of both high-speed passenger and heavy freight trains, and in shunting work. In the example illustrated, power is developed by a 1,300 h.p. Diesel oil engine, and converted to electricity by the main generator.

an hour, and the weight of one of them may be as much as five thousand tons.

For all practical purposes, therefore, the fastest trains are those with the highest average timings, and it was Germany that had the bulk of them. Building upon the knowledge they had gained with these early experiments, the German State Railways in 1932 startled railway circles by announcing a new service on the Berlin-Hamburg line

with an average timing of seventy-seven miles an hour.

The highest British average timing then was that of the Cheltenham Flyer, which did the daily trip between Swindon and Paddington at seventy-one miles an hour. This section of line, however, was almost perfect for speed work, and it was not supposed that the Cheltenham Flyer's average would become general. That train had, as a matter of fact, only been introduced the year before.

The German announcement, therefore, seemed surprising, considering the fifty-mile-an-hour speed limit from the capital out to Spandau, and the long curve through Wittenberge. How were such losses to be made up on the better stretches of line?

First Diesel-Electric Train

The secret lay in the high sustained speed possible with the Diesel-electric method of propulsion. For the first time this combination of oil engine, electric generator and electric motor was being used for high speed work, and the train in which it was tested was the Flying Hamburger.

The Flying Hamburger consisted of two streamlined coaches carried on three four-wheel bogies, one bogie under each outer end and one carrying the two adjoining ends in the middle. The train was thus a complete articulated unit. The electric motors were placed under the coaches in the two end bogies, an arrangement which had the double advantage of keeping the weight well down and reducing vibration.

For safety at high speeds, the cars were equipped with a double system of braking. They had the quick-acting Knorr brake for normal use, applied to the wheels, and a powerful electro-magnetic brake for use in emergencies, applied direct to the rails. This rail brake was powerful enough to bring the train to a standstill in three-quarters of a mile, even from a speed of a hundred miles an hour. Three-quarters of a mile is the distance customarily left in Germany between the distant signal and the stop signal. As a further precaution, if a distant signal were passed at caution, the brakes were applied automatically.

Carrying over a hundred passengers in comfort, and whirling them to their destination at a speed never known before in rail travel, the Flying Hamburger was an instant success. Even a refreshment buffet was provided, and the cars were connected by a gangway running their whole length, with three-abreast seats on one side and single seats on the other. Before long, the other great cities in Germany were clamouring for high-speed travel to the capital, and in this way Germany's chain of Diesel-electric flyers was started.

Most of the tracks over which they

GERMAN STREAMLINED STEAM LOCOMOTIVE. Design which looks rather strange to British eyes. The streamlined covering is carried down almost to the rails, and trouble has even been taken to bend the lower sections into a reverse curve, something like the bilge of a ship. Inspection covers are provided in the bottom part of the covering in order to facilitate attention to the cylinders and valve gear.

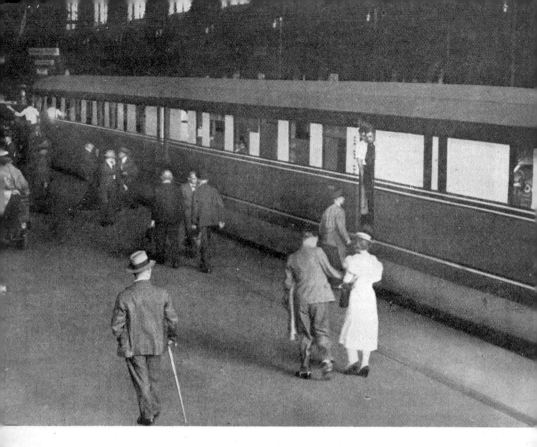

operated had to be rebuilt, some of them right from the foundations. The cant of the tracks on curves was increased to permit of hundred-mile-an-hour speeds with safety, and heavier rails were laid of a standard length of just over ninety-eight feet, the longest in the world to be produced as a regular practice. In addition, rail joints were welded to form continuous lengths as great as three hundred feet. In places, as in the Brandleite tunnel, in fact, there are rails with welded joints of a continuous length of over a mile and a half.

High Speeds in Germany

Add to all this the fact that in no other country in the world is there such a profusion of flying and burrowing junctions, and it will be obvious why the German State Railways, at the outbreak of the Second World War, had the fastest trains in Europe. They had built up gradually the right network of tracks and the right motive power for fast timings. To electricity,

122

which they had proved long ago to be faster than steam, they had added the oil-engine, so producing a self-contained unit capable of rapid acceleration and long-distance working. In 1939, they had eight Diesel-electric runs daily, with as high an average timing as eighty miles an hour.

Streamlined Steam Engines

Not many of their lines were electrified. Germany has ample coal resources, and the bulk of the services were still under steam. Pacific locomotives of various types were used for the principal passenger trains, some of them fully streamlined. One of these on test reached a maximum speed of a hundred and twenty-four miles an hour, only two miles an hour less than the world record of the British locomotive Mallard.

Electrification, however, is the keynote of the modern Italian State Railways. Unlike Germany, Italy lacked the coal for steam, whereas she had ample water power for a

GERMAN PASSENGER TRAINS. Two examples of the trend of design in Germany. Before the war, the Flying Frankfurter was one of the fastest trains in Europe. It covered the journey between Berlin and Frankfurt-on-Main, three hundred and thirty-eight miles, in just over five hours. It was a two-car self-contained unit like the Flying Hamburger, mounted on three bogies, with Diesel-electric propulsion. These German "Flyers" carried 102 passengers at a maximum speed of 99.3 miles an hour. The streamlined double-decked steam train in the bottom picture is in a different category, providing capacity rather than speed. The coaches are built with both upper and lower decks and, although rather cramped for space, have roughly double the passenger accommodation of the more usual type. They were designed for use on a busy route between Hamburg and Lübeck, and were known popularly as "upstairs-downstairs" trains. A similar type of double-decker coach has found favour in France as well as in Germany, chiefly on the very crowded Paris suburban lines. Double-decker cars are also used in the U.S.A.

hydro-electric system. Vast generating stations have been built, using water power from the mountain lakes, and all the main lines throughout the country are now electrified. The result is that the proverbially slow and dirty Italian trains gave place to swift and clean travel with electricity, and some of the Italian flyers have on occasion beaten even the German timings.

New Italian Routes

Far more than any other country, Italy has paid attention to the routes, in some cases rebuilding winding tracks entirely from one end to the other, and cutting through all obstacles regardless of cost. The new line from Rome to Naples, for example, flattens all gradients and eases curves so that unrestricted speed was permitted over the whole of its length.

Electrically hauled, the fastest Italian trains ran in three-car units, one of which has made the fastest start-to-stop run in railway history. This was a first-class train that left Florence and travelled by way of the new line through Bologna to Milan, doing the complete journey of a hundred and ninety-five miles at an average speed of one hundred and two miles an hour. The highest speed reached on the run was a hundred and twenty-six miles an hour.

The engineering of some of these lines is worth considering, particularly a still later one driven through the Apennines

OVERHEAD RAILWAY with the wheels on top of the coaches. Various types of suspension railways are used in Switzerland and other mountainous countries, but the Barmen-Elberfeld suspended railway in Germany was probably quite unique. A single-rail double-track was suspended from steel trestles, the coaches travelling below these on double-flanged pulleys. The line was made above a waterway.

STREAMLINED COVERING of steam locomotive partly removed to show boiler. The engine is of German construction, and is a high-speed 4-6-4 tank locomotive. The complete covering extends downwards well below the coupling rods, inspection plates being provided. Such streamlining adds greatly to the weight of the locomotive, but this is offset by the reduction of air resistance, especially at high speeds.

between Bologna and Florence. Previously, the main line from Milan to Rome was carried on a serpentine course over the mountains, but the new line effected a complete transformation.

How High Speeds Were Achieved

To begin with, it has cut the altitude to which the trains have to climb by half. Then it has shortened the Bologna-Florence distance from eighty-two to sixty miles, reduced all gradients and eased curves, so that speeds of seventy-five miles an hour were permitted throughout. The building of this new high-speed line involved the boring of thirty-one tunnels, with a total length of over twenty-two miles, and the building of forty masonry bridges and viaducts. It cost the enormous sum of twelve million pounds.

The Great Apennine Tunnel on this new line ranks as one of the railway wonders of the world. With a length of nearly twelve miles, it is the longest in the world which

has been bored sufficiently large to take a double track, and is the only tunnel which has a cross-over road and a signal-box, deep in the bowels of the earth.

The signal-box was installed to break up what would otherwise have been a very long signalling section on a busy line, and sidings were laid, communicating with both tracks, so that it is possible for slow trains to be shunted in the tunnel for the passage of fast expresses.

Underground Signal-Box

The signal cabin is located in a great central hall, far below the surface, over five hundred feet long, fifty feet wide and thirty feet high. It is entered from the main tunnel at both ends, and has subsidiary tunnels extending from the ends to house the siding tracks. The tunnel is ventilated by two inclined shafts sunk originally to facilitate removal of the excavated material.

Some extraordinary difficulties had to be overcome during its construction. Poisonous

gases, almost unknown in railway tunnelling, seeped into the workings and in some places caused outbreaks of fire. Another stubborn enemy the engineers had to contend with was water, which soaked in through the whole length of the tunnel. From May, 1925, to March, 1930, the quantity of water pumped out would have been sufficient to fill a lake a mile and three-quarters long, three-quarters of a mile wide and thirty-three feet deep. Extreme precautions had to be taken in consequence to waterproof the crown of the tunnel. Altogether, it cost over five million pounds to build.

In spite of their high-speed trains, it is a curious fact that the capital cities of neither Germany nor Italy had a single large railway station of any note. Much finer stations are to be found in the provincial cities of the two countries, particularly in Milan, where the Italian State Railways built the vast Central Station, containing twenty-two platforms, all but two of which are over eleven hundred feet in length.

Fine Station Buildings

Quite a large area of the city had to be cleared to make room for it. The station buildings, horse-shoe in shape, are among the most magnificent of their kind in the world. Italian marble and statuary have been used in profusion.

The desire for greater speed and faster timings was so general before the war that it spread all over Europe, each country doing its utmost to match up with the others, and each overcoming its own peculiar difficulties in various ways. No greater contrast could be found, for example, than

HIGH SPEED ON ITALIAN RAILWAYS was achieved partly by electrification and partly by the building of new high-speed, direct routes, which were carried over or through all obstacles, regardless of cost, in as nearly a straight line as possible. The viaduct bridge shown here illustrates one of the methods by which the improvements were accomplished. It is one of forty bridges on the Italian "Direttissima" route between Bologna and Florence, and crosses the river Setta at Vado. Each of the masonry arches of the viaduct has a span of over eighty feet.

1938. Before that year, the country had not a single run timed as high as sixty miles an hour, but exactly a year later the Dutch mileage scheduled at over this average was more than seven thousand, all in fairly short town-to-town runs.

Improvements in Belgium

Belgium, too, was influenced by the general railway speed-up in Europe. For years the Belgian State Railways had been noted for the quaint appearance of their locomotives, many of which were fitted with enormous square chimneys, but now they introduced some striking Atlantic types, specially designed and built for them. In addition, to by-pass congested cities, cut-off routes were laid, and the average timings of Belgian trains mounted rapidly. In 1939, they had reached over seventy miles an hour, chiefly on the line between Brussels and Ostend, and many other high-speed runs were introduced over the busy electrified main line between Brussels and Antwerp.

Work of Chapelon

But it is in France that the greatest strides have been made on steam lines, for it is in this country that the internal streamlining of the steam flow of the locomotive was originated. Most of the research work in this direction was done by an engineer named André Chapelon, who will always be remembered in connexion with the principle which bears his name. Before explaining it in detail, however, it is necessary to consider French practice in general, for French locomotive engineers have always

that between the mountainous terrain of Italy and the flat and low-lying nature of Holland and Belgium. In addition, there is in the Netherlands a greater density of population.

Consequently, train runs are short in Holland, and stops are frequent, and a type of motive power was needed that would permit of rapid acceleration and a high average speed between stops. Once again both electric and Diesel-electric haulage were introduced, the busiest routes, such as that between Amsterdam and Rotterdam, being electrified, while for the longer journeys a number of four-car Diesel-electric trains were put into service. These could be run in pairs or triplets, with multiple-unit control, when more seating accommodation was needed.

This speed-up in Holland took place in

127

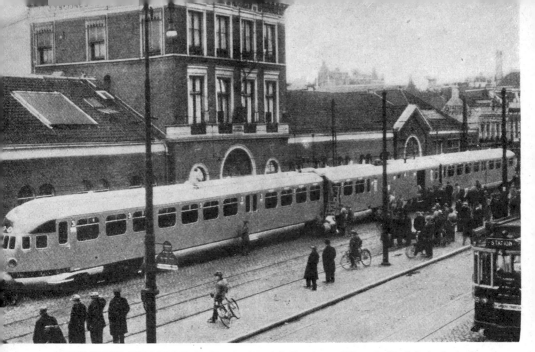

HIGH SPEED IN HOLLAND. Typical Dutch three-car Diesel-electric train in Haarlem. In areas where stations are not far apart, such as obtain in the Netherlands, stops are necessarily frequent, and increases in overall speed call for motive power capable of swift acceleration. Both Diesel-electric and electric traction fulfil this requirement, and before the war, improved average timings out of all recognition.

been to the fore, and French methods have left their mark in a large way on British engineering practice.

For years the use of compound locomotives, in which the steam, after being used in a high-pressure cylinder, is taken to a larger, low-pressure cylinder for further expansion, has been common in France, and the French engine has always been complex in design. Its appearance almost proclaims the fact, for it seems to carry most of its working parts outside.

Bonus System in France

The French driver is taught to make the greatest possible use of these complexities. He gets a bonus for fuel-saving, and lest there should be any temptation to economize in fuel at the expense of time-keeping, an additional bonus for regaining lost time. Further, to provide a safeguard against reckless running round curves and elsewhere, all locomotives used on fast trains have self-recording speed indicators.

The indicator contains a moving tape with

which the driver cannot tamper, and the tape shows the exact speed at any moment throughout the journey. This method of speed recording has since spread to Britain, but not until the first British high-speed streamlined train was introduced in 1935.

Low-pressure cylinders, as used in the compound principle, are necessarily of larger diameter than the high-pressure cylinders, and in fitting them the French have had the advantage of a more ample construction gauge than the British. They left more room round their tracks in the early days, although the track gauge used is the same, the standard four feet eight-and-a-half inches. They have, therefore, been able to make full use of the compound principle, which assists economy in fuel consumption. In addition, it is their practice to fit all principal locomotive types with such refinements as feed-water heaters, with the same object of economy in view.

Chapelon's whole idea was to advance economy in fuel still further, and the object he set himself was to reduce the fall in the pressure of the steam as it leaves the boiler and travels through the various cylinders. Steam retains its pressure only as long as it retains its heat; any fall in temperature means a resultant loss in pressure, and heat which has already been supplied and then lost before it can become effective is obvious waste. A further objective was to provide the exhaust steam with as free and rapid an escape through the chimney as possible, thereby reducing back-pressure.

Thermic Siphons

The changes began with the fitting of thermic siphons, which are narrow, wedge-shaped water-spaces in the inner fire-box, so improving the circulation and assisting in the generation of steam by increasing the heating area. At the same time, the working pressure was raised to two hundred and eighty pounds, the main steam pipe was considerably enlarged and all bends in it were replaced by sweeping curves.

A much larger superheater was also fitted, permitting the steam temperature to be increased to seven hundred and fifty degrees Fahrenheit, and poppet valves were used instead of piston valves, so improving the distribution of steam in the cylinders. Last of all, a double blast pipe and a double chimney were introduced to improve the exit of the steam.

The results were revolutionary. After some preliminary tests, the improvements were incorporated on some rebuilt Pacific-type locomotives, and one of these has developed a record horse-power for a locomotive of its weight. The indicator registered only fifty short of four thousand horse-power, and the weight of the locomotive, without tender, was a hundred and five tons. The same engine has also registered the greatest tractive effort of any

STREAMLINED FRENCH PACIFIC. French engineers are among the finest in the world, and it is in France that some of the greatest strides have been made in steam locomotive design. It was a Frenchman, André Chapelon, who developed the principle of internal streamlining, whereby the flow of the steam from the boiler through the valves and cylinders to the chimney is made as smooth as possible.

locomotive in Europe. Its draw-bar, or pulling, horse-power at seventy-five miles an hour was over three thousand, and it maintained as much as two thousand eight hundred horse-power for miles on end. The draw-bar horse-power is the pull of the locomotive on the train, after deducting that used in moving the engine itself.

Chapelon's achievement on a rebuilt engine was astonishing. He showed by such economical working that steam was by no means an outdated power, and most countries have followed the principle of internal steam streamlining. Double blast pipes and either double or huge circular chimneys are the chief signs of steam streamlining in Great Britain.

It is curious that such a simple and effective idea should have come from a country whose engines are so complex, but it was quite possibly the reaction from complexity that produced it. This is the case with signalling, at all events, for French

signalling was at one time even more complex than French locomotives. The number and variety of types of signals used in France were extraordinary.

Some French Signals

In stop signals there were no fewer than three different kinds. There was a curious type of chessboard stop signal for main lines, a square stop signal for subsidiary lines, and a circular type of signal known as the outer deferred stop signal. Then there were diamond-shaped distant signals, triangular reduced speed signals, block semaphores and direction indicators. At night, in addition to the customary red, yellow and green of other countries, the French indulged in violet lights as well. All this is now being simplified, however, and colour-light electric signalling is taking the place of such a bewildering variety.

There was another simplification just before the war, when all the French railways

VIAUR VIADUCT—one of the most remarkable bridges in France. It is a hinged cantilever structure, with two main T-shaped cantilevers, between them making an arched span of seven hundred and twenty-two feet, the longest in France. There are six main hinges, two at the foot of each cantilever and two in the centre where the two projecting arms of the cantilevers meet. The two piers which form the base for the foot of the further cantilever can be seen on the left of this photograph. The hinges provide the necessary play to meet the effects of variation in temperature.

Burma, the famous Gokteik Viaduct, which is actually a great deal higher, but the height of the Gokteik Viaduct depends upon a natural rock arch. The French Fades Viaduct is the highest built up by man. It has three enormous spans resting on huge, tapering granite piers, but so simple and beautifully balanced is the design that the height of the bridge, at first sight, passes almost unnoticed.

Another spectacular and ingenious bridge is the Viaur Viaduct over the Viaur River. This boasts the biggest span in France, one of seven hundred and twenty-two feet, but is far more notable in being a hinged or articulated structure. The viaduct consists of two cantilevers resting on hinged supports, and joined together by a third hinge which forms the crown of the arch. This giant structure spans a distance of roughly a quarter of a mile, yet the hinges on which it rests are unbelievably small in relation to its size. They were used, of course, to allow for expansions and contraction in such a large quantity of metal.

Electrification in France

There are two main electric lines in France, from Paris and Orleans to points on the Spanish frontier. Direct current of fifteen hundred volts and overhead conductors are used, the supply being obtained from hydro-electric power stations in the Pyrénées and the mountains of central France. This makes two stretches of track of roughly five hundred and six hundred miles respectively, with continuous electric haulage. Elsewhere, save for a few isolated sections of line, electrification is confined to

of former days were amalgamated into one national system. They are divided up into five regions known as the Northern, Eastern, South-eastern, South-western and Western Regions.

French engineers have also shown surprising skill in the building of their railway bridges. They have some magnificent examples to their credit, but most of them, unfortunately, are hidden away in remote valleys where the average traveller is unlikely to set eyes on them. One of these, the Garabit Viaduct, was designed by Eiffel, builder of the famous Eiffel Tower in Paris, and carries the railway on a magnificent arch more than four hundred feet above the River Truyere.

Not far away from this, in the Puy-de-Dôme region, there is the remarkable Fades Viaduct, which is the highest railway bridge in the world. It carries the lines four hundred and thirty-five feet above the level of the River Sioule. There is a bridge in

the Paris suburban services and the main line from Paris to Le Mans.

The suburban traffic at some of the Paris terminal stations is enormous. St. Lazare, for example, handles over a quarter of a million passengers every day. Even the Gare de l'Est handles daily between seventy and eighty thousand.

Double-Deck Coaches

The traffic at these two stations, in fact, has risen to such dimensions that it has been quite impossible to handle it all in ordinary coaches. The French have, therefore, provided double-deck coaches as are found in some other countries. The earlier versions of these were somewhat primitive vehicles, with outside staircases at the ends to reach the upper decks, but the latest bogie-wheeled double-deckers have large end vestibules with either stairs or ramps leading to the upper and lower decks, all inside and so under cover.

Paris is more than a capital with its own heavy traffic, however; it can rightly be called the terminus for the whole of Europe. Every day, before the war, there started from Paris some of the most famous luxury expresses in the world, carrying passengers all over the continent to the fringe of the Orient. These were the trains-de-luxe of the International Sleeping Car Company, made up entirely of sleeping and dining cars.

They were available to both first and second class passengers, and the traveller could book from Paris to cities as far distant as Athens or Istanbul. What is more, he could travel to his destination in the same coach. The running of such through trains all over Europe was a most complicated business, with steam haulage in some places and electric haulage in others, not to mention the crossing of frontiers and customs barriers; but European standard gauge made it possible mechanically, and all the other difficulties were more than anything a question of international agreement and organization.

Day and Night Comfort

Some of the cars of the Company are ingeniously arranged. The first-class passenger has a commodious room to himself, with a comfortable lounge seat across the width of the compartment by day, which is made up into a bed by night. If the room is required for second-class accommodation,

FAMOUS FRENCH EXPRESS. Well-known to every traveller between Paris and London, the Golden Arrow is seen standing at the Gare du Nord in Paris about to pull off on its daily morning run to Calais. The train is composed of luxurious first- and second-class Pullman cars, drawn by a four-cylinder compound Pacific locomotive of the Chemin de Fer du Nord, now part of the French National Railways.

CROSS-CHANNEL TRAIN FERRY. Running the sleeping cars of the through Paris-London night service on board the ferry, an operation calling for accurate alignment of the rails on deck with those on the quay. The ferry is run into a lock where the level of the water is under control, and further allowance for any difference in height or level is made by the hoisting gear of a connecting bridge or gangway.

133

however, there is a second concealed bed in the wall of the compartment, and this can be let down to make a two-berth cabin, as it were, with the two berths one above the other.

In this way the accommodation of the train can be varied quite easily, according to whether the greatest demand is for first or second-class travel.

World-Famous Expresses

Everybody has heard of the famous Blue Train to the Riviera. It earned its name not so long ago simply because it was one of the first to be changed from the original varnished teak to a livery of dark blue. Officially, it was known as the Calais-Mediterranean Express. Other famous trains were the Rome Express and the Simplon-Orient Express, which both began their fascinating journeys from the Gare de Lyon.

They followed the same route as the Blue Train as far as Dijon, but here the Rome Express branched off to Culoz and Modane, where the Italian State Railways took charge of it, while the Simplon-Orient Express, passing through the Mont d'Or tunnel,

made its way to Vallorbe with the help of the Swiss Federal Railways.

The Simplon-Orient had a long journey. It got its name from the Simplon Tunnel, through which it passed into Italy, and then went on by way of Milan, Venice and Trieste into Yugoslavia.

Besides the Simplon-Orient Express, there was the Orient Express, which crossed Europe by a more northerly route. It ran from Ostend by way of Cologne, Frankfort, Nuremberg and Vienna to Budapest, being joined on the way by a through portion from Paris. Yet another of these luxury travel trains was the Arlberg-Orient Express, which ran from Calais and Paris by way of the Arlberg route through Austria.

Language and Change Problems

It will be appreciated that the staffs of such trains must have a good knowledge both of languages and of money exchange rates. As each frontier is crossed, all the menu cards in the restaurant cars have to be changed, and bills made out in accordance with the currency of the country. This means keeping small change in the coinage of

AUTO RAIL-CAR. Used extensively on the smaller lines in France, as well as in other countries, this type of passenger car is usually powered by light-weight petrol or Diesel motors geared direct to the driving wheels and operating through a mechanical clutch. The cars are so light that the Diesel-electric principle would be uneconomical. Rail-cars of this type are used a great deal on the Riviera.

FRENCH DOUBLE-DECKER. Type of coach used on the Paris suburban lines to provide more seating accommodation on busy routes. Stairs or ramps lead from the vestibule to both upper and lower decks. The use of two floors practically doubles the number of seats available, but there is not full head-room on both decks. However, additional accommodation is provided in the vestibule for standing passengers.

every country through which the train passes, for few passengers think to provide themselves with all the variety of coinages they may need on a journey such as this.

Another and more serious difficulty is that every coach must be fitted to conform to the safety requirements of every country through which it passes. Further, it must have couplings suited to the many different types of locomotive that are used. Quite a lot has been done to standardize such fittings, but it is still necessary to fit these international trains with several different kinds of brake and other equipment.

Coaches fitted for steam-heating in winter have to be run over long stretches of electrified line, where there is no steam for any purpose, and this alone means either that electric heaters must be installed in addition to the steam radiators, or that a special boiler-wagon, producing steam for heating purposes, has to be attached to a train drawn by electricity. Again, owing to the problem of supplying the restaurant cars with gas over such long journeys, most of the cooking has to be done on coke ranges, and many of the sleeping cars are

fitted for coke heating in case of emergency. The cars pass over mountains and through deep snow cuttings in winter, and nothing must be left to chance.

Britain seemed to be isolated from this long-distance travel in the same comfortable coach, owing to the English Channel, but even this barrier was eventually overcome. Not by a Channel Tunnel, however, for this project, although a company has been formed to further it, has not been carried out. Nevertheless, in October 1936, it became possible to enter a sleeping car in London and travel in it to Paris and the Near East.

Dover-Dunkerque Ferry

The passage across the Channel was accomplished by means of the Dover-Dunkerque train ferry. Train ferries have been built in various parts of the world, and their principle is that they carry railway tracks on deck of a gauge to accommodate the trains. The boat train from London travels to Dover, where the cars are run on board the ferry, which is berthed in an enclosed dock with water at a constant level,

135

so that the same level may be maintained between the tracks on shore and those on the deck of the ferry.

At Dunkerque the reverse procedure takes place. The cars are transferred by a shunting locomotive from ship to shore, and there attached to an express for Paris. And from Paris, of course, they take their place in any of the luxury trains as desired.

Small Independent Lines

Apart from the main-line services and the national railways, most of the countries of Europe also have large numbers of small and independent narrow-gauge railways. France and Belgium, in particular, have quite a number that are little more than tramways. All were established long before the advent of the motor-car, and they were very successful in serving out-lying districts.

The great increase in road transport, however, sounded the death-knell of many of these lines, as far as normal operation was concerned, and only the more pro-gressive, which adopted the motor-car engine or electrification as their means of traction, have been able to survive.

The petrol engine was installed in rail-cars, and made a handy and economical vehicle for the transport of goods and passengers on little-used lines, having much less weight and consequently greater speed for the power developed. So success-ful was the idea, in fact, that petrol-driven rail-cars are now used on the main-line routes, chiefly in the south of France.

These petrol cars are different from the Diesel-electric locomotives of other countries, in that there is no electrical working, the motor being coupled direct to the driving wheels through a gear-box and clutch. Some of them, like the Micheline, are rubber-tyred vehicles, and provide the quietest form of rail travel yet devised. They have also been built to run either on the road or on rails, but this practice finds more favour in the northern countries.

Spanish Railways

The railways of Spain and Portugal can hardly be compared with those of the rest of Europe. To begin with, they are laid down to the much wider gauge of five feet

136

six inches, which prevents any through running of coaches from the standard gauge, and more or less cuts the two countries off from the general progress. All traffic for Spain has to be unloaded and reloaded at the frontier stations in the Pyrénées, a slow and costly business. In addition, the interior of Spain is very mountainous, and no speeds of any note are performed even on the main-line railways.

It is noteworthy, however, that Spain, like all the other countries of Europe, has amalgamated the larger private railway companies into one national system, in an attempt to bring them up to date. The change-over took place in 1941.

Past and present rub shoulders in Spain in a curious way. On the main lines, although high speeds are not obtainable, an express train may be hauled by a powerful locomotive of modern wheel arrangement suitable for heavy grades, with rolling stock including saloon coaches of the Pullman type. But a journey over a country branch in a mixed passenger and goods train is a very different experience.

Across the Pyrénées

Nevertheless, Spanish railways can show some fine engineering feats, chiefly in the Pyrénées Mountains, where the French and Spanish lines connect. There are some tunnels which had to be bored out of solid rock, one over three miles in length, and another in a spiral curve for the purpose of surmounting a sudden change in level. In addition, there are several viaducts, one, the Gisclard, designed on the lines of a suspension bridge, with a central span of over five hundred feet carrying the rails two hundred and sixty-five feet above the turbulent River Têt.

There are some excellent stations, too, in the larger Spanish cities, chiefly in Madrid and Barcelona. Barcelona also has a cable or suspension railway over the harbour, and Madrid has an underground system of the high-level variety, just below the surface. The Spanish railway system has made great strides recently, including a certain amount of electrification, but a great deal remains to be done to the minor and branch lines to bring them up to the level of the rest of Europe.

ELECTRICITY IN THE PYRÉNÉES. Most Spanish railways are steam-operated and many are comparatively old-fashioned, but a certain amount of electric haulage is used in the mountainous district of the Pyrénées. This electrified line to Nuria is supplied with current by overhead conductors and worked on the rack-and-pinion principle. The toothed rail in the centre of the track can be clearly identified.

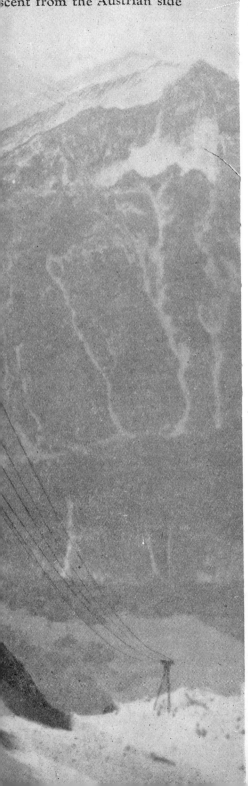

ugspitze Suspension Railway
the Bavarian Alps; the
scent from the Austrian side

CHAPTER SEVEN

AMAZING RAILWAYS OF THE ALPS

THE day is gone when one needed to be a competent mountaineer to get a good view of the Alps. Today it is the railway that goes mountaineering, while the tourist sits back in comfort and enjoys the scenery.

Even main-line travel in this part of Europe is unlike anything to be found in flat or level country. The track winds and twists in an extraordinary fashion, doubling back and forth among the mountains to gain height, and the train is constantly either ascending or descending a gradient.

Wonderful Engineering

France, Germany, Austria and Italy each control a portion of the alpine belt, but it is in the small, central country of Switzerland that the most amazing feats of railway engineering have been accomplished. The main lines are standard gauge, and the two most important are the Gotthard and Loetschberg routes.

The Gotthard line, a hundred and forty miles long, forms the most direct north-south link between Germany and Italy. Very heavy freight traffic is worked over it in consequence, and the line has been kept as level as possible. Even so, there are many miles with a gradient as steep as, roughly, one in forty. This is not far short of the Lickey gradient in Great Britain, which is the steepest in the country, yet in Switzerland it is an average main line.

Gotthard Line

The Gotthard line starts from the lovely lakeside city of Lucerne, and the winding nature of the track is evident immediately. In traversing the shores of the lake, and avoiding a mountain chain, it travels thirty-two miles to reach a point only eighteen miles from Lucerne direct.

It then enters the valley of the Reuss, where the river forces its tempestuous way

BERNINA PASS IN SUMMER, where the line is as much as seven thousand four hundred feet above sea level; this is not far below the perpetual snow line. The twisting nature of the track here as it skirts Lake Bianco is typical of most Swiss lines. It will be noticed that this light train has two power coaches at the head of it, for this line has gradients in some places as steep as 1 in 14, worked by adhesion.

through a number of gorges, and it is here, as the line rises from basin to basin, that some of the most extraordinary feats of engineering are found.

As the line approaches Wassen, there is the completely corkscrew Pfäffensprung tunnel, which rises in a spiral as it bores its way round within the mountain. The train travels for nearly a mile in this and comes out into the open again a hundred feet higher up, almost above the entrance.

Spiral Loops

Following this is a great double loop past the village, where the line, doubling back on itself by the aid of two more spiral tunnels, one on each side of the valley, climbs another four hundred feet. It crosses the Meienreuss River, in fact, three times at three different levels, and trains bound for Italy travel over it twice in a southerly

direction and once in the opposite direction. Spiral tunnels of this type are found all over Switzerland, on metre gauge track as well as on the standard gauge main lines. This is a favourite device of the engineer for gaining height without making the track too steep.

On reaching Göschenen, the line is two thousand feet higher than at its starting point, and here it enters the famous Gotthard tunnel, right under the main peaks of the Alps.

Third longest tunnel in the world, the Gotthard is over nine miles from portal to portal, and dead straight save for a slight curve at the southern exit. Little experience of tunnelling on this scale was available at the time of its construction, and the boring of it through solid rock took ten years.

For the whole of its length it is illuminated by electric lamps, and trains pass through it at sixty miles an hour. The tunnel is twenty-eight feet wide and twenty-one feet high, and is so bored that the floor is highest in the middle and drains gradually to both ends.

Once through the tunnel, the line begins to descend, and drops rapidly in one place for three hundred feet by means of four more completely spiral tunnels. Altogether it descends three thousand feet, but only to climb another eight hundred feet before it reaches the Italian frontier.

Mile Level Difference

On the north-bound journey, train-loads have to surmount a total difference in level of not far short of a mile vertically. Between the Italian frontier and Lucerne, there are no fewer than eighty tunnels in all, and well over three hundred bridges with spans of thirty-two feet and upwards.

The Loetschberg line is similar, almost rivalling the Gotthard line both in engin-

eering and scenic attraction, with a tunnel of roughly the same length under the Gastern Valley. The Loetschberg Tunnel, however, is not by any means straight, and for a tragic and dramatic reason.

Workmen Overwhelmed

Unknown to the engineers, there were beneath the Gastern Valley a number of deep fissures filled with water-bearing rock and silt, and when the northern bore had penetrated only three miles, the workers, on detonating a charge, broke into one of them.

Water gushed in so rapidly that twenty-five of the men were overwhelmed at the face, while stone, silt and other débris were carried back for a mile and a quarter along the tunnel, filling the bore completely. The whole stretch had to be abandoned, the end was blocked up and the tunnel was diverted eastwards, with a similar diversion from the south portal. Today, therefore, the

YET ANOTHER SUMMER SCENE—this time in the Oberalp Pass of the Furka-Oberalp line, which connects the valley of the Rhône with that of the Rhine. Except for a little traffic up the valleys at the two extreme ends of the line and for trains specially run for winter sports during the season, this railway is closed to traffic in winter. This line, here steam-operated, has since been electrified.

THREE DIFFERENT LEVELS OF TRACK. One of the most outstanding examples of spiral construction in Switzerland. This is the Gotthard line photographed from a point near Giornico, in the Ticino valley, where three sections of track can be clearly seen one above the other. Spiral construction is a favourite device of engineers to gain height without increasing the steepness of gradient, the large sweep of

142

the curve giving a greater proportion of length to the height the line must rise
in a specified distance. The main curves here, however, are inside the mountain
in the form of tunnels, the tunnels having been bored purely for the purpose of
extending the circle; both entrance and exit portals are on the same side of the
mountain. Two tunnels were necessary to achieve the rise on this section of track.

143

VALLEY TO MOUNTAIN TOP. Excellent example of how a Swiss track winds its tortuous way up a mountain side, gaining height without carrying the train any great distance as the crow flies from its starting point in the valley. On the left of the picture, beside the whitish-looking course of the stream, is a section of the track this electric train has traversed, hundreds of feet below its present altitude.

Loetschberg Tunnel has three curious curves, instead of the straight line originally planned.

This was not the only difficulty. At the southern portal, where the tunnel comes into the wild Lonza ravine, there was considerable peril in winter from avalanches. On one occasion a colossal snow-slide completely buried the construction camp, causing a number of deaths.

For this reason, as the line mounts high up the eastern wall of the mountain, it passes from time to time through massive avalanche tunnels constructed of concrete and steel, which are placed at every point where a recognized avalanche slide is crossed. These tunnels have roofs sloping from the mountainside towards the valley, so that melting snow passes harmlessly over the top. As a further precaution, many stout masonry walls have been built on the slopes, in the way of the avalanche trail, to break up the masses of snow.

From across the valley, it is a striking spectacle to see a train on the Loetschberg line high up the mountainside at Hohtenn, and to follow its rapid downward course,

into and out of tunnels, across bridges and viaducts until it reaches the international station at Brigue, where the Simplon Tunnel route starts for Italy.

Longest Main-Line Tunnel

The Simplon Tunnel is the longest main-line railway tunnel in the world. Actually there are twin tunnels, just over twelve miles and a quarter in length, and fifty-six feet apart. That on the right, looking from the Swiss side, was originally a smaller bore driven to aid in ventilating the larger tunnel, but was afterwards enlarged to accommodate railway trains.

The difficulties of driving the first Simplon Tunnel were formidable. At a point a few miles from the north portal, where the tunnel is roughly seven thousand feet below the surface of the Alps, the temperature rose to nearly a hundred and thirty degrees Fahrenheit, and men could only be kept at work by spraying the rock-face with ice-cold jets of water, pumped into the bore for the purpose. Irruptions of unwanted water into the workings were frequent, sometimes at the rate of three thousand gallons a

Bietschtal steel arch bridge
on the Loetschberg
main line, Switzerland

minute, and further trouble was caused by hot springs which also broke in, as hot as the rock-face itself.

Yet another danger came from rotten strata through which the bore had to pass. At one point the pressure was so enormous that it bent substantial steel linings well out of shape. Seven months of work passed in dealing with one length of only a hundred and thirty feet, through which the masonry lining of the tunnel is reinforced internally with curved steel girders.

Electricity in Switzerland

All the Swiss main lines are electrified. Not only is electricity of great assistance in working up heavy gradients, but water power for the production of current is cheap and plentiful. The ice-caps of the mountains provide a constant supply in the glacial streams which pour down their abrupt slopes, and suitable valleys all over the country have been dammed and turned into reservoirs for hydro-electric schemes.

Some of these schemes are on an immense scale, with reservoirs at great heights to make the fall of water as long as possible. The Barberine Lake which feeds the Barberine power-station, is an artificial sheet of water created by throwing a dam nearly a thousand feet in length across the valley.

At its highest point it is over two hundred and fifty feet, and at its base it is nearly two hundred feet thick. From the lake the pipe-line falls over two thousand three hundred feet into the power-station, where four Pelton turbines of sixteen thousand four hundred horse-power are coupled to generators producing current at fifteen thousand volts.

This is transformed up to sixty-six thousand volts and passed by overhead wire to the Vernayaz power-station in the Rhône, where there are five more great turbo-alternator sets. From Vernayaz the current is carried at a hundred and thirty-two thousand volts right across Switzerland, helping to feed its two thousand odd route miles of electrified line. The Gotthard line has its own power-stations.

The largest electric locomotives have either three or four motor-driven axles, with a bogie in front and a carrying axle at the rear, but for special purposes some enormous engines have been produced by coupling two of these units together, giving a combined output of twelve thousand horse-power. These giants were introduced on the Gotthard line to do away with the necessity for using two locomotives on the heaviest trains. Such a locomotive will work a five-hundred-ton train at a steady average of forty miles an hour over the steepest gradients of the main lines.

The fastest runs, of sixty miles an hour average, are those that cross the country from Geneva through Lausanne and Berne to Zurich, but even faster running than this

is made by the so-called Red Arrow rail-cars, used mainly for tourist traffic, which are permitted to travel at seventy-five miles an hour where the track is suitable. In considering speed, it must be remembered that even on the downgrades speed is strictly limited for the sake of safety, owing to the winding nature of the track.

Sharp Gradients

The average gradient, however, by no means represents the steepest slope up which a train can be worked by the normal grip of smooth-tyred wheels on rails. On some of the metre-gauge lines there are gradients as steep as one-in-fourteen, the steepest in the world for a normal track. These lines also have their engineering marvels, including the Landwasser Viaduct, which carries the rails on a curve over two

OVER THE ALPS IN WINTER. Two snow cuttings typical of Swiss lines in winter. That on the left is on the Bernina Railway. A snow cutting such as this is built up by several falls, the line being cleared by a rotary snow-plough after each fall. Although such depths of snow are by no means uncommon, services are rarely suspended. During heavy falls, the snow-plough patrols the line almost continuously. At a point on this route, Swiss engineers have erected a depth gauge in the form of a post with cross-bars to record the depth of snow, and the highest bar is over twenty feet above the ground level. The illustration on the right shows the view from the driver's cabin on a funicular railway in winter-time, but the photograph gives no indication of the steepness of the gradient, which in some parts of the Alps is at an angle of almost forty-five degrees.

DAM TO INCREASE DEPTH OF LAKE

ENTRY TO TUNNELS

SLUICE GATE
GANTRY &
CONTROL HOUSE

MOUNTAIN CUT AWAY
TO SHOW LAKE SUPPLYING WATER

TRIPLE STEEL
PIPE LINE

CATENARY WIRE
TO SUPPORT CONDUCTOR

15,000-VOLT CONDUCTOR

CURRENT COLLECTOR BOWS
ON PANTOGRAPHS

15,000 VOLT SINGLE-PHASE
ELECTRIC LOCOMOTIVE

—R·B·WAY—

HYDRO-ELECTRIC SCHEME for utilizing water power, a principle based on the early water-wheel, which was kept moving by the weight of water falling on to its vanes from above. The water-wheel has become much more efficient and is now known as a turbine. Water is carried from the source by pipelines and ejected after use into the river. Connected direct to the water turbines are electric generators, and the current

SINGLE-PHASE FEED
TO OVERHEAD LINES OF RAILWAY

HYDRO-ELECTRIC MACHINES
DEVELOPING 7500 KVA
FROM EACH SET

HIGH-VOLTAGE LINES
SUPPLYING OTHER AREAS

3-PHASE
GENERATOR

PELTON WHEEL
TURBINE

TRANSFORMERS
STEPPING UP VOLTAGES
FOR DISTANCE DISTRIBUTION

TAIL WATER
TO RIVER

generated by these is taken to transformers so that the voltage can be increased for distribution over long distances. It is then fed to the track by means of overhead conductors at a pressure of 15,000 volts. In actual practice, both the lake and the track might be situated several miles from the power-house, but each has been included in this simplified representation to explain the hydro-electric principle.

TRAVERSER GEAR OF PILATUS RAILWAY. Ingenious method for transferring cars from one track to another. A complete section of the rack-equipped track travels sideways on rollers, and is operated from the position immediately below the car on the right. By this means, all descending cars are transferred from the left-hand track to the right, after they have discharged their passengers, to load up at the right-hand platform, where the queue is seen forming for the next upward journey.

hundred feet above the river, straight into a tunnel in the face of a sheer precipice.

It is remarkable enough to find dining- and saloon-car trains, sometimes up to ten bogie vehicles, working over the less spectacular routes, but even on the one-in-fourteen gradients a restaurant car is a regular feature of the summer workings.

One of the most interesting of these trains is the Glacier Express, which runs daily in summer between Zermatt and St. Moritz, a distance of a hundred and sixty-five miles. This route connects no fewer than four rivers, the Rhône, the Rhine, the Danube and the Po. Thus, if the journey be continued to Tirano, just across the Italian frontier, it is possible in just over two hundred miles of travel to see rivers flowing to the Mediterranean, the North Sea, the Black Sea and the Adriatic.

Heavy Snowfalls

In winter, however, the Swiss lines are subject to very heavy falls of snow, which lies so deep in places it would completely cover the trains were it not for the precautions taken. At the Bernina Hospice Station, for instance, which is over seven thousand feet above sea level, there is a tall post with crossbars at intervals to indicate the depths of snow with which the railway has had to contend during its history, and the highest of these crossbars is over twenty feet above ground level.

Rotary Snow-Ploughs

The route is kept clear by rotary snow-ploughs, which are turned out to patrol the lines constantly during heavy snowfalls, and keep a cutting through the snow for the trains. On the front of the plough is a large wheel which has broad, curved vanes attached to its spokes, rotated by steam-driven machinery in the plough behind. The plough, which either moves up to the drift under its own power or is pushed by one or more locomotives behind, is set spinning rapidly, and throws the snow up through the plough casing in a tremendous arc, well clear of the track. In fine weather, the walls of the snow-cutting made by the plough stand up almost vertically and give no trouble. Over a summit like the Bernina the trains travel in

Restaurant car train climbing to the 7,400-ft. altitude of the Bernina Pass, Switzerland

INSULATORS

PANTOGRAPH

DRIVER'S
CONTROL
CABIN

PANTOGRAPH
STOWED

HIGH-TENSION
CHAMBER

AIR
GRILLES

AIR
GRILLES

FRONT HALF OF
LOCOMOTIVE
IDENTICAL WITH
REAR HALF

TRACTION
MOTORS

AIR-COOLING
RADIATORS

MOTOR GENERATOR
AND AIR BLOWER

8,500 H.P. ELECTRIC
LOCOMOTIVE
SWISS FEDERAL RAILWAYS
ARTICULATED TYPE

OVERHEAD DISTRIBUTING SYSTEM

PANTOGRAPH

LEADS TO HIGH-TENSION CHAMBERS

COLLECTOR BOWS

PANTOGRAPH EXTENDED

TRACTION MOTORS

CONTROL CABIN

COOLING AIR DUCTS

HIGH-TENSION CHAMBER AND SWITCHES

TRACTION MOTORS AND REDUCTION GEARS (16 MOTORS IN ALL)

DRIVING WHEELS

PLOUGH

AIR-BRAKE CYLINDER

LASHWELL WOOD

a deep snow cutting during most of the winter, often almost hidden by the snow.

There is something even more curious than this, however, and that is a bridge which has been made so that it can be taken to pieces in winter. It is in the wild Steffenbach Gorge, high up in the mountains on the Furka-Oberalp line, a gorge which in winter is the channel for the most devastating avalanches. The first bridge built here was completely swept away, but as the line is normally open only for four months in summer, there was no necessity for a bridge during the winter months. The famous Steffenbach removable bridge was, therefore, designed and built and has been in operation ever since. It is taken to pieces annually at the end of September and replaced in the following June.

Up or Down in a Day

The design was prepared with a view to rapid dismantling, with a permanent crane tackle at each end of the bridge and the middle sections built to fold and slide back. The bridge gang employed has now become so expert at taking it down or putting it up that neither operation takes more than a single day.

When we come to the real mountain railways, as understood in Switzerland and other parts of the Alps, the adhesion principle has to be abandoned and a very different type of track is used. This is the rack-and-pinion type, in the centre of which is a special rail formed with teeth, so that a cogwheel on the locomotive can mesh with it and so give greater grip. There are various types of rack. In the older type, known as the Riggenbach, the rack resembles a ladder, and the teeth of the cogwheel, or pinion, fit into the spaces between the rungs. In the newer type, however, known as the Abt system, the rack teeth are cut out of solid metal, and the rack resembles two combs set up on edge, so that the teeth of one fall opposite the spaces between the teeth of the other.

Highest Open-air Line

On this a special toothed wheel, driven by the locomotive, finds sufficient grip to pull a train up inclinations as steep as one-in-four, as on the Gornergrat Railway, which has the distinction of reaching the highest altitude in Europe of any line which completes the whole of its course in the open air. Its mountain terminus is over ten thousand feet above sea level.

Not all gradients of the cogwheel railways are as steep as this, of course, and not all rack railways are separate in themselves

REMARKABLE BRIDGE in the wild Steffenbach Gorge. The first bridge built here was carried away by an avalanche, but no such calamity has occurred to the present one. This is the famous Steffenbach removable bridge, photographed with the centre span being lowered and each half-section ready to be slid back for winter retirement. The drawing on the right shows in detail how the mechanism works.

DERRICKS

PULLEYS

WINCH

HINGE

TRESTLES

HINGE

STONE
ABUTMENTS

1

CENTRE SPAN
BEING LOWERED

STEFFENBACH
RAVINE

HINGE

DERRICK AND
PULLEYS

SIDE SPAN LIFTED
AND PULLED BACK

WINCH

FOOTWAY

LOCKING
BOLTS AND
HINGES

DETAILS OF
CENTRE SPAN

METRE GAUGE
RACK-AND-
PINION TRACK

TRESTLE

TO WINCH

WINCH

2

ROLLERS

CENTRE SPAN
LOWERED AND
SIDE SPANS
BEING PULLED
BACK

HINGED
TRESTLES

SIDE SPAN
RESTING ON
TOP OF TRACK

TRESTLE
RESTING ON
ABUTMENT

CUT AWAY
SECTION OF
AVALANCHE

3

SPANS PULLED
BACK AND
AVALANCHE
PASSES
HARMLESSLY BY

AN INGENIOUS
REMOVABLE BRIDGE
Steffenbach - Furka - Oberalp Line
Switzerland

L.ASHWELL
WOOD.

from the normal track. On many of the ordinary mountain lines there are sections where a rack has been laid to assist the climb, and on these the locomotives are fitted either for rack working or normal adhesion propulsion. Rack gradients range from one-in-twelve upwards.

These are the railways mainly used by sightseers. The Gornergrat carries passengers up to one of the most famous panoramas in the Alps, where a score or more of noted peaks can be viewed, including the notorious Matterhorn. Rival to the Gornergrat is the Jungfrau Railway in the Bernese Oberland, which attains a maximum height of over eleven thousand feet, and carries tourists up from the lakeside town of Interlaken to the eternal snows of the Jungfraujoch, in the pass between the Münch and Jungfrau peaks.

Climbing the Jungfrau

The Jungfrau Railway, however, does not finish the course in the open. It is really three railways working in conjunction. The Jungfrau Railway proper climbs only a short distance in the open before it is hemmed in on one side by the vast pyramid of the Eiger, with its north face a sheer precipice of over six thousand feet, and on the other by the impassable Eiger glacier.

Onwards from here the line disappears into the mountain, and travels for a mile and a half in a tunnel to a stop at Eigerwand, where the passengers, by means of a lateral gallery driven to the mountain face, are able to look down on the village of Grindelwald, six thousand feet below.

Three miles beyond Eigerwand is the Jungfrau terminus, also in a tunnel, and adjoining it is a palatial hotel, from which galleries in the rock lead out to the Jungfraujoch itself. Here the uncrevassed snow slopes of the thick ice-cap permit winter sports of all kinds to be indulged in during the height of summer, by tourists who, without this extraordinary railway, could never have reached such a mountain fastness unless they were competent alpine climbers. The railway even owns a team of dogs, mostly Canadian huskies, to take visitors for toboggan trips over the ice.

Most of the steepest gradients on the rack railways are those leading to mountain summits. One of the best known of these is the Pilatus Railway, which carries sightseers up from Alpnachstad, on the shores of the Lake of Lucerne, to the summit of the Esel, more than a mile above. The distance covered is a little less than three miles, and the line has a maximum steepness of nearly one-in-two.

Stepped Platforms

On such an inclination as this, the station platforms are flights of steps, parallel to the track, and the cars themselves are built with compartments stepped one above the other. One particularly nerve-racking stretch on this line is up the side of the Eselwand, where steel brackets projecting from a sheer wall of rock are all that support the line for some considerable distance. It is some comfort to passengers, however, to know that in the whole history of their mountain railways, the Swiss make the claim that they have never lost the life of a passenger as the result of an accident.

Next in order of steepness is the funicular type of railway, in which the cars are hauled up the slope by a cable, although still travelling on a normal, or nearly normal track.

In the funicular principle, two cars are used, connected by a haulage cable which is passed round a driving wheel of large diameter in the engine house at the top of the incline. The descending car, by its weight, thus helps to pull up the car which is making the ascent. A single track, used by both cars, is laid throughout the line except at the centre, where a loop is needed for the two cars to pass each other.

Water as Ballast

In some funiculars the only power used is provided by a dead-weight of water. Each car is fitted with a water-ballast tank, and the ascending car starts with its tank empty while that of the descending car is full. As soon as the journey begins, however, the weight of the steel rope paid out with the descending car begins to take effect, and water must be gradually discharged from its tank until, on reaching the lower terminus, the tank may be almost empty.

Other funicular railways have not the advantage of abundant water supply, and

RACK-AND-PINION LOCOMOTIVE. Designed to give sufficient grip on the rails on steep gradients. The more recent lines of this type use a double rack in the form of two combs set side by side with the teeth pointing upwards, each tooth of one opposite a space in the other. A double-toothed pinion on the car engages with this.

157

REDUCTION GEARS

WINDING DRUMS

CONTROL BOX

MOTOR

MAGNETIC BRAKE

PASSENGERS' ENTRY AND EXIT STAIRCASE

TRANSFORMER

HIGH-TENSION POWER LINES

HAULAGE CABLES

THREE-RAIL TRACK

GRADIENT OF TRACKS ABOUT 1 IN 2

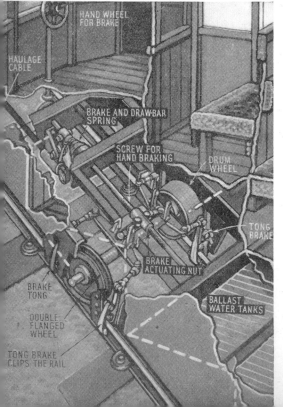

HAND WHEEL FOR BRAKE

HAULAGE CABLE

BRAKE AND DRAWBAR SPRING

SCREW FOR HAND BRAKING

DRUM WHEEL

TONG BRAKE

BRAKE ACTUATING NUT

BALLAST WATER TANKS

BRAKE TONG

DOUBLE FLANGED WHEEL

TONG BRAKE CLIPS THE RAIL

on these various forms of power are employed, chiefly electricity, to rotate the drum at the head of the line round which the rope passes. But on every line of this nature the weight of the cable must be considered, as there is perfect balance only when the two cars are passing on the loop, and at all other points some counter-balance must be brought into operation. On a lengthy line, the cable may weigh as much as forty tons.

The speed of travel on a funicular is necessarily slow, to avoid shocks or jars on the cable, and to prevent it from jumping off the pulleys, which are anchored down to the track for the cable to run over from top to bottom. On each line the maximum speed is strictly laid down, and is under the control either of the car drivers or of the engine-man in the top station, usually the latter.

Speeds vary roughly from two hundred to four hundred and forty feet a minute, and any excess over the limit for the line brings into operation powerful automatic brakes.

FUNICULAR PRINCIPLE, in which two cars are made to balance each other, one ascending as the other descends. In most cases they use the same single track, which is provided at the centre with a passing loop. This loop has no points, because a double-flanged wheel on the outer rail pulls each car on to its respective side of the loop. Very powerful automatic brakes in the form of tongs that grip the rail are also used and come into operation automatically in the event of a breakage in the haulage cable. A point that has to be considered is the constantly varying weight of the haulage rope, which increases on one side as it is paid out, and decreases on the side on which it is being wound in. To overcome this the cars are provided with water-ballast tanks and each car is filled as it reaches the top station. The water is then ejected slowly as it descends, so that the car gradually becomes lighter to counter-balance the increasing weight of the rope as the latter is paid out behind it. Some funicular lines are so steep that the car floors and station platforms are designed as a series of steps.

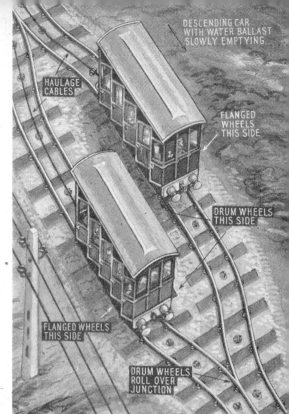

DESCENDING CAR WITH WATER BALLAST SLOWLY EMPTYING

HAULAGE CABLES

FLANGED WHEELS THIS SIDE

DRUM WHEELS THIS SIDE

FLANGED WHEELS THIS SIDE

DRUM WHEELS ROLL OVER JUNCTION

THREE-RAIL TRACK ON APPROACH VIADUCT

RAILS LAID ON STEEL SLEEPERS IN CONCRETE

POWER DRAWN FROM RIVER BY PIPE LINE HIGHER UP

ROPE JOCKEY PULLEYS

INSPECTION PIT BELOW RAILS

TURBINE DRIVEN POWER-STATION

Car climbing the St. Salvatore funicular railway from Lugano, Switzerland

ABOVE LOVELY LUCERNE. The suspension line from Beckenried to Klewenalp. In the whole history of their Alpine railways, the Swiss claim the astonishing record of not having lost a single life owing to accidents. This beautiful photograph shows the aerial car and, below, a glimpse of Beckenried beside the Lake of Lucerne.

On some railways these brakes are shaped like pairs of tongs, and are arranged to grip the head of the running rail on each side of the upper pair of car wheels. In the unlikely event of a haulage cable breaking, these tong brakes would come into action instantly, and there are two other types of emergency brake available to lock the cars in position until repairs have been effected.

In spite of their steepness, funicular railways are not the most startling of mountain lines. The most spectacular are the télépheriques, which hardly fall into the railway category at all, in that they dispense with rails altogether. The téléphérique has main cables from which the cars are suspended, and a haulage cable as a means of locomotion.

Two cars are used, as in the funicular principle, and are connected in a similar way by a single haulage cable, which passes over a drum at the top station. Each main cable is slung between towers and grooved

wheels travel on top of the cable, with a car suspended from them, in such a fashion that the supporting brackets do not foul the cable supports of the towers. The advantage of the téléphérique is that the main cables can be swung from tower to tower across a valley regardless of irregularities in the ground. The disadvantage, of course, is limited carrying capacity.

The téléphérique thus makes possible railway mountaineering of a type far beyond the scope of ordinary rails and permanent way. In the last quarter of a century, suspension lines have come into being all over the Alps, principally for the purpose of carrying sightseers to famous viewpoints, or tourists and others to high slopes for winter sports. There are many cableways in the Chamonix valley in eastern France, and it is here that there are some of the most amazing in existence.

They give access either to the outlying

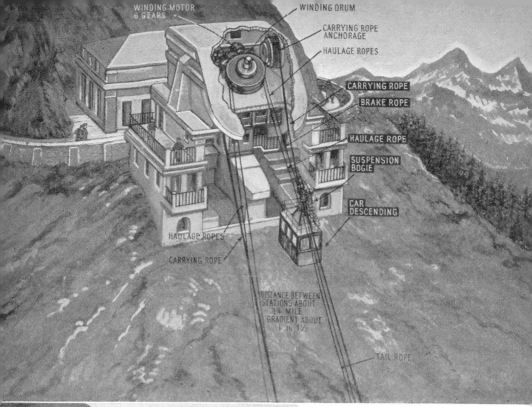

WINDING MOTOR 6 GEARS

WINDING DRUM

CARRYING ROPE ANCHORAGE

HAULAGE ROPES

CARRYING ROPE

BRAKE ROPE

HAULAGE ROPE

SUSPENSION BOGIE

CAR DESCENDING

HAULAGE ROPES

CARRYING ROPE

DISTANCE BETWEEN STATIONS ABOUT ¾ MILE GRADIENT ABOUT 1 IN 1½

TAIL ROPE

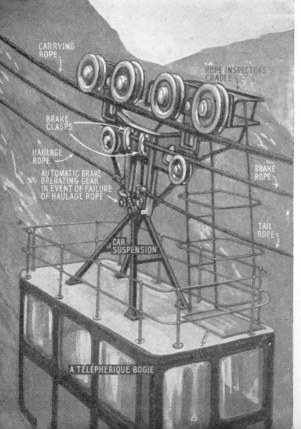

CARRYING ROPE

ROPE INSPECTORS CRADLE

BRAKE CLASPS

HAULAGE ROPE

AUTOMATIC BRAKE OPERATING GEAR IN EVENT OF FAILURE OF HAULAGE ROPE

BRAKE ROPE

TAIL ROPE

CAR SUSPENSION

A TÉLÉPHERIQUE BOGIE

TÉLÉPHERIQUE PRINCIPLE. Popularly known as a suspension railway, the téléphérique is the solution to the problem of providing transport to a mountain side or summit where the rugged and uneven nature of the ground makes the laying of an ordinary track impossible. Two main cables are slung from the lower station to the upper, with as many intermediate supporting towers as may be necessary, though spans of over three-quarters of a mile have been installed in extreme cases. A pulley-cradle rides on each main cable, and from this the passenger car is suspended. As on funicular railways, the ascending and descending cars balance one another, and are connected by a continuous haulage cable, which passes over a large drum at the top and round pulleys at the bottom. In this way the weight of one car descending is used to assist in raising the other. A second pair of cables is provided for control of speed, which is effected by brakes gripping the cable; the braking is automatic in the event of an accident to the haulage rope.

spurs of the famous Mont Blanc, or to high viewpoints from which the majesty of these snow-capped peaks can be seen to better advantage. One of them is up the side of the great Glacier des Bossons to a station known as Les Glaciers, at an altitude of over eight thousand feet, the ascent being made in two stages with a change of cars intermediately. The ultimate intention is to carry this line a stage further right up to the summit of the Aiguille du Midi, twelve thousand feet above sea level and one of the needle-pointed peaks, far above the line of eternal snow.

Over the Abyss

But the greatest thrill of all is on the north side of the valley, where a suspension line rises first from Chamonix up to Planpraz, six thousand feet above sea level, and then swings back on one long, unsupported span of over three-quarters of a mile to the crest of the Brévent, whose southern aspect is a sheer cliff over 1,000 ft. high.

Here the télépherique in truth becomes an aerial railway. The main cables have been strung across this vast gap in pairs, each one just over an inch in diameter. Their breaking strength is about a hundred and twenty tons, and the car, which holds only fifteen people, all standing, is of as light a construction as possible, but the cables themselves impose a tremendous strain by reason of their weight alone. On this aerial journey, which takes exactly seven minutes, the passenger obtains an unsurpassed view of Mont Blanc with the glaciers streaming down from its peak, and the Chamonix valley far below.

Amazing though they are, these are not the final objectives of the Alpine engineers. Plans are in existence to carry a railway right to the summit of the Matterhorn, the joy and despair of all Alpinists, nearly fifteen thousand feet above sea level. After reaching the hotel Belvedere, where climbers usually sleep before tackling the famous north-east ridge, the line would enter the rock, and reach the summit by three stages in the heart of the mountain.

Through the fir and pine forests
of Sweden with electric haulage

CHAPTER EIGHT

OVER WATER AND MOUNTAIN IN SCANDINAVIA

NOWHERE in the world does the railway cover a greater mileage over water than in the Scandinavian countries. At one extreme is Denmark, with wide waterways interrupting every possible railway route, and at the other is Norway, with the whole of its western seaboard indented by deep clefts which penetrate far into the mountains.

In between, there is the Baltic and the lakeland country of Sweden, offering the railway a choice between forests and more waterways, for the greater part of Sweden is covered by pine forests through which the railway has to find its way.

The contrast is certainly striking, for Denmark is extremely flat, whereas Norway is just a long ridge of mountains from north to south. Topographically, Sweden lies between, comparatively flat in the south, but with a mountainous area in the north on the Norwegian border.

Across the Waterways

In spite of all this, it is possible to go by train from Denmark to Norway and Sweden in the same coach or sleeping car. Many fine bridges have been built to carry the railway over the shorter water gaps, and where the gaps are too wide to be bridged, the coaches are carried by ferry steamers, a means of getting the railway across water that has been developed in Scandinavia more than anywhere else.

Most famous of the train ferries is that which in normal times crosses the Baltic from Sassnitz, in Germany, to the Swedish port of Trelleborg. The distance covered is fifty-eight nautical miles, and the service was started jointly by the Swedish and German governments, each contributing two steamers to the fleet.

The Swedish ship Drottning Victoria is a typical example. The stern is made very wide, and along the main deck are laid two railway tracks, each running nearly the

whole length of the vessel. They are actually just under three hundred feet in length, and can accommodate eight railway coaches between them.

The ship is backed into a dock, where the water can be maintained at a constant level, and the rail tracks are lined up with those on shore, which come right to the edge of the dock. A shunting engine usually pushes the coaches on board.

Securing the Coaches

For the sea trip, which takes four hours, they are securely shackled to the deck and to one another, as well as being fastened to the girders of the upper deck. The coaches are thus unable to come adrift in heavy weather, and passengers may either remain in them or transfer to the comfortable saloons or cabins on the ship itself. This passage across the Baltic is one of the longest in the world made by train ferry.

The Baltic coastline between Germany and Denmark also boasts the longest railway bridge in Europe, which just beats the famous Tay Bridge in Britain. The Storström Bridge, as it is known, connects Germany and Denmark across the Masned Sound, and is ten thousand, five hundred and thirty-five feet in length.

Numerous Spans

The Sound here is fairly shallow, so there was no need for any long spans. The longest are the navigation spans in the middle, giving searoom to shipping. The others, forty-seven in all, are much shorter, the shallowness of the Sound making it possible to build a number of supporting piers without difficulty. The bridge carries a single line of railway track and a road, and is one of the most recent to be opened in Europe, only two years before the Second World War. Its erection permitted a cut of fifty minutes in the time of the through

TO SASSNITZ

HARBOUR LIGHT

COMPASS PLATFORM

BRIDGE

BOILER-ROOM VENTS

SEA WALL

ENGINE-ROOM VENTS

SALOON AND DINING-ROOMS

BOILER UPTAKES

PASSENGER CABINS AT SIDE

NIGHT STEWARD

BOILER ROOM (4 SCOTCH BOILERS)

SIDE FUEL BUNKER

ENGINE ROOM (2 RECIPROCATING ENGINES)

ASHWELL WOOD

ENGINEERS CABINS

THRUST BLOCK

TRAIN FERRY STEAMER, showing internal arrangements and method of getting trains on board. The coach deck has a double track, and is long enough to take four full-length coaches each side. These are shunted on board over a connecting gangway which can be raised or lowered according to the level of the deck, the

PLATFORM
HOIST FOR
VARIOUS LEVELS
OF WATER

HOIST
ANCHORAGE

HOISTING
MOTORS

DOCKING
BRIDGE

SEARCHLIGHT

PULLEYS

4 COACHES
EACH SIDE
OF VESSEL

RAIL GRIPS
HOLDING
COACHES DOWN

RAIL
LOCKS

MOVABLE
PLATFORM

SLEEPING CARS
BEING SHUNTED
ABOARD

ends of the rails on ship and gangway being locked in position when the process
is complete. Rail grips hold the coaches down in case the vessel should roll, and
there are further ties, usually to the roof beams of the boat deck. The train ferry
solves the problem of getting trains across water which is too wide to be bridged.

167

COMING ASHORE BY TRAIN. Railway coaches from Warnemunde, Germany, running ashore from the train ferry at Gjedser, Denmark. Through coaches are run from many towns in Germany, not only to Denmark, but also to the other Scandinavian countries. The longest run of any train ferry in the world is from Sassnitz, in Germany, to the Swedish port of Trelleborg, a distance of sixty-seven miles across open sea.

sleeping-car trains from Berlin to Copenhagen.

Another interesting bridge is that built across what is known as the Little Belt, between Jutland and the island of Funen. The channel is a mile wide, and at one time was crossed by a ferry steamer, but a bridge gives so much more rapid transit that soundings were constantly being taken to see if a bridge were possible.

When it was started, embankments of very great height had to be tipped to form the approaches, for it was necessary to build the navigation span over a hundred feet above high water, and these approaches lead to eight immense arches of reinforced concrete. Between these is the main structure of the bridge, a con-

tinuous cantilever over two thousand, seven hundred feet in length.

It was the depth of the shipping channel, however, that was the real obstacle. In the shallowest part this was nearly a hundred feet deep, and foundations, to be secure, had to go considerably below the ocean bed.

The problem was solved by the caisson method of construction. A caisson is a huge cylinder sunk by various means to form a base for the piers. In this case, huge caissons of reinforced concrete were built up on shore, and launched from a slipway like ships. They were launched upside down, floated to their positions, and then capsized.

A caisson is usually filled with compressed air and forced down by added weights, so that men can work inside it and do the necessary excavations, but these caissons for the Little Belt Bridge were sunk by a new method in which the use of compressed air was avoided.

Concrete Tubes

A ring of concrete tubes was built around each one, and the work of excavating was carried out through the tubes, so that each caisson could sink gradually under its own weight. Finally, each one was sealed up with concrete. The bridge carries a double line of railway, a roadway and a footway in addition.

The speeds of trains in Scandinavia are, on the average, lower than over the rest of Europe, as can be understood from the nature of most of the country through which

the track has been laid. Diesel-electric propulsion, however, has come into use in places, where the lines are not electrified, particularly in Denmark.

In this country there is a series of streamlined trains known as Lyntog, running mainly between Copenhagen and Esbjerg, their times for a journey of nearly two hundred miles being four hours and three-quarters. These Diesel-electric flyers are permitted to travel up to seventy-five miles an hour, but the steam services seldom exceed a mile-a-minute as a maximum. A curious feature of Danish State Railways is that the locomotives carry the national colours in a band of red and white at the base of the chimney. Round Copenhagen, the capital, quite a number of lines are electrified.

In Sweden, on the main lines between

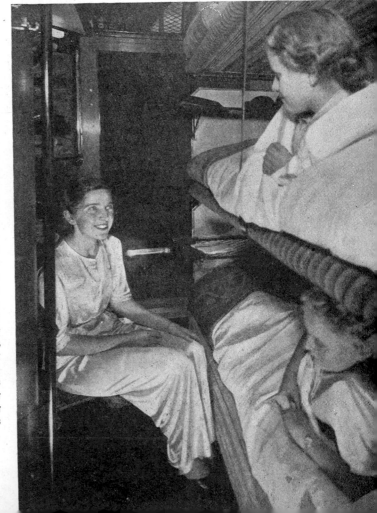

SWEDISH SLEEPING CAR. View of the interior of a third-class sleeping compartment, occupied by three charming Swedish girls. Sweden was one of the first countries in the world to introduce sleeping cars for third-class passengers. In order to make the most of the space available, the berths in each third-class compartment are in tiers of three. Second-class sleeping cars have two berths to a compartment, and first-class passengers have the exclusive use of one of the two-berth rooms. Many sleeping cars are needed, owing to the long journeys on most of the main-line services. When tourist traffic is heavy and hotel accommodation at popular resorts overtaxed, it is nothing unusual to see sleeping cars parked in a siding as a sort of hotel annexe.

T.W.R.—F*

ELECTRIFICATION IN SWEDEN. Electrically hauled train crossing Årsta Bridge outside Stockholm. Electrification of Swedish railways has been on such a scale that more than four-fifths of the traffic is now carried on electrified routes. The reason for such intensive electrification lies in the fact that Sweden has vast reserves of water-power, and hydro-electric generating plants are the natural outcome.

Stockholm and Malmö, over which the principal international services run, average speeds are roughly forty-five miles an hour, although some of the station-to-station runs are timed as high as fifty-five miles an hour. At one time, speeds exceeding sixty miles an hour were definitely discouraged in Sweden, but recently some new three-thousand-horse-power locomotives have been introduced on the electric lines, and these are capable of hauling six-hundred-ton trains on the level at as much as seventy-five miles an hour. These are the only high speeds of note in Scandinavia.

Sweden owns the longest stretch of continuous electrified railway track in the world. Like the Alpine countries, she has

inexhaustible supplies of water power, and all over the country this is turned into current by vast hydro-electric schemes. Electric trains travel the entire length of the country, from Trelleborg in the extreme south to Riksgränsen, in the far north, well within the Arctic Circle, a total distance of one thousand, three hundred and fifty miles. Alternating current at a pressure of sixteen thousand volts is employed in conjunction with overhead wires.

Turbine-Driven Locos

About half the Swedish railways are owned by the State, and the rest by private companies, some of the latter owning some curious steam locomotives which are turbine-driven. The turbine has been tried in various countries for locomotives, but has never found great favour. One of its disadvantages is that it is efficient only at very high speeds, which means that considerable gearing has to be introduced between the turbine and the driving wheels.

Altogether the State and private lines own some two thousand miles of narrow-gauge track, varying from two feet eleven inches to three feet six inches. The main lines, however, are laid to the standard of four feet eight-and-a-half inches.

Travel in Sweden is exceedingly comfortable and clean. In such northerly latitudes, provision must be made for severe cold in winter, and this leads to such refinements as double windows to the coaches. Accommodation is chiefly second or third class, first class being reserved for the through trains from the rest of Europe run by way of the train ferries.

Owing to the length of the journeys, sleeping cars are run in large numbers, and Sweden was one of the first countries in the world to introduce sleeping cars for third-class passengers. It is a country in which class distinctions are the exception rather than the rule.

Sleepers as Hotel Rooms

As an example, when tourist traffic is heavy and hotel accommodation at popular resorts is overtaxed, passengers are allowed to use the sleeping cars as hotel accommodation. It is nothing unusual to see twenty or thirty cars parked in a siding as a kind of hotel annexe.

The tidy appearance of the trains is remarkable. Cleaners are employed by the Swedish railways to perambulate the trains at all times and keep everything in spotless order. No litter is allowed. If any passenger should chance to drop any, he is very soon reprimanded.

The principal power-station of the Swedish State Railways is at Trollhättan, and

ROLLING LIFT BRIDGE with balanced lifting span which has a toothed quadrant on each side resting on a similarly toothed rack. There is also a toothed sector bolted to the side, and when the driving pinion meshing with this revolves, the bridge with its own balance rolls back on its supporting rack and quadrant. That is to say, it is not hinged, but balanced on a rolling quarter-circle.

RAIL AND ROAD-RAIL CARS, as used on minor and branch lines in France and some of the Scandinavian countries. The drawing shows the application of an idea that is the essence of simplicity and economy, that of using the same car to travel on both road and rail. It has both tyred and flanged wheels. The road wheels lift and are locked out of use when the car is on the rails; the front pair of rail wheels, which is provided with the normal steering arrangement for road travel, is also locked when the car is on the rails. For road use the tyred wheels are locked to the flanged wheels, and the car runs down a sloping section of rails on to the road. This type of car was designed to run over an ordinary railway track to the end of a branch, or to a station planned to serve as a rail-head, and from there to complete its journey with passengers and freight over the public highway. The rail-car shown in the photograph is of a type in common use in all parts of Europe. Driven by a lightweight petrol motor or Diesel engine, it forms a handy self-propelled unit which can be driven from either end and is most economical in working.

CAR IN ROAD POSITION

WHEEL SUPPORT STOWED

CAR IN RAIL POSITION

RAIL WHEEL

WHEEL SUPPORT BRACKET

ORDINARY STUB AXLE STEERING

LOCKING-PINS SUPPORTING ROAD WHEEL

LOWER ECCENTRIC

LOCKING-PINS SECURING ROAD WHEEL TO RAIL WHEEL

LOCKING-PIN HOLES

INNER HUB

RAIL WHEELS

UPPER ECCENTRIC

OUTER HUB

it supplies energy not only for the railways, but also for industrial purposes all over southern Sweden. The fall of the Göta River from Lake Väner, one of the largest lakes in Europe, supplies the water power for the turbines. Further down the Göta Valley, is the more recent railway power-station of Lilla Edet.

In the far north of Sweden lies one of the most interesting railways in Scandinavia. The Riksgränsen Railway, as it is called, although not quite the most northerly in Europe, is certainly the most northerly electrified railway in the world. This is the railway that carries the famous iron ore from the mines at Gällivare and Kiruna, sometimes known as the Narvik Iron-Ore Railway.

The two ore deposits at the places named are not only famous for their purity, but are estimated to contain over a thousand million tons. The mines were opened in the last century, and a railway became absolutely necessary for the transport of the ore.

Minerals are among the heaviest loads the railway has to carry, and their transport without the assistance of the iron road would be a very difficult matter.

Alternative Route

Apart from that, the mines are so far north that the nearest part of the Swedish coast is frozen over completely for six months out of the twelve, so the railway was planned not only to run to the coastline of Sweden on the Gulf of Bothnia, but also in the opposite direction to the Norwegian frontier, and a concession was obtained from the Norwegian government to continue the line across their territory for twenty-eight miles to the now famous port of Narvik.

In this way, the Riksgränsen Railway, or Narvik Iron-Ore line, came into being, and was one of the first to be electrified owing to the weight of the trains.

The mines are in a mountainous district,

173

and the line that runs from them travels on a downgrade in both directions in the main, a fact which necessitates very efficient braking for such heavy loads. All wagons are, therefore, fitted with the continuous braking system, like passenger coaches. The working of the line is shared by both Swedish and Norwegian locomotives, turn and turn about.

The ore is carried in six-wheeled hopper wagons of steel, each of which weighs forty-six tons when loaded. As each train is made up of forty or fifty of these wagons, its total weight may be well over two thousand tons.

This line is entirely within the Arctic Circle, a fact which gives rise to some odd features of its working. In the winter months, for example, it works for some weeks in continuous darkness. Conversely, at the height of summer, there is continuous daylight from the midnight sun, and no lighting of headlamps, coaches or stations is necessary. In midwinter the great ore-mines present a singular appearance, brilliantly illuminated for twenty-four hours a day by electric flood-lighting.

Underground Machine Room

Climatic conditions also influenced the design of the power-station for this line, which is at a place called Porjus, on a short branch line from Gällivare. As a protection against cold, the main machine room was blasted out of the mountainside, over a hundred and sixty feet below the surface.

ELECTRIC SIGNALLING. At work on an electric point machine. In Scandinavian countries, where winter snowfall is heavy, there are particular advantages in installing all-electric light signalling and electrical operation of points, as in this way the movement of signals by wires, and of points by considerable lengths of wire or rodding, made doubly difficult under a weight of snow, is avoided.

WORLD-FAMOUS RAILWAY TERMINUS. That of the Riksgränsen line at the iron-ore port of Narvik, in Norway. At this point only twenty-six miles of track separate the Swedish frontier from the waters of the North Atlantic, and this short line makes it possible for iron ore from the Swedish mines of Gällivare and Kiruna to be brought direct to an Atlantic port for shipment when Baltic ports are ice-bound.

Although the Narvik line is chiefly meant for the transport of ore, it is used quite a lot in the summer by holidaymakers who can travel by it to Abisko, in the heart of Swedish Lapland.

It is in Norway, however, that is found the maximum both for the sightseer and the engineer. Not only is the mountain scenery magnificent, but the very grandeur of it makes Norway a most forbidding country in which to build any railway at all. This in part accounts for the comparatively small mileage of track so far laid.

Terrain and Climate

Norway is eleven hundred miles in length, and yet so narrow that at one point it is not more than twenty miles across; half the country is at least two thousand feet above sea level. The whole of the western coast is indented with fjords, which are narrow sea inlets hemmed in by high mountains. What is more, although the temperature round the coast is kept moderate

by the Gulf Stream, the inland temperature in winter is of the Arctic variety.

Even in midsummer it is no uncommon thing to find the Taugevatn Lake, on the line from Bergen to Oslo, frozen over, for it lies over four thousand feet above the sea. At Finse, too, conditions are such that perfect ski-ing is possible even in the month of May, in conjunction with almost nightless days. This is, of course, magnificent for the holidaymaker, but in building railways there is a difference. Work in the open, in fact, can proceed in some parts only for three months in the year.

Nevertheless, the famous Bergen-Oslo line was built, including a hundred and eighty-three tunnels, and the dramatic story of its construction is worth telling.

To get the line finished, tunnelling was carried on day and night both in winter and summer, and for seven or eight months every year the workers were completely isolated. The boring was through solid granite, and pneumatic drills of the type used in building the Simplon Tunnel in the Alps, found it a very different proposition. In addition, the Italian workers, brought over specially for the task, were unable to stand the cold and had to be sent home.

In mid-winter, the workers of one construction camp were cut off from civilization by snowdrifts for over ten weeks, and nearly ran out of coal and wood for firing. This is easily stated in words, and does not look very terrible, but in Arctic conditions the complete failure of the heating arrangements would have meant death. On another occasion, a blizzard overtook a paymaster and his guide making their way over the mountains to an encampment, and not for six months was the mystery of their disappearance solved. Their bodies were found at the bottom of a deep crevasse.

Between Bergen and Voss the line is partly on a ledge blasted out of the mountainside, with fifty-two tunnels driven through projecting spurs of rock. For miles farther, it is covered by timber snowsheds to keep it from blockage by snowdrifts and avalanches. In this latitude, the permanent snowline is only three thousand feet above sea level, so that for miles the line runs in snow in winter and summer alike. For this reason, the tunnel mouths are also extended outwards by snowsheds, and there are many miles of fences to keep snow from drifting on to the line.

Wonderful Scenery

The scenic attraction of the line is magnificent. In places the train seems to come within touching distance of great glaciers, while at one point there is a sheer drop from the carriage window to the floor of the Flaam Valley, sixteen hundred feet below.

Many of the Norwegian lines are patronized by tourists simply because of the scenery they offer. There is one from Myrdal to Fretheim, which makes its way down a steep gradient with some extraordinary twists and turns, including a tunnel that is a complete S in shape. This is worked electrically, and it so happens that

EXPLANATORY DRAWING OF ROTARY SNOW-PLOUGH, showing the enclosed steam engine driving the vanes of the cutter. Some ploughs are self-propelling, but others need to be pushed to the scene of action. The cutter is rotated by means of bevel gearing, the driving pinion being coupled direct to the flywheel shaft. A flanged scoop fitted under the main frames clears the snow away from the rails.

SNOW THROWN TO ONE SIDE BY CENTRIFUGAL ACTION

STEAM PIPE

PUSHER ENGINE (SNOW PLOUGH DOES NOT DRIVE ITSELF)

CONICAL SCOOPS

BEVEL GEARS DRIVING CUTTER

CUTTER WHEEL IS GOING THIS WAY

VALVE MOTION

CUTTER SHAFT

REVERSING LEVER

RIGHT-HAND DRIVING ENGINE

BLADES HINGED FOR REVERSING ACTION

THESE BLADES CUTTING

FLANGED SCOOP

SNOW-PLOUGH IN ACTION, showing how the deep snow cuttings are formed after heavy falls. The vanes of the plough in front revolve at sufficient speed to throw powdery snow well clear of the track, high over the packed embankment at the side. The vanes are reversible, so that as the plough advances the snow can be thrown either to right or left, if possible to the side below the track level.

Fretheim is on one of the arms of the great Sognefjord, so the railway makes possible one of those combined rail and boat trips that are so popular in Norway.

Another line of note is the Rauma Railway, which was built originally to connect the port of Aandalsnaes with the Bergen-Trondheim route, and so expedite the carriage of fish, but this has become so popular with tourists on the cruising steamers which put into Aandalsnaes during the summer, that a trip from the port to Bjorli and back is all part of the entertainment.

The train carries them into the Rauma Valley, flanked on the left by the soaring needle of the Romsdalshorn, and on the right by the sinister peaks of the Trolltin-derne, and after travelling along the valley for a time, they see what appear to be two more railways, one above the other, high up on the north bank.

These are merely the continuation of the line. The train first swings to the left, and crosses the river by a bridge, nearly two hundred feet above the water, then doubles back through a spiral tunnel and so comes out on the higher stretches of rail. It is now four hundred and fifty feet above the track on which it was travelling before, which can be seen far down the valley below.

In sharp contrast to the mountains of Norway are the forests and lakes of Finland, the country of a thousand lakes, as it has been called, which, with only a comparatively small population, has no fewer

NORWEGIAN FREIGHT TRAIN, drawn by two locomotives, crossing a viaduct on its journey south. Few countries have such long lengths of railway track in mountainous districts as Norway. Many of the lines are patronized by sightseers for the scenery alone. They were engineered often under great difficulties, and men risked their lives cutting the track on sheer mountain sides.

SNOW-PLOUGH OF THE RAM TYPE, fitted to an ordinary steam locomotive. Over high-lying routes in Scandinavia, ploughs of this description are attached to the locomotive fronts during a large part of the year. Rotary ploughs do the main work of clearance, but the ram ploughs of the locomotives can clear the small drifts which quickly form in bad weather between the patrolling runs of the rotary plough.

than three thousand five hundred miles of railway. Through running between Sweden and Finland, however, is impossible, owing to the difference in gauge. The Finnish railways were originally part of the Russian system, and the railways have been laid to the Russian gauge of five feet.

Modern Finnish Railways

Finland is, therefore, isolated from the rest of Europe, although she has a surprisingly up-to-date railway system of her own, and its development has been on Scandinavian rather than on Russian style. Finnish culture itself is seen mainly in architectural masterpieces, such as the modern railway station in Helsinki, the capital, which is magnificent. The main line from here runs five hundred and fifty miles northward to the port of Tornea.

Elsewhere the lines travel through the forests and over the waterways connecting the innumerable lakes. Bridges are consequently found in great numbers, but are not outstanding in size.

The chief problem is fuel for the locomotives, for all coal has to be imported from a considerable distance, and there are no high mountain lakes to provide power for electric schemes, the country being surprisingly flat. Therefore, timber is used largely for fuel, and many of the locomotives are built with the large balloon chimney stacks seen in many forest countries in the early days of rail travel.

These chimney stacks are designed as spark-arresters, a very necessary provision where sparks might easily set huge forests on fire. The forests of Finland are the main source of the national wealth. Similar smoke-arresters are used to some extent on the smaller Swedish railways, but shaped like collars at the base of the chimney, rather than in the form of a wide top.

Typical Russian engine driver
of the Trans-Siberian Railway

CHAPTER NINE

NEAR EAST TO FAR EAST

THE longest train journey in the world is that which links the heart of Europe with the Pacific Coast of Asia, literally "Near East to Far East," without a change of trains.

For nine whole days the passenger lives in the train, while the engine labours on over the grassy steppes or through the forests of Siberia. The starting-point of this stupendous journey is Moscow.

Russian railways are peculiar in that they are built to an odd gauge, a trifle wider than the standard found over the greater part of Europe, yet narrower than the broad gauge of India. The actual width of the rails is five feet, and this has been Russian practice since the railway was first introduced into the country.

It is part of Russian military strategy. By having a gauge that differs from those of all the countries around them, the Russians are assured that no invader can use his own locomotives or rolling stock on their tracks, and all they have to do during a retreat is to remove their own wagons and engines and leave the tracks as they are.

Wasted Energy

During both the First and Second World Wars, an immense amount of energy had to be wasted by the invaders in consequence. All lines had to be converted to standard gauge as they advanced, before the invading forces could use the railway as a means of transport. Unfortunately, when invasion had flowed to its ebb and the defenders themselves advanced, a similar amount of energy was wasted in restoring the tracks to their normal width of five feet.

It is not only in the gauge width, however, that Russian railways are unusual. They have the largest loading or construction gauge in the world. Locomotives and rolling stock may be built to a total height of seventeen feet above rail level, and the width is so ample that all but the largest engines are provided with a wide platform extending right round the boiler. The platform has railings which continue unbroken even round the front of the smokebox, and so is a safe passage for driver or fireman even when the engine is running at speed. Access to it is given by doors in the front of the cab, which is itself completely enclosed, as a safeguard against the rigours of winter. All the larger locomotives are given names, usually of outstanding political figures, and these are displayed in Russian characters on the fronts of the engines.

Unusual Engines

The large loading gauge has given rise to some extraordinary engines. One class, built at the Voroshilovgrad locomotive works, has no fewer than fourteen coupled wheels with a 4-14-4 arrangement, which is unique. The driving wheels are five feet three inches in diameter, and the cylinders have a twenty-nine-inch bore with a thirty-two-inch stroke. The heating area provided throughout fire-box and boiler is enormous, being well over six thousand six hundred square feet, while the fire-box has a hundred and twenty-nine square feet of grate area. The working pressure is two hundred and forty pounds.

Enormous Tender

The tender alone is carried on twelve wheels, and has accommodation for eleven thousand five hundred gallons of water and twenty-three and a half tons of coal. Engine and tender together measure a hundred and ten feet eight inches, and weigh three hundred and five tons. The locomotive in running order weighs a hundred and ninety-four tons, and the tender, fully charged, a hundred and eleven tons. A great deal of care had to be taken to make the long rigid wheel base of the seven coupled axles as flexible as possible, although the engine is not really an articulated type. These mammoths of the rail are intended to handle the heavy coal trains of

the Donbas region at speeds up to forty-five miles an hour.

The biggest locomotive ever built in Great Britain was for the Russian railways. It was a Beyer-Garratt articulated engine, and was only twenty inches shorter, including the tender, than the giant Russian 4-14-4 type. Its four cylinders had a bore of twenty-two and a half inches with a twenty-eight-inch stroke, and the driving wheels were four feet eleven inches in diameter. The fire-grate, however, had an area of only eighty-six square feet, while the working pressure was two hundred and twenty pounds, against the Russian two hundred and forty.

Russian Locomotives

Altogether, Russian railways own about twenty-five thousand locomotives, including many standard types. Chief among the latter are the large 2-10-2 and 2-10-4 types for freight service, and the 2-6-2 and 2-8-4 class for passenger service. This last is the famous JS class, named in honour of Marshal Stalin.

With the spaciousness of the loading gauge, wagons and coaches in Russia are all very roomy. Class distinctions are not emphasized, but there are what are known as "hard" and "soft" classes. The latter is for those who desire privacy, and are prepared to pay extra for it. A typical soft-class compartment has one transverse berth and one arranged longitudinally, opposite the corridor. Hard-class compartments provide merely lying-down space at night on wooden bunks, but mattresses and bedding can always be hired from the conductor if desired. The bunks are usually in three tiers.

The equipment of main lines at one time was somewhat primitive compared with Western Europe, but great strides are being made with the help of the scientific and other development brought about by the Second World War.

October Express Trains

The fastest trains in Russia have been those of the October Express service, which covers the four hundred odd miles between Moscow and Leningrad in ten hours. These expresses are normally

RUSSIAN TYPES OF ENGINE. On the left is a condensing locomotive burning coal-dust as fuel. The condensing apparatus is in the tender, which is provided with slatted sides to assist the free circulation of air. Fans help to create a draught round the steam pipes while the engine is moving. A fan is also usually fitted to supplement the action of the blast pipe in the smoke-box, for when the engine is condensing, the exhaust steam is passed back to the condenser on leaving the cylinders, so there is no draught in the flues. Condenser tenders have been built in Russia for the long journeys the Russian railway trains have to cover over vast areas of desert, where water is scarce or even unobtainable, as on certain sections of the Turksib line, which connects Russian Turkestan with the Siberian railway. The lower picture shows two modern locomotives used for freight haulage in Russia. The Russian loading gauge is the largest in the world.

worked in three sections nightly, in each direction. This particular stretch of line is practically straight and level, and it is quite possible the time may be cut to six hours or so, and the night journey changed to one by day, probably with the aid of Diesel power.

In other directions, travelling times are very lengthy. From Moscow to Kharkov, for example, a distance of four hundred and eighty-five miles, the journey takes seventeen hours; from Kiev to Odessa, four hundred and six miles, fifteen hours; and from Moscow to Sevastopol, in the Crimea, nine hundred and fifty-four miles, the journey may take as much as thirty-eight hours. This gives an average timing over these three routes of only just in excess of twenty-six miles an hour.

New Russian Lines

Many new lines, however, are being laid in Russia, especially in the Ural Mountains and beyond, to connect the great iron and steel centres such as Magnitogorsk with the main railway system. The greatest of these is the Turksib line, which connects Turkestan with Siberia. This branches off from the Siberian railway at Novosibirsk, and though the original branch is relatively old, an immensely long tentacle has recently been laid from it through the wilds of Central Asia.

It extends southwards right down to Bokhara and Samarkand, within sight of the Tibetan frontier, and the laying of it was no mean achievement. Native labourers followed the track on yaks and camels, and the line grew steadily through what, up till 1935, had been one of the most desolate deserts in the world.

Oil-fired Locomotives

In the far south of Russia, in the prolific oilfields of the Baku region, most locomotives are fitted for oil-firing. Curiously enough, in this region where oil is so plentiful, there are also the high mountains of the Caucasus, and these offer abundant water supply for hydro-electric schemes. A certain amount of electrification has already been carried out over the heavy grades of the mountain lines. Various railways round Moscow have also been electrified, including the well-known underground railway, Moscow's Metro.

But Russian railways are not noted for electrification. They are noted more for the enormous distances they cover, and for the extraordinary rigours of the climate and the country through which they pass.

In the far north, there is a line that has the distinction of being the nearest railway in the world to the North Pole. For much of the way it travels entirely within the Arctic Circle, and at its northern extremity is far above the Narvik route in the Scandinavian countries. This is the Murmansk line, giving access to the port of Murmansk, which is free of ice throughout the whole of the year. Far away above Leningrad, the Murmansk line is over eleven hundred miles in length.

Parallel with it, is another northerly line from Vologda to the port of Archangel, covering nearly four hundred miles, and used much more in summer than in winter, for Archangel, like many other Russian ports, is frozen up for months at a stretch. Even on the Baltic, many ports can be used only in the summer months on account of ice-packs that develop during the winter.

Cold-Weather Precautions

Winter conditions are responsible for some peculiar developments on these far northern railways. One is the lining of the locomotive cabs with wood. In extreme cold, metal becomes almost dangerous to touch, tearing the skin from the hand if it is gripped at all hard, and even in the cab of an engine, with the furnace only a few feet distant, it has been found advisable to provide a wooden lining.

By far the longest route in Russia, however, is the Trans-Siberian Railway, which connects Moscow with the far Pacific. This is a line not far short of six thousand miles in length, running right through Siberia to the port of Vladivostok. It lies entirely in Russian territory to the north of China, but is not actually the shortest distance between Moscow and the port. A distance of nearly six hundred miles can be saved by leaving the Russian main line at Karimskaya and travelling due east to Vladivostok through China.

At one time, this constituted the Chinese

RUSSIAN ELECTRIFICATION. Electric locomotive in the Suram Pass of the Georgian mountains. There is not a great deal of electrification in Russia, chiefly owing to lack of a sufficiently distributed water supply, except among the high mountains of the Caucasus, where many of the heavier gradients have been electrified.

CHILDREN'S RAILWAY. Small-gauge line built just outside Moscow. The railway is about a mile and a quarter in length and is operated entirely by children, under supervision, providing them not only with a great deal of amusement but also with valuable experience should they choose to become railway engineers when they grow up. There are a number of similar miniature railways in Russia, each with its staff of grown-up instructors to put the young enthusiasts through a course of training during their holidays from school. The youthful crew is here seen making an examination of the engine before starting off on a trip.

Eastern Railway, built and owned by the Russians, but when Manchuria became an autonomous state it was absorbed as part of the Manchuria State Railways. The Russians, therefore, laid eighteen hundred miles of new track to the northward, so important did they consider it to have a line entirely within their own territory. So, on reaching Karímskaya, the Trans-Siberian Express divides into two parts, one part continuing to Vladivostok by the longer all-Russian route and the other travelling through China by way of Harbin, where there are connexions to Pekin and beyond.

World's Longest Run

The full journey from Moscow to Vladivostok takes nine days, and is the longest railway journey in the world that can be accomplished in the same train. The travelling speed is not high, averaging round about thirty miles an hour including stops, some of which last as long as twenty to twenty-five minutes.

Nowhere else in the world is there such a cosmopolitan train as the Trans-Siberian Express. On the departure platform at Moscow, when it is due to leave, there are to be found all the races of Asia, Chinese, Japanese, Mongolians and Tartars, together with a sprinkling of many other nationalities. This is the train that truly links East with West, and the two not only meet but get considerably mixed up in the jostling throng.

Although the train is provided with a restaurant car, most of these travellers

prefer to buy their food during the journey from the itinerant sellers who come to the platforms at all the stops. Tea is served from great samovars, and caviare is plentiful. Ample time is available for these refreshments, owing to the long stops. In the hard class, whole families may be found occupying the space between two tiers of berths, drinking tea, eating or sleeping. In Czarist days, the cars were lighted mainly by candles, but electric lighting is now found throughout all the principal trains.

Leaving Moscow about five in the afternoon, the Trans-Siberian travels first over the almost endless prairie country that stretches from the city to the Ural Mountains, and beyond these through the new indus-

186

trial areas, before reaching the limitless expanse of the Siberian steppes. So barren are the latter, that at Irkutsk it is astonishing to draw up in a great modern city which has a magnificent cathedral, fine wide streets and nearly a million inhabitants.

Lines Across the Ice

Beyond Irkutsk lies Lake Baikal, three hundred miles in length and a complete barrier to any direct continuation of the line. For many years, trains were ferried across it during the summer, and through-running became possible only in the winter, when the lines were laid across the ice. Laying lines in winter, which had to be removed again before the thaw, became a regular practice, though how the railway

officials decided just when to remove them, or what to do while waiting for the ice to disappear sufficiently to begin the ferry service, are points that must have made prospective travellers somewhat thoughtful.

Today, however, the track is laid right round the lake, through some of the most mountainous and difficult country in existence. It was the difficulty of engineering a line through such country that held up the work for so long, and forty-two tunnels had to be driven before it was complete.

So the days pass on this great Siberian route, until the train draws up in Vladivostok late in the evening on the ninth day after leaving Moscow. The time-table, with the usual meticulous accuracy of time-tables in general, records that at the end of this nine-day journey across the world's largest continent, the arrival is at three minutes past eleven o'clock in the evening.

The Trans-Siberian Express runs in each direction three times a week, and is supplemented by a slower daily service over the whole of the route. Altogether, nine complete trains are needed to maintain the express service, and over twenty trains for the slower daily service.

Beside the Gobi Desert

Connecting at Karimskaya with the Trans-Siberian, is the Manchurian train for Harbin and Pekin, a journey on which four days are spent, making eleven in all from Moscow.

This line is interesting in that it is laid for miles along the fringe of the great Gobi Desert, where the two chief worries of the railway officials are the sandstorms that sweep in from the desert wastes and bury the rails, and the brigands who have

a habit of pulling up the rails and removing them altogether.

Moscow is thus the junction for Asia, much as Paris is the centre of continental travel in Europe. In Asia, however, partly because rail travel is backward in development, but partly also on account of the great distances which have to be covered, the system has not reached European perfection.

This backwardness is due in part to the violent opposition to the railway met with in the far eastern countries. In China, for example, there was the most extraordinary antagonism to a steam engine running on rails, although the British had proposed a short railway line from Woosung to Shanghai as far back as the 1860s.

This line was intended to be both an object lesson to the Chinese of the value of railway travel, and the beginning of a main line between Shanghai and Nanking, but some very serious objections were raised to it by the Chinese authorities. One was

FASTEST TRAIN IN ASIA. This is the well-known Asia Express at Mukden Station, South Manchuria Railway. It is only seventy years since the superstitious Chinese bought the first British railway in China for the sole purpose of tearing up the rails and dumping them, along with all locomotives and rolling stock, into the sea. Later, they even built a temple to placate the offended spirits.

CHINESE EASTERN RAILWAY, showing open wagons used as coaches. Coolies travel in them at very low rates exposed to all kinds of weather. The Chinese Eastern Railway was laid originally to the Russian gauge of five feet, but it has since been converted to standard gauge. Although the Asia Express in Manchuria is timed at high speed, rail travel in Asia in general is below European standards.

that the proposed route lay over a number of ancestral tombs, and these could not be disturbed on any account. Eventually, however, the route was varied to avoid the tombs, and permission was given by the Chinese for its construction.

Offended Spirits

The line was opened on the outskirts of Shanghai in 1876, but almost immediately a coolie was knocked down and killed. Riots ensued, and the line had to be closed, whereupon the Chinese Government agreed to purchase it, and completed the payments the following year.

Their purpose in doing so soon became clear. Tracks were torn up, and all rails, engines and carriages were dumped in the sea. To placate the offended spirits, a temple to the Queen of Heaven was built on the site of the Shanghai station.

An even more curious story is told of the first steam locomotive that ran successfully in China. An ordinary track for coal trucks, either pushed by hand or drawn by mules.

had been laid from the coalfields at Kaiping to a canal which gave access to the sea, and the engineer of the mining company decided to build a locomotive in secret.

Using materials from the colliery scrap-heap, he put together a small tank engine and named it Rocket of China, with a representation in brass, on the side, of a Chinese dragon. For a time, the partly-built locomotive was buried to keep it out of sight, but eventually it was put to work and came under the notice of a powerful Chinese mandarin, Li Hung-chan. Strangely enough, Li Hung-chan was favourably impressed, and his influence was sufficient to give the railway a proper start.

Till now, however, development has been extremely slow. The principal lines consist of two great north-south routes and two east-west routes, but the most modern is the Manchurian system, which is by far the most fully developed of all railways in East Asia.

For this, the Japanese are in the main

responsible. They converted certain of the lines of the system, which were laid originally by the Russians to the five-foot gauge, to the standard of four feet eight-and-a-half inches, and over one of them, from Harbin to the port of Dairen, runs the fastest train in Asia. This is the streamlined Asia Express, composed of up-to-date coaches with a fully streamlined Pacific locomotive.

Between Dairen and Tsinking, the distance is four hundred and thirty-five miles, and the time allowed is only eight-and-a-half hours. This requires an overall speed, including stops, of fifty-one miles an hour, and maximum speeds in excess of sixty miles an hour.

The Japanese were always ahead of the Chinese in railway development, but they made the initial mistake of deciding on the narrow gauge of three feet six inches. This is the main-line gauge throughout the length and breadth of the islands. Some fast trains are run on this gauge, as in the island of Java, at speeds even exceeding sixty miles an hour, but the Japanese had aspirations to travel as fast as anybody in the world.

Japanese Plans

Consequently, they prepared some ambitious plans, even to the extent of building a standard-gauge main line to run the whole length of their main-island groups, from north to south. As a first instalment of the scheme, they tunnelled under the sea separating the main island of Honshu from Kyushu, and reduced a journey which used to take an hour by sea to a through run of only ten minutes. Trains began to run on this line between Tokyo and Nagasaki in 1942.

The total cost of this standard-gauge main line is estimated at about eighty million pounds, and it is considered that it will take at least fifteen years to build. Work has already started on two very lengthy tunnels, but whether the line will be completed or not is a moot point.

For the journey of seven hundred miles between Tokyo and Shimonoseki, the best trains have hitherto taken about twenty hours, but on the new line it is proposed to run streamlined trains in nine hours. As the route surveyed will reduce the distance to just over six hundred miles, this will need

190

an overall speed of seventy miles an hour. Until now, the fastest trains in Japan have been the Swallow expresses between Tokyo and Kobe, which do the journey of three hundred and seventy miles at an average speed of forty-one miles an hour.

Long Under-Sea Tunnel

Many other even more grandiose schemes have been formulated by the Japanese Government Railways. One is nothing less than a tunnel under the sea, a hundred and twenty miles long, to connect Japan with the mainland of Asia. If world events make the standard-gauge line throughout the Japanese islands difficult of construction, it would seem that this under-sea tunnel, fascinating though it is in concept, is almost out of the question politically. With a little imagination, perhaps, we might tunnel under all the oceans of the world at their narrowest points and provide through rail communication everywhere!

Another Japanese idea was to link up the various Chinese railways and build new connexions in such a way that trains could be run straight through from Japan to Malaya, Burma and India.

But the most remarkable plan of all, also originating from Japan, was a main line, over ten thousand miles long, to link Tokyo with the former Axis capitals of Berlin and Rome. An Imperial Railway Association was actually formed in Japan in 1942 for the furtherance of this scheme, and the proposed route was through China, Afghanistan, Iran, Iraq and Turkey. But subsequent events have put these and many other Japanese schemes into the realm of the visionary rather than the practicable.

Cheap Railway Fares

One point about Japanese railways is that travel on them is very cheap. Even the first-class rate is less than third class in Great Britain. For all that, however, first- and second-class passengers together form less than a fifteenth of the whole passenger traffic in the country, for tourist and excursion tickets are issued at even lower rates still, many being in connection with annual visits to shrines and temples.

A great deal of rail travel in Japan, in

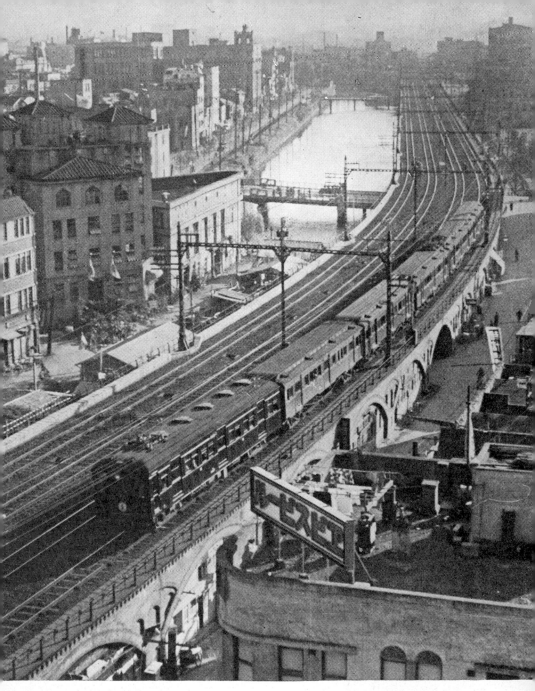

NOT NEW YORK, BUT MODERN TOKYO. Electric locomotive hauling a passenger train on one of the city's approach viaducts, using the overhead system of electrification. Japanese railways have the disadvantage of being laid on the narrow gauge of three feet six inches. A standard-gauge line running the whole length of Honshu and Kyushu from north to south has been planned, with a tunnel under the straits that separate them, but little has yet been done towards its completion.

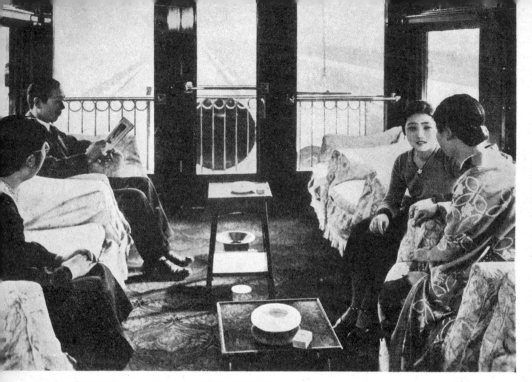

OBSERVATION CAR IN MANCHURIA, used on the Hato Express of the South Manchuria Railway. As a result of Japanese efforts Manchurian railways are the most fully developed of all railways in East Asia. The streamlined Asia Express runs on the Manchurian system and attains maximum speeds of more than sixty miles an hour.

fact, is for the purpose of visiting shrines, and many of the mountain railways have been built solely to give access to shrines perched on the tops of high hills. Most of these are built on the funicular principle like some of the steeper Swiss railways, with a continuous rope working two cars in opposite directions.

Mount Rokko San Line

One of the best-known funicular railways in Japan, however, is purely tourist in character. It is the line to the famous Mount Rokko San, between Kobe and Osaka, a very popular resort for visitors and holiday-makers.

The Mount Rokko San line, just over a mile in length, overcomes a difference in level of more than sixteen hundred feet, with an average gradient of one-in-three-and-a-half, though it steepens to one-in-two near the summit.

It is divided into two sections, and passengers change cars intermediately,

but the same continuous haulage cable works both sections, a most unusual arrangement. On both sections, therefore, all cars start and stop together, two ascending while the other two descend.

Travel on Japanese main lines has features which are typical of the country and its people. Although dining cars are provided on all the principal trains, their use is confined mainly to the wealthier classes and to foreign visitors. The ordinary people, in this land of shrines, prefer to buy from the vendors on the platforms.

These throng all the more important stops, selling "honourable tea, honourable milk and honourable food," usually so cheaply that for the equivalent of a penny one can buy the pot and the cup as well as the tea. Neat wooden boxes containing all the necessaries for a good meal, as understood in Japan, can be bought for about tenpence.

The largest compartment in the box is packed with hot boiled rice, and other compartments contain delicacies to eat with it. The collection is completed with a paper serviette, chop-sticks and a tooth-pick.

Vans for Live Fish

One curious feature of Japanese railways is the live-fish vans. These vans are built specially for the transport of live fish, chiefly carp, from Lake Biwa and elsewhere in the Tokyo area. Each van is provided with four large fresh-water tanks, which are kept at a suitable temperature to ensure that the fish will arrive in a satisfactory condition. It is the Japanese equivalent of a refrigerator van, although refrigerator vans are also used on a large scale for the transport of perishables.

Japan is also well up to date in the matter of electrification. Both Tokyo and Yokohama are modern cities with more the appearance of New York than any far Eastern port, at least as far as railways are concerned. They have a dense passenger traffic, and electricity has been introduced on the railways to deal with it.

The overhead conductor system, with fifteen hundred volts direct current, has been adopted and altogether there are over six hundred and fifty miles of electrified route in Japan.

As a final example of Japanese railway development all rolling stock, wagons as well as coaches, is fitted with the automatic coupling device, and nearly all wagons as well as passenger coaches are now equipped with the Westinghouse continuous brake.

HONEYMOON TRAIN. Evening express to Atami, Japan's Riviera. This train, which is used by many of the bridal couples leaving Tokyo, and run specially for their benefit, leaves Tokyo Station at 9.15 p.m. The late departure gives plenty of time for the elaborate banquets and wedding receptions customary in Japan. Atami is only a short run from the capital and is a favourite honeymoon resort.

PRINCIPAL RAILWAYS OF
ASIA

0   MILES   1000

Permanent way repair train in the famous Khyber Pass on the North West Frontier of India

CHAPTER TEN

ANCIENT INDIA'S MODERN TRANSPORT

THE railways of India show some vivid contrasts, beginning with the fact that in this country there are some of the broadest and narrowest gauges in existence. The main line rails are set at as great a width as five feet six inches, and yet a number of lines are built to a gauge of only two feet. In between these extremes, there are at least ten thousand miles of track on a gauge of one metre.

Narrow-Gauge Flexibility

This curious inability of the Indian railways to make up their minds which gauge they prefer, is explained in part by the well-known fact that a narrow-gauge line is much more flexible on curves. For this reason, narrow gauge is to be welcomed in mountainous country, and some of the mountain railways in the mighty Himalayas certainly need it. On the contrary, over vast plains, where the necessity for a winding track does not occur, it would obviously be impracticable to keep to a line of toy-like dimensions.

High Standards

A further contrast is found between the extremely modern main-line railways and those in outlying districts which, in some respects, seem a trifle behind the times. All in all, however, Indian railways are of a very high order, certainly among the most advanced in Asia. The wide gauge makes it possible to design very spacious coaches, which alone give a sense of luxury to Indian rail travel. All the chief lines are owned by the State, and are under the control of a central Railway Board in Delhi.

Some of the most striking engineering features are found on the lines giving access to the wild North-West Frontier. Here the track winds among mountain defiles, climbing sometimes as much as a mile in height on very steep gradients. The

most spectacular part of the line lies in the Chappar Rift, a gorge about three miles long with sheer sides from two hundred to three hundred feet in height.

From Peshawar, the railway runs to Landi Kotal, at the head of the far-famed Khyber Pass, and continues on to Landi Khana, right on the borders of Afghanistan. On the continuous steep up-grade from Jamrud, no fewer than thirty-two tunnels had to be bored through the most treacherous shale, and the whole construction was carried out under the constant menace of attack by Pathan tribesmen.

Crowded Trains

At first, the railway was something very strange in India's ancient civilization, but today the teeming population of three hundred and fifty millions makes use of it on a considerable scale. Trains are always crowded, and long before a main-line train is due to start, hundreds of people gather

on the platform; some even spend the previous night there. The arrival of the train sets this crowd in violent motion. Mixed with the crowd are sellers of tea, sweets and fruit, and pandemonium reigns until the train gets away again.

Third-class travel is very cheap, but the average Indian peasant is so poor that travellers without tickets are detected to the extent of between two and three millions every year. How many there are who are not detected, it is impossible to estimate.

Because of these crowded conditions, corridor trains are not in favour. Instead, first-class passengers are accommodated in large separate compartments each communicating with a bathroom and lavatory. The compartments are each designed for six people by day and four by night. The two settees for use in the daytime become beds at night and two further berths usually let down from the partitions. There are also a couple of armchairs, a collapsible table,

COMFORT IN INDIAN RAIL TRAVEL. Electrically-hauled Deccan Queen and interior of air-conditioned coach of the Great Indian Peninsular Railway. The Deccan Queen is one of the fastest trains in India. It runs between Poona and Bombay, a distance of roughly a hundred and twenty miles, night and morning, and does the journey at an average speed of forty-four miles an hour, in spite of a number of very steep gradients on the Western Ghats. It carries first- and second-class passengers only, and is one of the very few corridor trains in the country. Air conditioning of coaches has not made very great strides in India, but the one shown is typical of those in general service. Air-conditioned coaches are not quite as simple to operate as may seem possible at first sight. To reduce the temperature of the air indoors in a hot country, is to give incoming passengers rather an unpleasant chill; and once they have become used to the interior temperature, going out again into the heat is equally trying. It should prove possible, however, to strike the happy mean, and an air-conditioned coach is an improvement on the blocks of ice previously carried on the floors of most Indian first-class compartments.

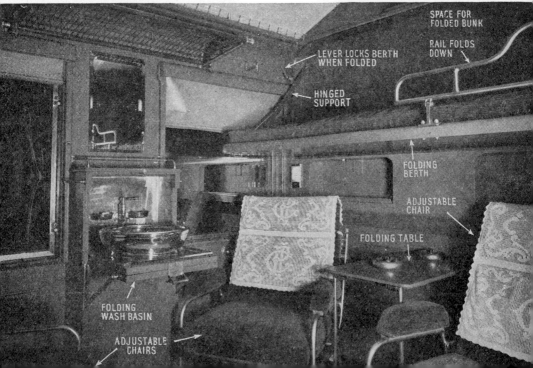

SPACE FOR FOLDED BUNK

RAIL FOLDS DOWN

LEVER LOCKS BERTH WHEN FOLDED

HINGED SUPPORT

FOLDING BERTH

ADJUSTABLE CHAIR

FOLDING TABLE

FOLDING WASH BASIN

ADJUSTABLE CHAIRS

a small chest of drawers, electric fans, wooden shutters to mellow the glare of the sun, and a covering of fine mesh gauze over the windows to keep out dust.

Heat and dust are the worst trials of travel in India. Air-conditioned coaches have been tried, and are run on some lines, but have not so far become standard. In the meantime, it is possible to buy large blocks of ice, which are placed in containers on the carriage floors, and these help to keep the temperature down to something like a reasonable level.

The absence of a corridor makes it necessary to change to the restaurant car while the train is standing at a station, and to wait for another stop before getting back, but the privacy secured is considered to outweigh any such minor disadvantage.

Speeds in India

High speeds cannot be expected in India. Tracks are often unfenced, gradients on some routes are severe, and it is difficult to keep track maintenance up to the standards which obtain in a country like Great Britain. On certain lines, speeds up to and even slightly exceeding sixty miles an hour are permitted, and in these cases fairly fast timings are possible. The electrically hauled Deccan Queen, for example, running between Poona and Bombay night and morning, does the journey at an average of forty-four miles an hour, including some severe gradients on the Western Ghats.

With first- and second-class accommodation only, this is one of the very few corridor trains in India. Another is the Imperial Indian Mail, or Blue Train, which runs once a week in each direction across northern India, between Calcutta and Bombay. The Blue Train connects with the steamer services to Britain, and saves a long sea journey round the southern tip of India and Ceylon.

Electrification in India is confined to the area around Bombay, where there is a busy suburban service running multiple-unit trains.

Some fine bridges have been built

PILGRIMS TO THE TEMPLE. Station scene at Rameswaram, site of one of the largest Buddhist temples in India. Such passengers, with their bales and baggage, are only to be found in the East. When Asia accepted the railway, she did not change her ancient customs and religions, but merely permitted it to facilitate their practice.

RAILWAY STATION AT BHOPAL. India's teeming millions use the railway to a surprising extent and its railway system is far and away the most up-to-date in Asia. High speeds are not usual, nor are corridor trains, but rail travel is comfortable, even luxurious. The country is linked by rail both from north to south and east to west.

T.W.R.—G*

201

GALLERY BRIDGE, type used on some of the mountain railways in India. The bridge is built up as a series of arches, about the only method of construction possible with small brick or rubble. Some of these gallery bridges have as many as five tiers of arches. The bridge illustrated above is on the Kalka-Simla narrow-gauge railway.

NARROW-GAUGE MOUNTAIN RAILWAY. Station on the Darjeeling-Himalaya line. This line is laid on the narrow gauge of two feet and the coaches are only six feet wide with very low floors to keep down the centre of gravity. Even six feet, however, gives an overhang each side of roughly two feet, but their weight helps to keep them stable. In these coaches passengers are carried round the famous Agony Point.

particularly across the Indus and the Ganges. Both these rivers are liable in the rainy season to become swollen to an immense size, and the bridges are of great length in consequence. The Lansdowne Bridge, at Sukkur, was the largest of its kind in the world when it was opened, and was the first really large-scale application of the cantilever principle. Similarly, the Upper Sone Bridge and the Lower Godavari Bridge are each nearly two miles in length. One of the most recent projects, the Willingdon Bridge over the Hooghly at Bally, near Calcutta, has seven spans each of three hundred and fifty feet. This great road and rail structure contains seventeen thousand tons of steelwork and cost over three and a half million pounds to build.

Famous Mountain Railway

The most famous of the mountain lines is the Darjeeling-Himalaya Railway, which possesses the famous figure-eight curve. With its summit at Ghoom, seven thousand four hundred feet above sea level, it is also the highest mountain line in the country. This is a two-foot-gauge railway, and it climbs its seven thousand feet over a distance of less than fifty miles.

The ascent is fairly easy at first, but from Sookna the climb begins in earnest, and the line crosses and recrosses itself as it winds spirally upwards. The sharpest curve is at Agony Point, where the radius is only seventy feet. The steepest gradient on the line is about one in twenty-three.

Limited Speeds

Speed is strictly limited, and trains are even slower coming down than they are going up. On the upgrade, the maximum speed allowed is twelve miles an hour, but on the downgrade it is only nine. The coaches are very light and carried on only four wheels, and are pulled by locomotives weighing no more than fourteen tons. First-class carriages are thirteen feet six inches in length, six feet wide and seven feet six

Spectacular figure-eight loop of
the narrow-gauge Darjeeling-
Himalaya mountain railway

inches in height, with floors set very low. The lower-class carriages are open, with hoods and curtains.

Far away to the south is the one and only rack railway in India. This is the Nilgiri branch of the South Indian Railway to Ootacamund, summer headquarters of the Madras government. It is laid on metre gauge, and on the first part of the ascent the line clings to a precipitous cliff along galleries blasted in the rock.

The rack system used is the Swiss Abt system, and the locomotives for this line were actually built in Switzerland. They are combined rack-and-adhesion locomotives, the rack pinion not being required on the flatter grades.

The Burma State Railways are laid out on the metre gauge, and are surprisingly modern and efficient. Heavy traffic is worked over them on the main lines. Rangoon, the capital, with its four hundred thousand inhabitants, has a fine modern station with seven main-line platforms and twenty suburban platforms.

The Burma railways have come into prominence with the much-talked-of Burma Road into China, which itself will soon become a railway, and one probably without a rival in the world for the difficulty of the country through which it is laid.

Burma Branch Line

The starting point of the Burma Road is at Lashio, and already the branch line which connects Lashio with Myohaung Junction, just to the south of Mandalay, is one of the most spectacular in the world. Not only does it climb the precipitous western escarpment of the plateau, which at Maymyo is three thousand eight hundred feet above sea level, but the plateau itself is riven by deep gorges which force the line to become a sort of switchback railway, with steep gradients and reverse curves.

Beyond Maymyo, it crosses the highest railway bridge in the world. This is the well-known Gokteik Viaduct, two thousand two hundred feet in length and eight hundred and twenty feet above the level of the torrent.

In fact, however, the built-up height of

MODERN TREND ALL OVER THE WORLD is the Diesel-electric method of propulsion, illustrated above by an oil-driven train on the Colombo-Galle service of the Ceylon Government Railway. It offers a striking contrast to the conventional steam-hauled train on the left, actually the Viceregal train of Lahore. Both trains could be equally comfortable, and could offer high-speed service, but the Diesel-electric type has certain definite advantages, and it is no accident that it is gradually replacing the steam locomotive. In a country like India, which has little or no coal of its own and is comparatively close to the Persian oilfields, the oil engine gains its first point; and in combination with the electric generator and motor, it has more rapid acceleration and can maintain high speeds for long periods. Diesel-electric locomotives can be in operation nearly twenty-four hours a day. In addition, they are cleaner and more compact, more easily driven, by finger-tip control, and can be coupled in units and controlled by one driver up to any reasonable power.

the bridge is much less than this, for it rests on a natural arch of rock above the river. The bridge itself is carried on sixteen lattice steel towers, the highest of which is three hundred and fifty feet above the rock arch. The mouth of the arch is almost directly under the bridge, with the river flowing underneath it, so that it seems possible from the train to toss a stone straight down in an eight-hundred-foot drop into the water.

Within British territory, a new hundred-mile extension of this branch railway from Lashio will be needed to reach the town of Kunlong, on the banks of the Salween River, which came into such prominence during the Burma fighting during the Second World War. This has already been surveyed, and in the other direction, the Chinese are coming from Chungking with their connecting line. When the whole railway is complete, it will be possible to make a through railway journey of sixteen hundred miles from Rangoon, capital of Burma, to Chungking, capital of China.

Railways of Java

Burma, however, is not the end of our railway tour of the Indies, for there is still the island of Java, in the Dutch East Indies. Here is a country which has a most up-to-date and efficient railway system, laid out mainly on a gauge of three feet six inches, and yet all trains must cease running after dark, owing to the hazards of the jungle.

One of these hazards is the water buffalo, an animal of considerable weight and dimensions, yet hardly large enough, you would say, to hold up a modern train. Nevertheless, one of these animals may easily stray at night on to the unfenced track and cause a derailment, particularly

MOUNTAIN LINE IN JUNGLE COUNTRY, Penang Hills Railway. The line is worked on the funicular principle, with wire rope haulage for the cars, the wire travelling over pulleys set between the rails. A footway has been provided alongside the viaduct for ease of maintenance. The photograph gives a good idea of the nature of the wild, jungle type of country through which the line has been constructed.

OBSERVATION CARS IN MALAYA. One of the cars at Tumpat Station, Kelantan, Federated Malay States. Railways here are laid on the metre gauge, as in Burma. This particular line passes through some of the most picturesque parts of the country, making an observation coach, with plenty of window space, a very welcome addition to a passenger train. The connecting Burma lines are developed on quite up-to-date lines.

with the rather light coaches used in the island.

A curious feature of the railway in Java is a certain section of track which has been laid to two different gauges. Engines and trains of both gauges can run over it, and the double track, although apparently complicated, really represents the simplest way out of a difficulty that had grown up between the State lines and a private company.

For a number of years the State lines, grouped at the two ends of the island, were separated by a private line in the middle, the private line being of the standard gauge while the State lines were narrow gauge.

As a result, all freight travelling from one end of the island to the other had to be transhipped twice, a most troublesome and costly business. Finally, however, by friendly arrangement between the two managements, a second pair of rails was laid inside the wider track, and now the narrow-gauge locomotives use it as well as the others.

Apart from a few Diesel-electric rail-cars that run in other countries on narrow-gauge track, the Java State Railways run the fastest narrow-gauge service in the world. Even more astonishing is the fact that they hold the narrow-gauge record for the world's longest non-stop run.

This is made by the Batavia-Sourabaya Limited, which is booked to make a run of over a hundred and thirty miles without a stop. It travels between Batavia and Cheribon, and its full time allowance is a hundred and seventy-two minutes, which works out roughly at an average of forty-six miles an hour, and requires maximum speeds of sixty miles an hour.

Steep Gradients in Java

Java also has its heavy gradients. The important town of Bandoeng is over twenty-three hundred feet above sea level, and is approached by some long stretches of steep gradient. Its branch line, leading to Garoet, ends at four thousand feet above sea level, with gradients up to one in twenty-six.

Round Batavia, the local lines are electrified, and over some of them there is a fifteen-minute service. Even the privately-owned steam tramway companies are so highly developed that some of them own express trains with restaurant cars. Without doubt, although there are jungle hazards, and all train services cease after dark, Java can claim the most progressive and efficient railway network in the tropics.

PASSENGER TRAIN IN THE CAPE PROVINCE, narrow-gauge express. Although all railways in South Africa are laid to the narrow gauge of three feet six inches, the coaches and locomotives are of normal carrying and hauling capacity. Many South African locomotives are heavier and more powerful than British standard-gauge engines.

CHAPTER ELEVEN

RAIL ENTERPRISE IN AFRICA

ALL railways in Africa, south of the equator, are laid on the narrow gauge of three feet six inches, a gauge that looks like a toy when compared with the standard of four feet eight-and-a-half inches, yet the South African lines on this system are among the most progressive in the world.

Of course, their narrow gauge imposes certain limitations, chiefly as regards speed, but the extraordinary part is that many South African locomotives are bigger, heavier and more powerful than the largest British engines.

Enormous Boiler

As an example, one of the latest types put to work in South Africa has such an enormous boiler that practically no room has been left above it for the ordinary boiler mountings, such as dome and chimney. The chimney and dome are just visible, but that is all.

These locomotives have driving wheels five feet in diameter, and the 4—8—2 wheel arrangement, with cylinders of twenty-four-inch bore and twenty-eight-inch stroke, and a working pressure of two hundred and ten pounds. This gives them a tractive effort of forty-eight thousand pounds, as against the forty thousand pounds of a streamlined L.M.S. Pacific.

In weight, also, they beat the L.M.S. streamliner. The engine alone is only a ton heavier, but with its eight-wheeled tender, which carries over six thousand gallons of water and fourteen tons of coal, it beats the streamliner by thirteen tons.

Keeping Down Costs

Narrow gauge was chosen originally to keep down the cost of construction. As always, a narrow-gauge track can be laid with sharper curves, and in a country like South Africa, where long distances have to be covered over a rugged terrain, it is frequently possible, by taking a sharp turn round the contour of a hill, to avoid the heavy cost of embankments, cuttings, bridges or tunnels.

The only real disadvantage of narrow gauge is the speed restriction imposed, and this arises from the fact that there is more overhang of coaches, wagons and engines on a narrow track if they are to be built with normal carrying capacity. So in building powerful and heavy locomotives, to pull equally heavy loads, South African railways are automatically reduced to speeds well below those obtainable on standard track.

Average timings of just over thirty-five miles an hour are about the highest reached, even by the Union Limited, the most famous train in South Africa. The Union Limited does the journey of just over nine hundred and fifty miles between Cape Town and Johannesburg in roughly twenty-seven hours.

The highest speed ever attained, as far as is known, was on a test run near Cape Town, when a Pacific type locomotive reached seventy miles an hour. In the ordinary course of working, even over favourable stretches of line, it is rarely possible to reach a speed of more than fifty or fifty-five miles an hour.

Lower Weight Level

It is sometimes difficult to understand how adequate stability is maintained with overhanging engines and coaches on a narrow-gauge track. The explanation is that the weight is kept at a much lower level than on a standard-gauge track. Engines and coaches may look much the same as those of standard gauge, but the centre of gravity is lower. The boiler is not pitched so high above the rails, and this, in turn, means that driving wheels have to be smaller, yet another reason for lower speeds.

It is amazing how such limitations have been overcome. The narrow track, sharp curves and light rails are among the main reasons for the development that has taken place for South African working of the Beyer-Garratt articulated locomotive.

This is a type built specially for heavy haulage, and has its weight spread over far more than the usual number of driving wheels. The boiler is slung between two separate engine units, which also carry the coal and water supplies, and the three sections are joined on pivots, so that they are flexible.

Beyer-Garratt articulated locomotives are used a great deal on standard-gauge track, but in South Africa and on other narrow-gauge routes they find their greatest usefulness.

On the Johannesburg-Zeerust-Mafeking line, for example, which is laid with light rails weighing no more than sixty pounds a yard, there are some steep gradients and sharp curves, and it was necessary to design some very flexible engines with great pulling power and a weight of no more than fifteen tons on any one axle.

Beyer-Garratt Principles

This has been accomplished by means of the Beyer-Garratt principles, and though the giant locomotives produced weigh over a hundred and seventy-five tons, the weight restrictions have been most carefully observed. They have the 4-8-2-2-8-4 wheel arrangement, so that there are fourteen axles to carry the full weight of the locomotive.

The length of these narrow-gauge giants is nearly ninety-four feet, yet they negotiate the curves without difficulty. The boiler is seven feet in diameter, probably the largest ever mounted on a narrow-gauge locomotive, and each of the four cylinders has a twenty-and-a-half-inch bore and a twenty-six-inch stroke. There is even mechanical firing equipment.

Auxiliary Water Tanks

One result of the weight restriction, however, is that the water tanks had to be reduced in size, so each of these narrow-gauge mammoths hauls an auxiliary tank holding another six thousand seven hundred and fifty gallons of water, which brings the total water capacity up to eight thousand three hundred and fifty gallons, and the weight of engine and tank up to two hundred

and twenty-five tons. Each of these locomotives is capable of hauling a seven-hundred-and-fifty-ton train up the steepest gradients on the Johannesburg-Mafeking line, and the line capacity has been increased by half as much again.

Another assistance to working up heavy gradients is electricity, and a great deal of electrification has been carried out on the modern South African lines, particularly around Johannesburg. All lines from the coast have to climb the high central plateau, between five and six thousand feet above sea level, and one of the busiest of these lines, that between Durban and Johannesburg, is now electrified for the greater part of its length. Soon, indeed, it will be possible to travel the whole of the five-hundred-mile journey between these two cities by electric railway.

The standard electric locomotives use direct current at three thousand volts. Each one is of twelve hundred horse-power, but two or three are usually coupled together, giving two thousand four hundred or three thousand six hundred horse-power respectively. They are worked from the front driving cab as multiple units.

Improved Services

Electrification has made it possible to increase trainloads by more than a half, and to cut running times by more than a third of that possible with steam.

Owing to the relatively low speeds, most South African long-distance journeys involve a lot of night running, and sleeping accommodation is, therefore, general on all trains making journeys of any length. Such accommodation is provided almost entirely by compartments which can be converted at will from their ordinary day use into two- and four-berth sleeping rooms at night. Restaurant or buffet cars are also to be found on all long-distance trains.

Suburban electrification has also been carried out round Johannesburg and Cape Town, and altogether there are roughly five hundred and eighty route miles of line now electrically worked in South Africa.

Farther north, there is a very different type of country, mainly tropical jungle, until the great desert of the Sahara is reached, and it is here, in the jungle, that

PRINCIPAL RAILWAYS OF
AFRICA

MILES
0   1000

ZAMBESI BRIDGE, a magnificent engineering feat in a magnificent setting. The great arch of this bridge has a span across the gorge of five hundred feet and the rails are four hundred and fifty feet above the torrent. The bridge is a favourite spot for tourists wishing to view the world-famous Victoria Falls. It was built to carry a double line of rails but one track has since been removed to make way for a road.

one of Africa's most outstanding feats of railway engineering is to be found.

This is the great steel arch of the giant railway bridge over the Zambesi River, where the river pours over the world-famous Victoria Falls. The river tumbles into a narrow gorge, over four hundred feet deep, and the bridge has been built a little way below the cataract, where the gorge, although only four hundred feet wide at the bottom, opens out to seven hundred and fifty feet at the point at which it has been crossed.

This is the second highest bridge in the world, and was built originally as an essential link in the projected Cape-to-Cairo railway, but whether such a railway will ever be completed, is now uncertain, chiefly owing to the development of road and air travel.

A route from Cairo to the Cape is actually in existence, but the link is by air, and with steamer transport on the great lakes of Victoria, Tanganyika and Nyasa, the railways of north and south can be almost, if not quite, linked up by road.

As a matter of fact, the bridge itself has been altered to carry not only the rails but a wide motor road and footway as well. Originally, it carried a double track of three-foot-six gauge, but one of the tracks has been removed to make way for the road, leaving only a single line for the railway.

If ever rail connexion is fully established between Cairo and the Cape, it is likely to be by a route much farther to the west, for the original line, as planned, would have taken the railway through many hundreds of miles of unexplored virgin jungle, over a total length of more than four thousand five hundred miles.

But the bridge itself is an achievement, and a vantage point for viewing one of the wonders of nature. It has no pillars or central supports, but crosses the gorge below the roaring falls in one clear span from cliff to cliff, and many a sightseer must have wondered how ever such a bridge could be built.

The very first step in the construction of the Zambesi Bridge was provided by a rocket apparatus. A rocket attached to a line was fired across the gorge, and the line was then fastened to a steel wire. When this wire had been drawn across, it was attached to a much stronger cable, and so the first temporary cableway was established across the gorge.

Aerial Transport

Following this, a more permanent conveyor, working on a steel cable eight hundred and seventy feet in length, was installed. This carried a five-ton car, capable of transporting loads up to ten tons, and propelled by electricity, the current being supplied by an upper trolley wire. While it was in use, this aerial railway transported altogether a hundred thousand tons of material.

With connexion established across the

UNION LIMITED OF SOUTH AFRICAN RAILWAYS, three-foot-six-gauge express on the run to Cape Town after emerging from the Tulbagh Kloof. A "kloof" is a cleft or valley between two hills. The train is descending the single-track route through the valley of the Hex River. The line enters Cape Town from the northern side, negotiating the famous Table Mountain by a detour round the corner known as Devil's Peak.

gorge, work was begun on the bridge itself, the arch of which was built in two halves, cantilevered out from each side until they met in the centre. It stands on two solid foundations of reinforced concrete, built on ledges cut in the rock on each side of the gorge, about a hundred and ten feet below rail level. Each of these main bearings is designed to stand a thrust of sixteen hundred tons.

The first test of the bridge was made by a train weighing six hundred and ten tons, travelling at a speed of fifteen miles an hour. Crossing over, it caused a deflection of no more than one inch in the centre of the five-hundred-foot arch, which is four hundred and twenty feet above the water.

The Zambesi Bridge carries the rails of the Rhodesian Railways, which are independent of South African Railways proper and connect with the latter at Vryburg.

They then skirt the Transvaal through Bechuanaland and so reach the capital, Bulawayo, which is noted for a platform at its main station two thousand three hundred feet in length.

Crossing the Continent

The railways of Rhodesia are more or less central, and there is a line joining them that runs through Portuguese East Africa from Beira, on the coast. In the other direction, there is another line to Lobito Bay, in Portuguese West Africa, and this connects with the Rhodesia Railways by way of the Belgian Congo.

Thus, it is possible to cross Africa from Lobito Bay to Elisabethville. Through trains, with restaurant and sleeping cars, are run every week, and take about three days to complete the journey.

Some idea of the enormous distances to

TRESTLE TYPE BRIDGE IN WEST AFRICA, just outside a station with a famous name —Waterloo. The district is Sierra Leone, one of the hottest areas in Africa, which explains the white sunblinds outside the coaches. West African railway trains traverse a great deal of jungle territory and have been the means of opening up country that until comparatively recent years was almost inaccessible to white men.

AFRICA'S WATERLOO STATION, rather different from Britain's largest terminus. This picture gives a good idea of the broad and low-swung coaches used on these narrow-gauge jungle lines, offering plenty of comfort to the passenger. Raised platforms at stations are the exception rather than the rule, and the open ends of the coaches are provided with steps. First-, second- and third-class accommodation is available.

be covered is given by the lengths of the various lines making up this route. From Lobito Bay to Tenke, the distance is roughly eleven hundred and sixty miles, and from Tenke to Beira it is about seventeen hundred and eighty miles. Southward from Tenke to Cape Town, the distance is nearly two thousand five hundred miles.

Distance alone, however, gives no idea of the country or difficulties through which the lines had to be laid. In Portuguese West Africa, for example, the line runs for two hundred and fifty miles through what is known as the Hungry Country which, although not without water, is entirely unsuitable for cultivation. It is just a stretch of sand and scrub through which it would

have been futile to lay a railway track were it not for the copper mines at Katanga to which it gives access.

Another interesting section of line is found on the Kenya and Uganda Railways, where, after descending through tumbled hills and steep ravines, the track crosses the forbidding Taru Desert. Construction could proceed here only after arrangements had been made to bring regular supplies of water over considerable distances to the workers. As a contrast, the last stage of this line runs through a luxurious, fruit-growing, tropical belt to Mombasa.

But the most entertaining section of all, perhaps, is that just beyond Nairobi, before

217

the line reaches the Taru Desert, and where it passes through a kind of natural zoo. Here there is a vast game reserve, and animals of all kinds—antelope, zebra, waterbuck and even lions—can frequently be seen from the carriage windows. Work on one bridge on this section, as a matter of fact, was delayed considerably by lions, who developed the habit of appearing at night and doing their hunting among the workers in the construction camp.

Equator Station

These lines are very near the equator, and on one section there is a station called Equator, being situated at the exact point where the rails cross this imaginary line round the earth.

The Kenya and Uganda Railways have some of the most remarkable articulated locomotives ever built for a narrow-gauge track. These again are of the Beyer-Garratt type, with the boiler slung between two separate chassis, each with its own cylinders and driving motion. The weight of the boiler, frame, water tanks and coal bunker is transmitted to the chassis by great pivots, and through these are carried the steam connexions from boiler to cylinders.

The main reason for this method of construction is to spread the weight over as great a length of track as possible, and the engine has to be made flexible to negotiate the curves. On these locomotives of the Kenya and Uganda Railways, there is a bogie truck under the end of each pivoted chassis, so that the total number of wheels is divided into six groups, each group having its own independent swinging motion.

The wheel arrangement is 4-8-4-4-8-4, so although they weigh a hundred and

BEYER-GARRATT ARTICULATED LOCOMOTIVE hauling a goods train in Kenya. The Beyer-Garratt type of engine is used all over Africa. It has the advantage of a long wheel-base, so that the weight can be spread over as large a number of axles as possible, and yet, owing to its flexibility , offers less restriction to curves in the track. This type of locomotive is illustrated in detail in the drawing overleaf.

DARKEST AFRICA, lightened a little by the railway. A wayside station on the Kenya and Uganda railways, with a Masai warrior in full regalia seeing his friends off by train. The Masais once terrorized East Africa with their raids, but the coming of the railway helped the government to divert their activities to peaceful pursuits. The railway seems to hold the same fascination for these people as it does for us.

eighty-six tons, these Garratt locomotives impose no more than just under twelve tons on each pair of wheels, and they can thus be used safely over the light rails commonly used on narrow-gauge track.

Each of the four cylinders has a sixteen-inch bore and twenty-six-inch stroke, and the driving wheels are four feet six inches in diameter. The boiler pressure is two hundred and twenty pounds, and six thousand gallons of water and twelve tons of coal are carried in the tanks.

Although the railway from the Cape to Cairo seems unlikely now ever to be completed, there is another Trans-African line which, although of lesser extent, is not only in course of construction but should very shortly be completed. This is the French line across the Sahara Desert, the greatest wilderness of sand in the world.

The Sahara Desert lies north of the African jungle belt, and the line is intended to link the French North African territory with the port of Dakar, on the west coast, and also with the Lake Chad region. The importance of Dakar, the nearest mainland port on the North Atlantic to South America, was proved in the Second World War, when it was used so much for supplies from America.

Lines from Dakar

Various lines have been built from Dakar at different times, and these have now been linked up and the track brought up to modern standards, until there is a through railway route from Dakar for nearly nine hundred miles to the Niger River. The Niger, incidentally, flows through the famous town of Timbuctoo, once so far off the beaten track as to be almost inaccessible, and should the branch line ever link up, as planned, with those in the Belgian Congo, the day may come even yet when it will be possible to travel right through

219

TOP FEED CLACKBOXES

REGULATOR VALVE

STEAM STAND VALVES

STAYS

BOILER-TUBES

INNER FIRE-BOX

OUTER FIRE-BOX

BRICK ARCH

FIRE-DOOR

REGULAT HANDLE

REVERSING WHEEL

WATER CONNEXION TO CLACKBOXES

FRONT WATER TANK 2650 GALLONS

FRONT PIVOT STEAM & WATER CONNEXIONS

WATER PIPE BETWEEN TENDERS

PIVOT CENTRE BEARING

ASH-PAN DAMPERS

FRONT UNIT

SAFETY VALVES

STEAM DOME

TOP FEED CLACKBOXES

SUPERHEATER FLUES

SUPERHEATER HEADER

STEAM PIPE FROM BLAST-PIPE RING

SUPERHEATER ELEMENTS

SPARK ARRESTER

COUPLED WHEELS

STEAM PIPE TO FRONT UNIT

BLAST PIPE

STEAM PIPE TO HIND UNIT

EXHAUST FROM FRONT UNIT

REVERSING LEVER

EXHAUST FROM HIND UNIT

TRAIN PIPE

WATER PIPE

FRONT PIVOT

BEYER-GARRATT ARTICULATED LOCOMOTIVE
For the Far East and Kenya - Metre Gauge

HIND PIVOT AND FLEXIBLE TRAIN-PIPE

REVERSING ROD

WATER

STEAM AND EXHAUST CONNEXIONS

AIR VENT

COAL BUNKER 7 TONS

TANK BAFFLE PLATES

PIVOT CENTRE BEARING

WATER OUTLET

REVERSING ROD

HIND WATER TANK 1550 GALLONS

SIEVES

STEAM PIPE TO CYLINDERS

PISTON VALVES

EXHAUST FROM CYLINDERS

WALSCHAERTS VALVE MOTION

FLANGELESS COUPLED WHEEL

HIND UNIT

PISTON 24-IN. STROKE

L. ASHWELL WOOD

Africa from north to south by rail. But this would still not be the Cape-to-Cairo route, as dreamed of by Cecil Rhodes, for the traveller from the beautiful temperate climate of Table Bay would arrive in Algeria rather than in Egypt.

As is well known, the Sahara Desert is not only the world's greatest sandy wilderness, but also provides some of the world's hottest temperatures, and one of the difficulties facing the engineers is to arrange for reasonable living accommodation for the staff who will have to live alongside the track when the line is opened.

Underground Stations

It is suggested that the difficulty may be overcome by means of underground air-conditioned stations, containing everything necessary for living and working, where the staff can be housed at least during the noonday heat. Water would also have to be supplied to them, for there is none, or practically none, in the Sahara.

This is one of the reasons why Diesel-electric propulsion is most likely, for the Diesel locomotive requires very little water throughout a journey, merely sufficient for cooling purposes, and thereby offers great advantages over steam for desert working.

When the Saharan line is completed, it will be possible to bring all produce from Nigeria, the Gold Coast and the surrounding country on a speedy route to the north, where transhipment will rapidly carry it into Europe. There is even a further proposal to develop the Niger Valley by irrigation, a project that would add great quantities of rice and cotton to the traffic.

In North Africa, the most advanced railway development is found in Algeria and Egypt, where the lines are laid on the

A HALT IN OWERRI PROVINCE, NIGERIA, where some third-class passengers alight. Third-class rates here are the cheapest in the world, being only a farthing a mile, and good use is made of the railway by the natives, who enjoy travelling merely for the fun of it. Second-class is a penny a mile but the luxury of first-class travel costs fourpence a mile, which helps to offset the low third-class rate.

MOROCCO, the clean and up-to-date station at Rabat, used mainly by tourists from Southern Europe. The service is electrified, current being supplied by overhead conductors. Although there are a number of railways in North Africa, principally in Tunisia, laid on metre-gauge track, the majority are built to the standard gauge of 4 ft. 8½ in., as distinct from the narrow-gauge tropical and South African lines.

standard gauge of Europe. So also are the Moroccan lines, with which the Algerian system is connected. The latter system actually forms part of the French National Railway system.

Two-thirds of the Tunisian lines, however, are on metre gauge, which is narrower even than the three-foot-six of the South African lines, although they are reputed to hold the record for the highest speed ever attained on such a gauge. A twin Diesel-electric rail-car, which used to cover the two hundred and sixty-three miles between Tunis and Gabes in six hours, has reached a speed of seventy-eight miles an hour on test.

Once again, on the Algerian railways, we find the heavy Beyer-Garratt type of locomotive, but here it is built to standard

gauge and has been introduced for express passenger service rather than heavy freight hauling. These machines were built to British patents, but at a works in Belgium.

They have the biggest driving wheels ever fitted to locomotives of this type, only an inch under six feet in diameter, and the engines concerned have attained the highest speed ever known for any articulated type. The speed reached was over eighty miles an hour, and the record was obtained on African lines.

They have the 4-6-2-2-6-4 wheel arrangement, or are like two Pacific-type engines coupled back to back, and each one weighs nearly two hundred tons in running order. They have a pulling power of fifty-three thousand six hundred pounds, and their four cylinders have a bore of nineteen and a quarter inches and a stroke of twenty-six inches.

Their introduction on the Algerian lines brought about a tremendous difference in the weights of trains. Whereas the heaviest train previously had been round about two hundred and fifty tons, the new giant Garratts promptly tackled test trains weighing as much as five hundred and fifty tons, notwithstanding some heavy gradients between Algiers and Oran. With improvements in track and signalling, it is hoped eventually to cut the time over this two-hundred-and-sixty-mile stretch from nine hours to about six and a half hours, including all stops, and with much heavier trains.

Travel in Egypt

In Egyptian rail travel, the present rubs shoulders with the distant past in a remarkable way. In the parlour of a Pullman car, the modern passenger in Egypt can travel swiftly from the port of Alexandria to Cairo, the capital, in two hours and three quarters. There, he can change into a luxurious dining- and sleeping-car train, and be carried south under the shadow of the Great Pyramids, past Luxor and the tombs of the Pharaohs, to the terminus at El Shellal, five hundred and fifty miles south of the capital.

Great Britain is mainly responsible for the development of the Egyptian State Railways, with the result that Egyptian rail travel is more similar to travel in Britain than to that of any other country. The locomotives, which include some 4-4-2 Atlantic-type engines, are beautifully painted and maintained. As the coaches are painted white, the trains make a handsome picture in the Nile valley.

Apart from the main lines, one of great importance is that from Cairo to Ismailia, where it branches into two, the northern line going to Port Said and the southern arm to Suez. This is now linked at Kantara with the Palestine Railways by a connexion which crosses the Suez Canal and makes its way round the south-eastern corner of the Mediterranean. This link is of very

FASTEST TRAIN IN EGYPT, King Fuad I, operating between Cairo and Alexandria. This train has covered the distance between the two cities in two hours, its average being seventy-eight miles an hour, almost a world record for the distance with steam. These railways have been developed mainly by British enterprise and capital.

RAILWAY SCENE IN THE LIBYAN DESERT. Passengers rush to get seats on the roof, where they can enjoy a cooling breeze on the hottest day. The great difficulty with the working of a desert railway is the provision of an adequate supply of water for the steam locomotives, but the introduction of the Diesel-electric principle, in which oil engines provide the primary power, has considerably simplified the problem.

recent construction, having been completed during the Second World War.

Another interesting railway in Egypt is the narrow-gauge line which provides rail travel over the Nile delta. This is laid on a gauge of only two feet six inches, but extends throughout the fertile lands of the delta for over six hundred miles, crossing waterways in all directions by means of navigable swing bridges.

South of Egypt are the railways of the Anglo-Egyptian Sudan, although there is a Nile steamer service between them. The Sudan railways are laid on the three-foot-six gauge, like those of South Africa.

The gap between the Egyptian and Sudan Railways is one of over two hundred and twenty miles, from El Shellal to Wadi Halfa,

but both towns, of course, are on the banks of the Nile, and there is an excellent service of steamers between them.

From Wadi Halfa, it is possible to take a comfortable restaurant- and sleeping-car train southward to the famous city of Khartoum, on a journey which lasts for twenty-four hours, partly across the Nubian Desert and partly alongside the Nile.

Southwards from Khartoum, there is yet another long main line, which runs along the Blue Nile to Sennar, site of the great dam, and then turns westward to Kosti, on the White Nile, and finally to El Obeid, exactly a thousand miles from El Shellal. And as far as North Africa is concerned, this is the farthest point reached towards a rail link-up between Cairo and the Cape.

Auckland express approaching
Wellington, New Zealand, on
the new Tawa Flat cut-off line

CHAPTER TWELVE

THROUGH DESERT AND CITY
IN AUSTRALASIA

AUSTRALIA possesses the longest straight line of any railway in the world. It is part of the transcontinental line linking the states of South and Western Australia, and has not the slightest curve in it for over three hundred miles.

Such a line could only have been laid in the perfectly flat country found in the great desert of the Nullarbor Plain. Not only is this one of the flattest areas of the earth's surface, but it is almost unbroken throughout the whole of its hundred-thousand square miles by either tree or habitation.

Desolate Countryside

Since the railway has come, of course, there are the lineside structures and a number of small settlements along the track, inhabited chiefly by the railway workers themselves, but the country each side of the route is so unproductive that it supports only a few roaming aborigines, who wander in now and then to beg from passengers at the various halts.

For four hundred and fifty miles the line runs through this desolate, barren and almost waterless country. The ground is composed of limestone and is full of cavities and blowholes. What little rain falls is soaked up immediately. Once upon a time it was the bed of a prehistoric ocean, but was forced upward at some period to become the driest of dry land.

Water-tank Cars

Additional water-tank cars have to be attached to the tenders of the locomotives working this route, for there is little possibility of taking in water on the journey. Even Kalgoorlie, the starting point, has no natural water supply, and water has to be piped to it for a distance of three hundred and fifty miles.

Only sparse and stunted vegetation grows on the Nullarbor Plain, and the journey across it by rail is one of the loneliest that can be found. Altogether, from Kalgoorlie to Port Pirie, the distance is over a thousand miles, nearly half of which runs through desert.

Almost on the mid-point of the run, at a place called Cook, is a lonely locomotive depot, where locomotives are changed. Two engines are used for the thousand-mile run, each working for about fifteen hours. From time to time stops are made at the tiny settlements alongside the track, and it is then that the aborigines come across from their primitive encampments to beg from the trains.

In spite of the monotony of totally unchanging scenery, the passenger is comfortable enough on the train. Sleeping cars are provided as well as a dining car, and the journey is unique in that the cost of sleeping berths and meals is included in the price of the ticket. Another special feature of the train is that there is a piano in the lounge car, so that passengers who weary of the scenery may have other means of passing the time.

Government Line

The line was laid by the Commonwealth Government, for no individual state could have afforded to lay down and work a track through such barren country. There are no goods or passengers to be picked up for hundreds of miles.

At one time, this desert country was shunned by the aborigines as being a land of evil spirits. The wind at times whistles through the cavities in the limestone desert with a weird and mournful noise, quite uncanny enough to startle the least superstitious.

The trans-Australian railway links the lines of all the states together, so that passengers can travel by rail the whole distance from Brisbane, capital of Queensland, to Perth, in Western Australia, but there is still no continuous north-south route through the country. In the Northern Territory there is a line which runs south as far as the central desert, and from Adelaide, in South Australia, there is another extending nearly a thousand miles north to Alice Springs, right in the central desert, but as yet the space between them has not been covered. When this gap has been filled in, it will be possible to travel across the whole continent both east to west and north to south, but in neither case will the journey be made in one through train.

Numerous Gauges

This is on account of the number of different gauges that were laid in Australia before a complete link-up of the various railway systems was visualized. Each state laid its track to whatever gauge it pleased, with the result that at one time there were no fewer than six changes. That is to say, although certain sections were of similar gauge, they were separated by different gauge track in between.

This has now been altered, and besides the east-west link-up, the six changes have come down to four. Starting from Perth, the passenger travels on a three-foot-six gauge to Kalgoorlie, the great gold-mining centre of Western Australia, and changes here on to the standard gauge of the Transcontinental, in which he spends two nights and a day to reach Port Pirie. Here, there is another change on to the broad gauge of five-foot-three across Victoria to its capital city Melbourne.

More Changes

New South Wales, however, is again standard gauge, so from Melbourne to Sydney there is another change at the frontier station of Albury, whence the standard-gauge line runs right through into Brisbane in Queensland. In earlier days, owing to Queensland having the narrow gauge of three-foot-six, there was still another change, and although a standard line has now been taken through to the capital, most of the Queensland railways are narrow gauge. Thus there are still certain breaks of gauge, where all freight has to be unloaded and reloaded on to another train and, in view of the cost

PRINCIPAL RAILWAYS OF AUSTRALIA

involved in any change of track on a large scale, such breaks are likely to persist.

In vivid contrast to its central and western deserts, Australia possesses the busiest railway station in the world at Flinders Street, Melbourne. On a single day, no fewer than three hundred and twenty thousand passengers have passed through the barriers of this station. Most of the trains are of the suburban electric type, running over a hundred and seventy miles

of broad-gauge tracks round the suburbs, but there are steam trains as well, up to a hundred and fifty a day. Over two thousand electric trains are handled each twenty-four hours, and the maximum frequency is a hundred and fifty-eight trains an hour.

The latest Australian steam locomotives are among the most powerful in the British Empire. Although most of Australia is flat, there are certain mountainous districts through which the railway has been engineered, these producing with their rainfall the most fertile belts of land, and on these lines there are some steep grades requiring powerful engines.

Locomotives with the 4—8—4 wheel arrangement, some of them streamlined, are used for the principal passenger trains, and the same wheel arrangement is also used on engines for the heavy freight trains. The huge 4—8—4 locomotives of the broad-gauge Victorian Railways and

229

their tenders weigh two hundred and sixty tons in running trim, over a hundred tons more than a British engine of the same type, and there are others almost as large on the New South Wales and South Australian Railways.

Caves Express

As an example of uphill work in the mountains, the Caves Express, which runs from Sydney to the famous caves of the Blue Mountains, climbs practically to the height of Snowdon in a run of just under seventy miles from Sydney to Katoomba, and over three thousand feet of this climb are surmounted in thirty-three miles. The longest non-stop run in Australia is that of the famous Victorian streamliner Spirit of Progress, which runs from Albury, on the New South Wales border, into Melbourne at an average of fifty-three miles an hour, covering a hundred and ninety-one miles.

Diesel power is used for working at least one Australian streamlined train, the Silver City Comet, which provides a fast service between Sydney and the manufacturing centre of Broken Hill.

In the country districts of certain states there are some unusual trains. In Victoria, a Better Farming train, with fifteen passenger and freight cars all painted bright yellow, makes visits lasting ten days to the farming areas and acts as a university on wheels. The train carries an electric power plant, livestock, models of farms, farming equipment, exhibits of wool, soil and grass and many other things of interest to farmers.

Another curious train, also run in Victoria, is that known as the Reso train, Reso standing for National Resource Development. The idea of this train is to give Victorians a better insight into the resources of their state, a charge of about fifteen guineas being made for a whole week's trip round the country.

On the South Australian Railways, there is a weed-killer train, specially provided for destroying the weeds on certain

FLINDERS STREET STATION IN MELBOURNE, reputed to be the busiest station in the world. Much of its traffic is of the suburban electrified variety. Australian railways present the startling contrast of the world's busiest station and its loneliest and longest straight track, the one laid across the desolate Nullarbor Plain in the West.

COOK STATION IN WESTERN AUSTRALIA, loneliest railway halt in the world. It lies about midway on the four-hundred-odd-mile transcontinental journey across the Nullarbor Plain, a desert completely bare of habitation except for lineside structures for the railway workers. The train stops here in order to change locomotives.

sections of track. These weeds grow so rapidly and in such profusion that if they were not destroyed they would seriously interfere with the drainage and safety of the permanent way. The train has tanks containing arsenical weed killer, and, passing slowly over the weed-infested part of the line, sprinkles this in much the same fashion as a water cart sprays water on to a dusty road.

Railway electrification in Australia is confined mainly to the great cities of Melbourne and Sydney, capitals of Victoria and New South Wales respectively. Fifteen-hundred-volt direct current is used with overhead wires, and on the suburban electric service of Melbourne, the trains travel thirty million miles annually. Between Flinders Street and Spencer Street stations, which are connected by a viaduct, fifty-two trains an hour pass along a double-line track. Melbourne is also noted for a flying-junction in the suburb of Burnley, where crossing-tracks have been separated by means of a viaduct. Of twenty-one electric sub-stations on the Melbourne lines, twelve are operated automatically and need no attendant.

The greatest piece of engineering in Australia, however, is undoubtedly Sydney Harbour Bridge, one of the most astonishing structures ever erected. So exceptional is it, that when drawings of the proposed bridge were first exhibited, prominent German and American engineers declared that it would be impossible to erect.

The Australians wanted the bridge, and persisted in the matter. It was needed to connect one half of Sydney with the other, for the northern suburbs of the city were separated from all the others by the entrance to Sydney Harbour. At this entrance, shut in by high cliffs, the gap is only a third of a mile wide, yet to get from one side to the other without a ferry, meant a long journey right round the huge bay. Furthermore, the traffic had reached such dimensions that the harbour ferry service was becoming inadequate.

Tenders Invited

So after a great deal of discussion and a lengthy public enquiry, the New South Wales Government eventually invited tenders for the building of a bridge, and the successful tendering firm, which happened to be British, produced no fewer than seven different designs. All of these, however, were variants of three basic designs, one a cantilever bridge, another a cantilever arch, and the third the bridge eventually built.

The gap to be spanned was sixteen hundred and fifty feet, and across it the builders were required to carry four railway tracks, a fifty-seven-foot roadway and two ten-foot footways, which needed a total width of one hundred and sixty feet.

Building the Arch

It was not the width, however, but the immense main arch that provided the chief problem. This rises four hundred and forty feet above the sea level, giving ample head-room for the largest liners and dominating the whole of the city. The difficulty was that each half of the bridge would have to be built out from the harbour side for some

eight hundred feet without support, until it could be joined to the other in the middle.

Eight hundred feet of metal projecting into the air, and weighing as much as fourteen thousand tons, had to be held only by its supports on the shore side ! In addition, on the extreme end of each arm, there was mounted a creeper crane to hoist from water level the steel required as each successive panel was built outwards. These cranes alone, with their equipment, imposed a load of six hundred tons on the end of the projecting arm, like a weight at the end of a giant lever.

Nothing like this had ever been known before in bridge construction, and it was probably one of the main reasons why the Germans and Americans had declared the

BURNLEY FLY-OVER NEAR MELBOURNE, photographed while two suburban electric trains were on the point of crossing. Victorian Railways are laid on the unusually wide gauge of five-foot-three, and the coaches seem almost square in appearance. Electrification is on the overhead system, with direct current at fifteen hundred volts.

SPIRIT OF PROGRESS, super-train of the Southern Hemisphere. It belongs to the Victorian Government Railways, and is a streamlined, all-steel, completely air-conditioned express. It runs non-stop each way daily the one hundred and ninety miles between Melbourne and Albury at an overall average speed of fifty-one miles an hour.

construction to be impossible. Nevertheless the giant arch was erected without any serious hitch from beginning to end of the work.

As each half-arch was built out from the harbour side, it was held in position by a hundred and twenty-eight steel cables, attached to all four top corners of the arch and led back through anchorages deep in the rock. These cables were each two and a half inches in diameter, and each had a breaking strain of over a hundred tons.

Stress Testing

During the course of construction, various members of the arch were stressed far more severely than they are now that the bridge is completed, and this fact had to be taken into account in making the design. The builders installed a testing machine of over twelve hundred tons capacity, one of the largest ever built, and this was used to test to destruction large-scale models of various parts of the bridge.

Some of the facts of this colossal structure are almost unbelievable. Altogether there are fifty-one thousand tons of steel in the bridge, most of which had to be shipped from Britain to Sydney, a distance of over twelve thousand miles. This weight of metal is considerably more than is found in a large battleship, so the Sydney bridge is equivalent in weight to a very large battleship supported high in the air only at its ends. Thirty-eight thousand tons are in the giant arch alone, so balanced that both weight and strain are as evenly distributed as possible.

To allow for expansion and contraction of such a quantity of steel, the arch rests on four enormous hinges, two each side. They are sunk from thirty to forty feet deep in the rock, and each one is designed to withstand a thrust of nearly twenty thousand tons. The actual road of the bridge is about a foot longer during the daytime than at night, and this is allowed for by special expansion joints.

During erection, the builders had made allowance for the fact that when the two

SYDNEY HARBOUR BRIDGE

One of the World's greatest Railway Links

SECTION OF UPPER CHORD

INSPECTION FOOTWAY

HANGER BRACKETS

SECTION OF LOWER CHORD

DECK HANGERS

ELECTRIC LIGHTS

6-WAY ROAD

SOUTH PYLONS

FOOTWAY

SECTION OF DECK

FOOTWAY

ELECTRIC 4-RAILWAY TRACKS

HANGER PINS

INSPECTION FOOTWAY

FROM SYDNEY CENTRAL STATION

170 FT

AMPLE HEADROOM FOR 22,000-TON LINER

DEPTH OF WATER 60 FT

SANDSTONE ROCK

NORTH PYLONS

FOOTWAY

SECTION OF DECK
AT PYLONS

GRANITE
FACING

STEELWORK OF
APPROACH ROAD

SUPPORT FOR
APPROACH ROAD

END POSTS

WER CHORD
CHORAGE

CONCRETE
PYLONS

16-FT STEEL RODS

STEEL ROLLER (EACH SIDE)
BEARINGS TAKING WEIGHT
OF ENTIRE BRIDGE

CONCRETE
FOUNDATION
IN SANDSTONE

ASHWELL
WOOD

TASMANIAN GOODS TRAIN, hauled by Q class Mountain-type locomotive. These engines have the 4-8-2 wheel arrangement, and cylinders of twenty-inch bore and twenty-four-inch stroke. Dimensions are limited by the fact that Tasmanian railways are laid on the narrow gauge of three feet six inches, with rather light track.

half-arches met in the middle, they might be some few inches out of alignment. Such was the construction that the meeting was perfect, not even an inch out of true. At the same time, there was a certain amount of unavoidable sag in the structure, all the stress being exerted through the main lower chords of the arch. The top members were resting on the lower, as it were, and not bearing their own weight.

Steel Wedges

To make the whole structure into one rigid piece, resting properly on its feet, these upper chords, at their meeting point, were forced apart by hydraulic jacks exerting a pressure of over three thousand tons, until they were wide enough apart to permit the insertion of specially machined steel packing pieces. The arch was then complete, and the supporting wire ropes could be removed.

The next job was to hoist into position the

great hangers, from thirty to a hundred and ninety feet in length, by means of which the bridge floor is suspended from the arch. The centre hangers were erected first, then those on each side, until the outermost hangers were reached. This was done to distribute the weight of the floor and its supports evenly over the arch above. The biggest hanger, slender though it may appear, weighs ninety tons. Connexion at floor level across the harbour was established in February, 1931, and the bridge was opened formally just over a year later, in March, 1932.

A point of interest is that all four of the railway tracks laid across the bridge are for electric trains, which serve the suburban areas on the north side of the harbour. The opening of the bridge brought these outlying suburbs within much easier reach, and resulted in a great deal of development.

Away to the south of Australia lie the two

mountainous islands of New Zealand, where railway engineering has to contend not only with a great mountain chain that rises on the west coast of South Island to Alpine altitudes, but also with a volcanic structure that gives rise sometimes to earthquake shocks.

In the building of the new terminal station at Wellington, for example, special precautions were taken to make the building shock-proof. The piles on which it stands were joined by continuous ties, making the foundations a complete whole, and the steel superstructure was specially jointed to offer the greatest possible resistance to vibration.

The mountainous nature of the islands caused the narrow gauge of three feet six inches to be chosen for the railways, and this has since become standard. The narrow gauge gives greater freedom of curvature on mountain lines, and consequently permits the line to be laid in places where a wider gauge would make the task extremely difficult.

The Raurimu spirals in the heart of the Maori country are an example of the surprising curves that are sometimes necessary on mountain tracks. These spirals are on the Auckland-Wellington main line, and form the culminating stretch of track as it climbs to two high summits.

Beginning at Raurimu and mounting steadily, the track first doubles back to the north-west, then turns north-east, and finally goes south. After this it describes a complete circle, and arrives at a point which, although two hundred feet higher up the mountainside, is still only a quarter of a mile from the start in a direct line. Continuing southwards, the line makes a final bend and climbs another two hundred and thirty feet, but has still travelled only a mile and a quarter, as the crow flies, from the start. The spiralling loops allow the track to be laid at an incline of one-in-fifty, thereby gaining height over a long stretch without making the climb short and abrupt. Only two tunnels were needed to complete this striking piece of mountaineering.

The North Island main line extends for fifty miles at more than two thousand feet

Passenger train on the Bridge-
water Causeway, Tasmania

above sea level, hemmed in on both sides by immense mountains. Between Auckland and Wellington there are thirty tunnels and twenty-two viaducts, a fine example of the latter being the Makatote Viaduct, which carries the rails two hundred and sixty feet above the river over a deep gorge.

There is one remarkable incline in North Island which is world famous, and this is the steep climb through the rampart of the Rimutaka Mountains to the rolling grass-lands and dairy-farming country beyond. It begins some thirty-four miles from Wellington at Cross Creek, which lies at the entrance to a valley leading steeply up into the mountains, and climbs eight hundred and seventy-one feet in a distance of two and a half miles, with gradients varying from one-in-sixteen to one-in-thirteen. On gradients of this description, the grip of the driving wheels on ordinary track is unequal to the task of pulling a train, so special track was laid on what is known as the Fell centre-rail system.

The centre rail is like the bull head type of track rail used in Britain, save that the head and the foot are the same size, and in section the rail has the shape of a dumb-bell. This is laid on its side and secured to sleepers running lengthwise with the track, and these in turn are fastened down to the ordinary cross-sleepers.

Each Fell locomotive, besides its normal driving wheels, is provided underneath with a pair of driving wheels which are laid on their side. By a powerful arrangement of springs, these extra wheels can be pressed into contact with the centre rail, gripping it between them and providing additional adhesion on the gradient. Because of the steepness of the incline, the weight of these locomotives has been kept down to thirty-nine tons, and they are tank engines with the 0—4—2 wheel arrangement.

This centre rail also enables special precautions to be taken for braking pur-poses when trains are descending. The horizontal driving wheels are moved out of contact with the rail, and four cast-iron

NEW ZEALAND K TYPE ENGINE. Powerful 4-8-4 locomotive class built entirely in the Dominion. New Zealanders are very proud of these engines, which represent notable development on narrow gauge track. Engines of this type haul the principal trains in North Island over the four-hundred-mile route between Auckland and Wellington.

NEW ZEALAND ELECTRICALLY-HAULED MAIN LINE TRAIN, fine example of narrow-gauge passenger stock. All the local lines round Wellington, the capital, have now been electrified, including the new main trunk line out to Packakariki. Over two million pounds have been spent on this work and the fine new station at Wellington.

brake shoes instead are pressed into contact with it by screw gear. In addition, special brake vans are attached to each train also having such shoes as their equipment, and a guard on each van applies further braking effort to the centre rail as required, it being vital that no train shall get out of control on such an incline.

It is also important to avoid putting too great a strain on the coach-couplings, so on the ascent each locomotive pulls no more than the train weight for which it has been designed, about sixty or sixty-five tons. At the foot of the incline, therefore, every train is remarshalled, extra locomotives being placed at the head of every sixty-ton section.

So when a train mounts the famous Rimutaka incline, it is nothing uncommon to see three or four locomotives belching out smoke and steam at different points throughout its length. The additional brake

vans come up in a string at the tail of the ascending train, and on the descent are placed at the end of each sixty-ton section.

Speed is limited. On the ascent it is no more than six miles an hour, and coming down the incline trains must not travel at more than ten miles an hour. What with this and all the marshalling and remarshalling that takes place at both top and bottom, the Rimutaka incline is a troublesome patch on the route concerned, holding up trains and causing a low average speed for the journey.

Recently, however, fast Diesel-electric rail-cars have been introduced between Wellington and Masterton, and for the first time are providing a swift passenger service up and down the incline. They are also, of course, equipped with the additional driving wheels and brakes, and cut the time taken on the journey by a full hour.

The South Island of New Zealand has the

HAPUAWHENUA VIADUCT, on the main line between Auckland and Wellington, carrying the track one hundred and fifty feet above the river bed. Not far away are the famous Raurimu spirals, by which the summit level of the line is reached at Waimarino.

longest railway tunnel in the British Empire. This is the Otira Tunnel, with a single-track bore five miles and a quarter in length. It was bored to pierce the mass of the Southern Alps, which had previously cut off Westport and Greymouth, on the western side of the island, from the main railway system, and the east portal is nearly two thousand five hundred feet above sea level.

Electrification was introduced through the tunnel, and the resultant fast traffic has opened up parts of the country which were previously accessible only by mountain passes or by the sea. Diesel rail-cars run over this route also.

One special problem which faced railway engineers in South Island was the number of great rivers rushing down their wide beds from the glaciers of the Southern Alps. The crossing of these rivers, in fact, determined the stages by which the main line down the eastern side of the island was completed.

First came the Rakaia River, with a viaduct a mile and an eighth in length, and then the bridges across the Rangitata and Waitaki Rivers. The whole line from Lyttleton to The Bluff is three hundred and ninety-two miles in length.

Travelling times between the two islands, North and South, will soon be greatly reduced. At one time it was necessary to take an eleven-hour steamer journey between Wellington and Lyttleton, but a railway is now being built to cover the distance to the narrow Picton Strait. When this is completed, only the strait will have to be crossed by steamer, and passengers will then be able to travel by train the whole length of the South Island main line.

Indeed, New Zealand railways have been improved greatly in recent years, and the growth of traffic has caused the size and power of locomotives to increase until they have reached the maximum limits that can be permitted on a narrow gauge of three feet six inches. New Zealanders are particularly proud of their big hundred-and-thirty-five-ton locomotives of the K class with the 4—8—4 wheel arrangement, built entirely in the Dominion to suit New Zealand conditions. They haul all the principal trains in North Island over the four hundred odd miles of mountainous country between Wellington and Auckland.

241

Empire State Express, stainless steel
train of the New York Central Railway

CHAPTER THIRTEEN

SUPER FLYERS OF AMERICA

THE fastest and most luxurious trains in the world are found in the United States of America, where the railroad received its most enthusiastic welcome. In America, the railway helped to build the nation, fighting and defeating the red man on the gold trail to California, and welding the eastern states with those of the west.

As a result, it is venerated as one of the sturdiest of pioneers, and there is a genuine deference in the general attitude towards it. It can never be regarded as a child that grew slowly to manhood, altering the general scheme of existence as the years went by, for it arrived as a healthy youngster nursed to comparative maturity in Great Britain, and more than capable of doing a man-sized job.

Coming of the Railway

Before it came, the only land link for people between New York and San Francisco was the covered wagon, with its trail of hardship and danger, and even death. Then the railroad arrived and unfolded itself with surprising speed across the prairies of the far west, and the blood and smoke that heralded its approach are mainly responsible for the romance and drama that have grown up around it.

Even today, romance can be seen in the names given to some of the most modern Diesel-electric flyers, such as the El Capitan and the Super Chief, one Spanish and the other a direct descendant from Indian days. Yet these trains were not even in existence before 1935.

It is not surprising, therefore, that a country which admittedly owes so much to the railroad should have built within its borders nearly a third of all the railways in the world. If all the running lines, branch lines and sidings were laid end to end, it would take a train travelling at a mile a minute roughly nine months to complete

THE NEW AND THE OLD, a striking comparison. On the left is a streamlined Diesel-electric locomotive used on the City of Los Angeles, one of the latest American flyers. Alongside it is the veteran No. 22, wood-burning steam engine of the early days of the Union Pacific. This was the type in use in the days when Indians were still sufficiently numerous to take to the warpath, and attacks on trains were frequent.

the journey, or conversely, there would be sufficient track to make a hundred and twenty-four parallel lines from New York to San Francisco, in place of the one winding route that originally linked the two cities together. And all this in spite of the fact that America has only one-sixteenth of the world's surface area, and considerably less than a sixteenth of its population.

Many hundreds of independent railways make up the American network. There is a tendency, however, for some of the larger and more famous systems to group other connecting lines under their control as subsidiaries. The New York Central System affords a good example, combining no fewer than six different railways, with altogether more than eleven thousand miles of line.

Its hub is the Grand Central Terminal in New York, one of the most palatial railway

stations ever built, with more than fifty million people passing through it every year. Its entrance hall (or main-line concourse) alone is a vast vaulted structure over a hundred and twenty feet high, the same in width and more than twice this in length, filled always with a moving crowd.

Sunlight streams through three immense south windows during the day; concealed fluorescent lighting makes day out of night. Shops are grouped round the hall, and a cinema, an art gallery and a restaurant open off it. Altogether, that part of the station structure seen above ground is over seven hundred feet long and nearly four hundred feet wide, yet this is only a small fraction of the whole, for the greater part is underground.

Here there is an enormous cavern blasted out of solid rock and roofed in with concrete and steel. This is the part in which the tracks are laid and in which the trains are constantly moving. At twenty feet below the surface there are forty-one tracks for long-distance trains, and twenty-four feet below that is the suburban station with another thirty-nine tracks, making eighty tracks in all on the two levels. And because this is a terminus, at the entry end of the tracks on both levels there are loop tunnels, so that the trains, after running into the arrival platforms, can be worked round to the departure platforms without fouling the tracks and holding up the flow of traffic.

Trains enter the Grand Central Terminal by way of a long four-track tunnel under the famous Park Avenue. Under Fifty-Seventh Street the lines begin to fan out, with a down-gradient on the west side to the suburban platforms and an upgrade on the east side leading from it.

Three boxes, with modern electric signalling, control the movement of trains. Tower A, in which there are always five signalmen at work, controls all train movements into and out of the forty-one main-line platforms; Tower B controls all trains using the suburban tracks, while the third box controls the running round the loops.

Reversible Signalling

The electric signalling of the four tracks through the entrance tunnel is reversible, and enables traffic to be regulated ingeniously during the rush hours. In the morning, only one of these tracks is kept for outgoing trains and the other three are used for trains coming in, whereas in the evening, roughly between five and six o'clock, the process is reversed. Then three tracks are used for outgoing trains and only one is reserved for trains arriving.

Beyond the end of the tunnel, there are acres and acres of carriage sidings at Mott Haven, and one-fifth of the train movements through the tunnel are of empty

INTERIOR OF CLUB CAR on the City of Los Angeles, popular streamliner running between Chicago and Los Angeles. The passenger has a sense of luxury and comfort here equivalent to that to be found in any first-class hotel, in spite of the fact that he may be speeding through a western desert at a speed of over eighty miles an hour.

GRAND CENTRAL TERMINAL
NEW YORK CITY

LOWER PARK AVENUE BRIDGE

42ND STREET

MAIN-LINE
ENTRANCE

MAIN WAITING-ROOM

← ENTRANCE
FROM SUBWAYS

CINEMA, SHOPS
RESTAURANT, ETC.

SUBURBAN RAMP
DOWN

RAMP FROM 42ND STREET

INTERBORO
SUBWAY

HUDSON AND
MANHATTAN
TUNNEL

BELMONT
TUNNEL

MAIN - L

THESE LOOPS ENCIRCLE THE
ENTIRE STATION FROM ARRIVAL
TO DEPARTURE PLATFORMS →

SUBURB

FROM HOTELS
AND STREET

L. ASHWELL
WOOD.

43ʳᴰ STREET

44ᵀᴴ STREET

STREET ENTRANCES

CAB ENTRANCE

CAB DRIVE

MAIN-LINE TRAIN ROOM

MAIN-LINE CONCOURSE

ENQUIRIES

RAMPS DOWN

TICKET ENTRANCES

SUBURBAN CONCOURSE

RAMPS DOWN

SUBURBAN TRAIN ROOM

DEPARTURE PLATFORMS

LOOP

LOOP

Two Levels of Platforms - Upper 41 Tracks, Lower 39 Tracks

trains being worked between the station and the yards, where they are serviced. Everything is electric, and even the long-distance trains are electrically worked for thirty-three miles out of New York to Harmon, on the Hudson River. The building of the Grand Central Terminal cost the equivalent of thirty million pounds.

Pennsylvania Terminal

Another giant station in New York is the Pennsylvania Terminal, similarly below ground level, though in this case it was necessary to tunnel under the broad Hudson River to bring the trains into the city from the New Jersey side of the water. Pennsylvania Terminal, however, is not really a terminus, as the lines continue on to Sunnyside, a suburb of Brooklyn on Long Island, and are used by the Long Island suburban trains. The Pennsylvania Terminal is also used by long-distance trains coming from Boston and continuing to Washington and Philadelphia, and these trains cross the river by the massive Hell

Gate Bridge, a four-track steel arch with a thousand-foot span.

These great stations in New York are typical of main-line stations in many American cities, and in some of them, such as Washington, Cincinnati and St. Louis, the various railways serving the city have combined to build one vast Union Terminal, which is used by all their trains. St. Louis has a station of this kind, with forty-two tracks to accommodate the trains of more than a dozen different railroads.

American stations rarely provide any comfort on the actual platforms, which are often no more than covered footways at ground level alongside the track. All the comfort is provided in the palatial station buildings, and passengers generally remain in the building until the time comes to join the train. This is a practice that has grown out of climatic conditions, for in a North American winter it would often be far too cold to wait on any exposed platform, no matter what precautions were taken.

It is not stations alone, however, that have

PALATIAL RAILWAY STATION, Grand Central Terminal in New York. More than fifty million people pass through it every year. The main concourse, shown here, is over a hundred and twenty feet in height and width, and more than twice this in length.

TYPICAL AMERICAN STATION. Most American stations have low-level platforms, although high-level platforms are also occasionally seen. The steps beneath the coach door are folding, so that they offer no obstruction while the train is in motion, and when they are pulled up the underside forms part of the lower curve of the coach.

grown in America to a size and magnificence far outstripping anything on European railway systems. The locomotives have developed far beyond European standards, and have changed almost out of recognition from the chugging old-timers with their balloon chimneys and grill cowcatchers. Some of the latter, curiously enough, had names that were definitely un-American, and showed quite distinctly their country of origin, such as Old Ironsides and John Bull.

Room for Development

The fact that they left more room round their tracks in the beginning has made it possible for the Americans to develop the size of their locomotives. The rail gauge is the same as over most of Europe, namely the standard of four feet eight and a half inches, but they can build as high as

sixteen feet above rail level and to a width of ten feet without fouling bridges or lineside structures.

This makes a surprising difference. As an example, the big streamlined Hudson steam locomotives that work the famous Twentieth Century Limited from New York to Chicago weigh as much as a hundred and sixty-one tons. With their tenders, which are of the twelve-wheeled variety now almost standard in America, they turn the scale at three hundred and ten tons.

This is fully loaded, with the tender carrying twenty-eight tons of coal and fourteen thousand gallons of water. The working pressure of the Hudsons is two hundred and seventy-five pounds, and they have the 4—6—4 wheel arrangement. Their cylinders are twenty-two and a half inches in diameter with a twenty-nine inch stroke. These alone account for four feet of

249

OUTSIDE AND INSIDE. Two views of a New York Central semi-streamlined Hudson steam locomotive of four thousand seven hundred horse-power. The Hudson is the engine that draws the famous Twentieth Century Limited between New York and Chicago, and was travelling at eighty miles an hour when the photo on right was taken. The locomotive works at a pressure of two hundred and seventy-five pounds, and has the 4-6-4 wheel arrangement, while its tender is of the twelve-wheeled type now very common in the United States. Fully loaded, with the tender carrying twenty-eight tons of coal and fourteen thousand gallons of water, it turns the scale at three hundred and ten tons. Its cylinders have a bore of twenty-two and a half inches, with a stroke of twenty-nine inches. A view of the driver's cab is given below. The lettering indicates the uses of the various controls and gauges. The engine is fitted with mechanical firing, the principle of which is described in detail in a drawing overleaf.

ELECTRO-PNEUMATIC TRAIN CONTROL VALVES

PYROMETER

STEAM HEAT

BOOSTER STEAM GAUGE

STEAM HEAT REDUCING VALVE

WATER GLASS

WATER GLASS

BOILER GAUGE COCK HANDLES

FEED WATER HEATER GAUGE

STEAM PRESSURE GAUGE

WATER LEVEL GAUGE

STOKER GAUGE

STOKER JETS

AIR BRAKE GAUGES

VALVE PILOT

INJECTOR OPERATING LEVER

STOKER GAUGE

BACK PRESSURE AND CUT-OFF GAUGE

FIRE DOOR

AUTOMATIC BRAKE VALVE

POWER REVERSE GEAR

the permissible width. The Hudsons take over at Harmon, at the end of the electrified section thirty-three miles out of New York, and then run on unchanged for the full nine hundred and twenty-five miles to Chicago.

For over a hundred miles of the journey, from Elkhart to Toledo, they average as much as seventy-two miles an hour, and this is pulling a train weighing sometimes nearly nine hundred tons. For all that, they are not by any means a record in size for the United States.

On many of the main lines with heavy grades, the favourite wheel arrangement for fast passenger and freight work is 4—8—4, that is, eight coupled driving wheels with a leading bogie, and a bogie at the rear end to carry the fire-box. The handsome streamliners used by the Southern Pacific Railway on their Daylight expresses between San Francisco and Los Angeles are an example, with three-hundred-pounds boiler pressure and cylinders of twenty-five-and-a-half-inch diameter and thirty-two-inch stroke. Each engine turns the scale at two hundred and twelve tons, and engine and tender together weigh over four hundred tons.

Needless to say, manual firing of such engines would be completely beyond the power of any human fireman. On most of these larger types, therefore, automatic firing is installed, and this, by means of a worm-type conveyor, brings the coal from the tender and deposits it in the fire-box. The fireman is able to control the speed of firing with the same exactitude as he could with a shovel on a smaller engine.

Coal Stages

The consumption of fuel by such giants is so heavy that on many main lines there are coal stages for the replenishment of tenders. These are erected across the main track, and under these the locomotive stops in the course of its run to fill up.

Water, as usual, is a simpler proposition, being scooped up at speed from troughs, or track-pans as they are known in America, in the same way as in Great Britain and other countries, save that in America the speed at which the locomotive can travel while taking on water has been greatly increased. Formerly, about forty-five miles an hour was the limit, but on the New York Central line this has now been raised to seventy-five miles an hour.

It has been made possible simply by

redesigning the scoops so that they reach their maximum efficiency at the higher speed. At this speed, it has been found possible to take in as much as seven thousand gallons at a single gulp, from a track-pan a third of a mile in length. Some difficulty was experienced at first, owing to the sudden terrific rush of water up the delivery pipe, for in some cases the overflow from the tank top broke windows, not only in the train behind, but in trains on the next track. The difficulty was overcome by arranging overflow vents, which carry any surplus water downwards.

The absolute maximum in size for a locomotive is reached in the so-called articulated types, which are of such a length that, in order to get round the normal curves, they are built in two sections and hinged in the middle. In these the greater headroom in America gives scope for a different design from that used in the British-built Beyer-Garratt articulated locomotives. Because there is three feet more headroom above the rails, American articulated locomotives have the boiler mounted entirely above the two sections of chassis, instead of on a girder frame slung between them, so that they are very little different in appearance from a locomotive on a rigid frame.

The record is held by the colossal Big Boy class of the Union Pacific Railroad, used to haul heavy freight trains over the Wasatch Mountains, between Ogden, in Utah, and Green River, Wyoming.

They have the 4—8—8—4 wheel arrangement, or a four-wheeled bogie in front, followed by two groups of eight coupled driving wheels, and then a trailing four-

MECHANICAL STOKING ON AN AMERICAN LOCOMOTIVE, showing how the coal is carried from tender to fire-box by a series of screw feeds. The main screw is horizontal, and forces the coal through a flexible connexion into a junction box under the cab, from which it is lifted by vertical screws so that it can be blown into the furnace by a jet of steam. The floor of the tender coal space is built so that it slopes down to the main screw, and the rate of feed can be adjusted with exactitude by the driver.

MALLET-TYPE ARTICULATED LOCOMOTIVE of the Norfolk and Western Railway, used for hauling the long and heavy coal trains, which may weigh from five thousand to as much as ten thousand tons. The leading chassis is arranged to pivot, to enable the immense length of the locomotive to adjust itself to the curves in the track.

wheeled bogie under the cab. Their full length, without tender, is seventy-two feet six inches.

The rear driving wheels and bogie are fixed, integrally with the main frames of the engine, while the front bogie and driving wheels are pivoted under the smoke-box end of the engine. This means that all eight front driving wheels and bogie make a sideways sliding movement under the boiler on rounding a curve, while the boiler partly overhangs the track. The boiler itself is tapered, from just under eight feet in diameter at the front to nearly nine feet at the rear, and supplies steam at three hundred pounds pressure to four cylinders, two on the front chassis and two on the rear one. Each cylinder has a twenty-three-and-a-half-inch bore and thirty-two-inch stroke.

The tenders for these monsters are built with fourteen wheels, and carry twenty-five tons of coal and twenty-five thousand gallons of water. These alone, when filled, weigh nearly two hundred tons. Engine and tender together weigh five hundred and thirty-four tons, or more

than three times as much as a British Pacific engine and tender. On test, they have developed as much as seven thousand horse-power.

Many of these massive engines have been built for oil-firing, particularly those used on the main lines near the Californian oilfields, and in one type at least, the 4—8—8—2 of the Southern Pacific, the design of the locomotive has been reversed completely. That is to say, the driving cab is in front and the chimney is at the rear.

Fuel Pumped Forward

Such an engine does not run backwards. Its tender, carrying oil fuel, is at the rear behind the chimney, and the oil is pumped right forward to the fire-box, which is just behind the driver and fireman. This is possible with liquid fuel, of course, and one of the advantages is that the driver and fireman are ahead of the fumes from the chimney when passing through tunnels. The chief advantage, however, is the obvious one that they have an excellent view of the track ahead.

The tasks such mammoth locomotives are

set to perform are in proportion to their size. Apart from the passenger trains, which on the chief main lines may often be more than a thousand tons in weight, freight trains are made up exclusively of high-capacity bogie wagons on eight wheels, and a hundred or more of these on one train is quite a normal load. In other words, a normal freight train in America weighs upwards of five thousand tons.

They travel at high speeds, too, as much as sixty miles an hour, an astonishing sight if one is not accustomed to it. On suitable routes in the States, however, a freight train of a hundred wagons whirling up the dust at this speed is no uncommon spectacle. All wagons are fitted with the same continuous brake as passenger vehicles, one of the chief reasons why such speeds are possible with safety.

A more fascinating sight is the fully steamlined train, in which America excels.

All the cars have vivid external colouring, schemed from head to tail of the train in a way that varies with each company, and their brilliance as they streak through the countryside is striking. In addition, they are furnished luxuriously with all kinds of novel interior arrangements, so that a journey becomes a pleasure in itself.

Streamlining in America

American streamlining started in 1934, and is one of the most amazingly rapid developments in railway history. The railways were suffering severely at that time from competition from both road and air transport, which, coupled with the world depression, roughly halved their passenger traffic. It was obviously necessary to do something to recover at least a part of the lost ground, and when the Germans showed the possibilities of high-speed streamlined travel with the

CAPITOL LIMITED, drawn by a Diesel-electric locomotive of three thousand six hundred horse-power. The photograph was taken in the Potomac River Valley as the Capitol Limited was on its way from New York to Chicago. All the principal Baltimore and Ohio Railroad express trains are now hauled by Diesel-electric power.

NOT AN AIRSHIP—only a railway coach! This experimental streamlined coach was designed in America for high-speed work and built by Cortlandt T. Hill. It has an unusually low centre of gravity and, consequently, greater stability and safety than a coach of normal design. Its floor level is only thirty inches above the rails, and the roof only eleven feet, compared with the maximum of sixteen feet.

Flying Hamburger, the Americans followed suit in a way that rapidly eclipsed German streamlining methods. Since then, they have gone further than any other country with this form of travel, and the response of the public has been overwhelming.

The attraction does not lie only in speed, although on suitable stretches of line speeds of a hundred miles an hour are quite common, even with quite lengthy trains. The chief attraction is the pleasure of travelling in such trains, with their surprising variety of cars, including buffet cars as well as dining cars, and the solarium lounges or observation cars at the rear.

The extraordinary success of these streamlined flyers can be shown in a very simple illustration. One of the first to come into service was a train called the Four Hundred, which ran between Chicago and the twin cities of St. Paul and Minneapolis, a distance of just over four hundred miles. Previously, the journey had taken nine and a half hours, and most passengers had

made it by sleeping-car train. The new Four Hundred did the trip in six and a half hours, with a steam locomotive, slightly modified for the purpose, and six cars of conventional design.

Next, over a different line, but still between the same cities, came the Burlington Zephyr, a three-car train with Diesel-electric propulsion, and following this, over yet a third route, came the maroon-and-orange Hiawatha, a train of six cars pulled by the first fully streamlined steam locomotive in America.

Service Doubled

Before very long, the Four Hundred and the Hiawatha had been doubled in service, with morning and afternoon streamliners, and the accommodation of the trains had been greatly increased, with the Four Hundred being replaced by a brand-new luxury train with Diesel-electric propulsion. Ten years later, the Four Hundred had grown to an eleven-car train, the Burlington Zephyrs were each nine-car

DENVER ZEPHYR AND SOUTHERN BELLE, two of America's famous luxury flyers. The attraction about these streamlined Diesel-electric trains is not merely the fact that they carry the passenger at high speed to his destination. It is a pleasure to travel in them, with their extraordinary variety of cars and armchair lounges, and people look forward to the journey for its own sake. Smooth and easy travel is accompanied by an absence of steam, smoke and cinders, which further increases the popularity of the Diesel streamliners. Well over one hundred of these streamline trains are now in service and many more are being built. On some routes there are separate flyers for Pullman and ordinary passengers. The Denver Zephyr is one of the expresses run by the Burlington line between Chicago and Denver, Colorado, and covers the thousand odd miles between the two cities in sixteen hours. The Silver King locomotive illustrated is hauling a train of coaches built entirely of stainless steel. The Southern Belle (below) runs between Kansas City and New Orleans, famous Mississippi port, and links the geographical centre of the United States with the Gulf of Mexico in a run of eight hundred and seventy miles.

trains, and the Hiawatha had expanded to a fifteen-car formation morning and evening. That is to say, instead of the total of fifteen cars which began the service, fifty-nine cars were now needed in each direction to carry the traffic, which amounted to between three and four thousand passengers daily over a distance greater than from London to Glasgow.

Most impressive of the American flyers are the luxury services operating between Chicago and the great cities of Los Angeles, San Francisco and Portland. Various companies run them over different routes, and their names are world famous. The Super Chief and El Capitan run twice weekly in each direction over a route of roughly twenty-three hundred miles, and over routes of similar length the City of Los Angeles and City of San Francisco run every fifth day. The City of Portland runs once every ten days.

All these services have a uniform schedule of just under forty hours. They start in the evening, and the passenger, spending two nights and the intervening day on board, arrives at his destination first thing in the morning. Roughly half the journey is through the Rocky Mountains, with mile after mile of heavy grades and severe curves, and very high speeds are necessary when the trains reach the open plains to keep up the average of just under sixty miles an hour for the whole journey. Runs booked at seventy and eighty miles an hour on flatter routes are common, even with trains of thirteen cars.

Night Streamliners

Among the fastest of the American flyers are the two night streamliners between Chicago and Denver, capital of Colorado, in the foothills of the Rockies. These are the Denver Zephyr and City of Denver, and they cover, roughly, a thousand and forty miles in sixteen hours, which entails an overall average speed of sixty-six miles an hour, all stops included. Four trains are required to maintain the service, and each one reels off at this speed more than thirty-one thousand miles a month.

Diesel Power Advantages

The advantage of Diesel power lies in the fact that on the longest journeys the locomotives can be worked right through without change. Crews are changed at divisional points, but the locomotive carries on. The bigger trains are headed by power plants of formidable dimensions, consisting of three seventy-foot power cars weighing well over four hundred tons and developing as much as six thousand horse-power. The lighter loads, such as those of the Super Chief and El Capitan, can be handled by two power cars of only four thousand horse-power.

This is another advantage of Diesel-electric propulsion. The number of power cars employed can be proportioned to the trainload, grades and speeds, and whether two, four or six thousand horse-power are needed, the single, twin or triple power units can all be controlled electrically from the one driving cab in front.

As a final example of the possibilities of Diesel power, the Denver Zephyr, consisting of six cars and a locomotive of four thousand horse-power, has made an experimental non-stop run for over a thousand miles between Chicago and Denver, completing the journey in just over twelve hours, or at an average speed of eighty-three miles an hour. It would be difficult, if not impossible, to make a non-stop run of this length, and at such a speed, with steam.

Not all the long American routes are double-track. Because of the loads and speeds of their trains and the frequency of the services, single track over considerable distances is often sufficient to carry the traffic on American railways, but the signalling engineers have had to develop the most elaborate methods to get the best use out of busy single tracks.

The most modern and extensive development is that known as centralized traffic control, and a controlled section may be anything in length from a few miles up to

NOT SO MECHANICAL. Track maintenance gang at work on a section of the Southern Pacific line. In spite of mechanization, which in America has reached its highest pitch of perfection, railway operation and maintenance still require a great deal of manual labour. The men here are using crowbars to lift ordinary, non-welded track.

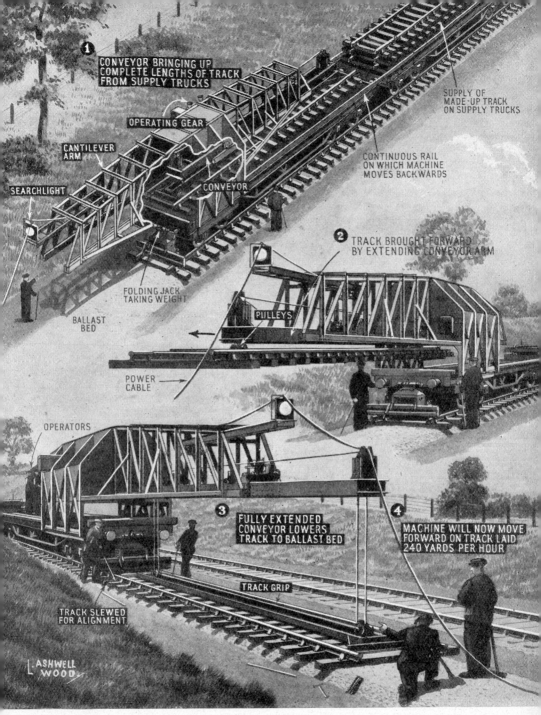

① CONVEYOR BRINGING UP COMPLETE LENGTHS OF TRACK FROM SUPPLY TRUCKS

OPERATING GEAR

CANTILEVER ARM

SEARCHLIGHT

CONVEYOR

SUPPLY OF MADE-UP TRACK ON SUPPLY TRUCKS

CONTINUOUS RAIL ON WHICH MACHINE MOVES BACKWARDS

FOLDING JACK TAKING WEIGHT

BALLAST BED

② TRACK BROUGHT FORWARD BY EXTENDING CONVEYOR ARM

PULLEYS

POWER CABLE

OPERATORS

③ FULLY EXTENDED CONVEYOR LOWERS TRACK TO BALLAST BED

TRACK GRIP

④ MACHINE WILL NOW MOVE FORWARD ON TRACK LAID 240 YARDS PER HOUR

TRACK SLEWED FOR ALIGNMENT

L. ASHWELL WOOD

MECHANICAL TRACK-LAYING—rapid modern system. The track is carried on flat trucks in ready-made sections, and a conveyor moves backwards and forwards on rails on top of the trucks picking up the sections and lowering them in position. As each section is laid, the whole train moves forward ready to lay the next one.

259

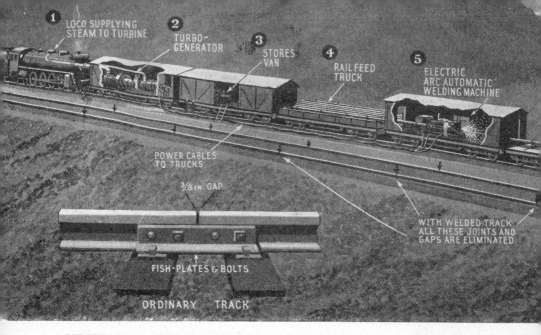

MECHANICAL WELDING OF RAILS. A welded rail has many advantages over one laid in separate sections with joints and fish-plates. For considerable distances, it can be welded into continuous lengths, the welds being virtually as strong as the rail itself, and there is consequently no jolting of wheels over joints, while the costs

more than a hundred miles. Somewhere along its length is situated the control cabin, which consists of an office containing an illuminated diagram of the whole length of track under control, and from this is operated the complete signalling installation of the section. All is done by means of electrical circuits, and in some cases even the switches giving access to the passing loops are operated from the same box.

Track circuits show on the diagrams where trains are standing or in motion, and in this way the crossing of trains at the loops is arranged with the least possible loss of time. On some routes, this has reduced the times of journeys by almost a half, which makes it possible to pass nearly twice as much traffic over the line as before.

Other main lines, however, are so busy that a single track is not sufficient to carry the traffic, and here the lines are doubled, or even quadrupled. On the New York Central System, between New York and Chicago, there are no fewer than four hundred and seventy miles of continuous four-track route, save for one short break of double-track two miles in length.

Great precautions have been taken to

promote the safety of the modern flyers. The favourite signalling method is automatic block signalling, usually with electric colour-light signals, working in conjunction with continuous inductive cab signalling on the engines. Continuous light signals are exhibited in the cab all the while the engine is running, and the driver has before him a constant picture of the state of the line ahead. In this respect, American signalling is well ahead of the signalling on European railways.

Time-Table Control

At the same time, however, on many of the country and branch lines, no signalling at all is in use. This sounds extraordinary, but America is well known as a land of extremes. On such lines, the movement of the trains is controlled entirely by the time-table, which gives the driver the authority to proceed. That is, he starts when it is time to do so, and any variation in the schedule from what the time-table lays down must be covered by a written order handed to him by the train despatcher at the station concerned.

The despatchers are in contact with one

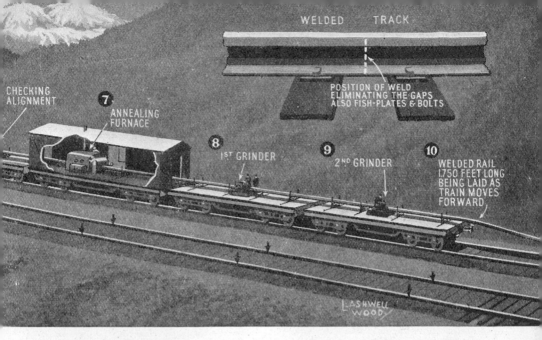

WELDED TRACK

CHECKING
ALIGNMENT

POSITION OF WELD
ELIMINATING THE GAPS
ALSO FISH-PLATES & BOLTS

7 ANNEALING
FURNACE

8 1ˢᵀ GRINDER

9 2ᴺᴰ GRINDER

10 WELDED RAIL
1,750 FEET LONG
BEING LAID AS
TRAIN MOVES
FORWARD

L. ASHWELL
WOOD

of track maintenance are reduced owing to the absence of rail points. Hitherto, to allow for the expansion and contraction of the steel resulting from changes of temperature, gaps have been left between each pair of rails. It is now known, however, that in a rigidly-held rail the tendency to expand can be ignored.

another by telegraph, and the importance of their written instructions, as, for example ordering one train to pass another at a different loop on a single line, needs no emphasis.

One serious handicap on American lines is the level crossing. The States are full of them. All lines originally were laid so that they crossed, not only highways but other railroads, at grade, or on the same level, and it is now costing tens of thousands of dollars in and around cities to build bridges or viaducts. The schemes are known as grade separation schemes, and streets and roads, as well as other lines, are being carried under or over the main lines for the first time. Obviously, with train speeds increasing as they are, the unprotected level crossing is a source either of great danger or tiresome delay.

It is because the great majority of the thousands of level crossings through the States are unprotected, that is, have no gates or signalmen, that American locomotives are required by law to be provided with a cowcatcher and a searchlight.

The cowcatcher, so-called, is also needed because many of the tracks are unfenced,

and is a kind of apron in front of the engine just above the track level. In the old days, this was one of the most distinctive features of American locomotives, but today, on the streamlined units, it has grown into a curved steel fender of almost futuristic design. Its purpose is to clear obstructions off the track; literally, to catch cattle that may have strayed on to the line.

Night Warning

The searchlight acts as a warning to all road users at night, and can be seen for miles as the express roars along the track. To make assurance doubly sure, many of the Diesel streamliners carry two headlights, one a fixed beam which throws a light along the track ahead, and the other a rotating light, known as the Mars headlight, which throws a tremendous oscillating beam high into the sky, so that the express can be seen at night by the glow above it long before it is anywhere in view from ground level. Apart from this, the only visual warning at the crossings are prominent signs inviting the unwary to "Stop, Look, Listen."

It is also compulsory to fit every loco-

261

motive with a bell and a hooter. The bell is for tolling when slow movement is taking place at stations, along streets, in yards and elsewhere, and the hooter must be sounded when travelling at speed on approaching a level crossing. Two short blasts and one long one, make up the recognized signal.

Main-Street Track

In pioneering days, it was not uncommon when the railway reached a town, to carry the track along the main street to the station, or depot, as though it were a tramway, and some of these street routes still persist, even in large cities. Until 1936, for example, such famous trains as the Twentieth Century Limited and the Empire State Express passed for a mile and a quarter up Washington Street in Syracuse, a main shopping centre in a city of two hundred thousand inhabitants in New York State. This has now been altered by building a new high-level line through the outskirts of the city to a new station, but it took six

years' work and cost the equivalent of six million pounds.

The larger a city grows, the more difficult and costly it is to build a new track. The railway suffers great loss of time in such locations, as speed must be reduced to fifteen miles an hour for the safety of road users. Level crossings of railway over railway are equally liable to cause delay.

There are also elaborate safety precautions, apart from signalling, on the trains themselves. Every axle-box throughout each high-speed train is provided with a thermo-couple installed in the journal, which causes a red light to glow in the driver's cab if the journal runs hot. Another light also glows on the affected coach as an indication of the seat of the trouble. Safety derailment flanges likewise form a part of every coach bogie, and keep the bogies from slewing round in the event of a derailment, so holding the cars more securely in line.

On long descending gradients through

ROCKY MOUNTAIN ROCKET, new American streamliner with Diesel-electric power for fast passenger traffic. This train runs daily between Chicago and both Denver and Colorado Springs, Colorado. It is in the United States that the Diesel-electric locomotive for fast passenger trains has reached its greatest development.

Through the Royal Gorge of the Arkansas River beneath the world's highest suspension bridge, more than a thousand feet above water level

AMERICAN LOADING GAUGE is less than three feet higher and eighteen inches wider than the British, but this difference has a remarkable effect on the size of American lomocotives and rolling stock. The largest American articulated locomotives, on the Union Pacific Railroad, are over a hundred and twelve feet in length and weigh, in running trim, some five hundred and thirty-four tons apiece. This represents the limit in size so far reached in the construction of steam locomotives and, on test, engines of this type have developed over seven thousand horse-power. The locomotive illustrated is one of rather smaller dimensions and is shown on an electrically operated turntable at Shaffers Crossing, Norfolk & Western Railroad, with an engine-shed of typical American round-house type in the background. The caboose below has no actual counterpart in Britain, though it approximates to the guard's brake. It houses the travelling office, headquarters and sleeping accommodation of the freight train crew and, for this reason, is much larger than its British relation. The raised "birdcage" on the roof is provided in order to give the train-crew a good look-out along the length of the train.

the mountains, water sprays are applied automatically to each wheel to prevent its overheating as the result of long brake application. An electric control governs the pressure of the brakes in relation to speed, and so helps to prevent skidding. Also, for the same purpose, there is an automatic sanding device which comes into operation ahead of each wheel in the event of an emergency application of the brakes.

On the Diesel-electric locomotives themselves, if any one of the Diesel engines should overheat, an alarm bell rings in the cab immediately. Another control would automatically stop the engines if the lubricating system were to fail, and a governor is provided to keep the speed of the locomotive within the prescribed limit over those sections of line where a speed restriction operates.

As regards electrification, all the noted expresses running from New York to Chicago and New Orleans on the Penn-

sylvania route are worked for a hundred and ninety miles by electrical power, that is, between New York and Harrisburg. This is part of the great Pennsylvania electrification scheme, which already covers over seven hundred and forty route-miles of line, and a total of more than two thousand three hundred miles of single track.

World's Busiest Line

The most important section electrified is that which connects New York with Washington, the administrative capital, by way of Philadelphia and Baltimore. For its length of two hundred and twenty-five miles, this is easily the busiest main line in the world. Also, in the average speed of its trains, it is the fastest, for no fewer than sixty expresses use it daily. Between them, they maintain an all-round average of fifty-seven miles an hour, including stops, for the whole distance.

Over this route, also, pass the famous

streamliners that link New York with the beautiful Florida-coast resorts, such as the Silver Meteor and the Tamiami Champion. Other famous trains using the line are the Southerner for New Orleans, and the Congressional and Senator for Washington. These latter run at even hourly intervals, and usually take just under four hours for the journey.

Such journeys are undertaken almost casually by the American. In a country where thousands of miles separate the principal cities, mileage has less meaning. All journeys are a question of proportion, and it is the longest journey possible in a country that sets the standard by which all the others are judged.

Comparative Distances

As an example, the longest journey for practical purposes in Great Britain is roughly one of four hundred miles, and a trip of a hundred miles, therefore, becomes a full quarter of the whole, and is subconsciously regarded as such. Applying the

same attitude in a country where the longest trip is, say, two thousand miles, it would be necessary to travel five hundred to produce the same effect on the mind.

It is not possible, however, to make so long a through journey in the United States as in Canada. In Canada one can stay in the same train right across the continent, from Montreal to Vancouver. In the States, the great middle-west city of Chicago acts as a kind of barrier to all through travel, and no coaches or sleeping cars whatever are worked through from the lines east of it to those leading west from the city. All passengers from the east to San Francisco and Los Angeles, or any other Pacific coast port, must, therefore, change trains in Chicago, and very often change stations as well.

Nevertheless, the distances covered in the same train are considerable, and much greater use is made of sleeping accommodation than in Great Britain. The sleeping cars are built by the well-known Pullman Company at their works just outside Chicago,

CORONATION SCOT, photographed alongside the Royal Blue express of the Baltimore & Ohio Railroad, during the Coronation Scot's tour of Canada and the United States, which ended at the World Fair in Chicago just before the Second World War. For some miles the two trains ran side by side on a specially-cleared track, not racing, but keeping steadily together, and making an impressive finale for the tour, after which the Coronation Scot was on view at the Fair. Millions of people saw it there and during the tour, and were able to compare it with Canadian and American trains. The difference between the British and American construction gauges for rolling stock is clearly apparent in this view. The Royal Blue has since been turned over from steam to Diesel-electric power, and streamlined Diesel-electric locomotives are now being built to take over the working of the Empire Builder, seen in the lower view. This express, which is worked by the Burlington and Great Northern Railways between Chicago and Seattle, is here photographed being hauled by a Great Northern 4-8-4 steam locomotive over a typical stretch of line in the Rockies.

the builders, also, of most of the luxury vehicles used in the daytime.

At one time the Pullman cars were not only built by the Pullman Company, but were owned and run by them as well. The company paid a rental to the railways for permission to run the cars in their trains, and made its profit by the supplementary fares charged for the use of the accommodation. Over seven thousand such cars were maintained in a far-spreading car pool, and in one year alone Pullman cars ran altogether over a thousand million miles.

Anti-Trust Law

That was all altered in 1914, however, when a law known as the Sherman Anti-Trust Law was passed, under which the Pullman Company was compelled to separate its building business from the operating side of its activities. It chose to continue in the car-building business, so now the cars are operated by a separate company.

The first American sleeping accommoda-

tion was in cars which could be changed at will from day cars to sleepers, and quite a number of them are the same today. As night draws near, on a long journey, the porter in charge of the car prepares it for night use. Seats are drawn out to form the lower berths, and the sides of the car are let down to form the upper berths. On these the bedding is placed, and curtains are then drawn along both sides of the centre aisle to give some measure of privacy. The beds are wide and comfortable, and the only disadvantage in such an arrangement is the acrobatic performance necessary to dress and undress inside the berth, behind the shelter of the curtains. Large toilet rooms are available at each end of the cars.

At the rear of this older type of sleeping car is a compartment known as the drawing room, a completely enclosed room with two or three beds, which can be engaged at a slightly higher cost than one of the sections. At one time, this was the most

SWEATING-ON THE TYRE OF A DRIVING WHEEL, achieved by the natural expansion and contraction of metal according to temperature. The tyre is heated until it expands sufficiently to be forced over the rim of the wheel, and by contraction in cooling, it fits so tightly as to assist considerably in keeping the tyre securely in position.

RAILWAY SHOPS AT SACRAMENTO, CALIFORNIA, where heavy repairs to Southern Pacific locomotives are carried out. They can be seen in various stages of assembly. In the foreground is a pair of locomotive main frames: the boiler of the next engine has the lagging partly removed, showing the fire-box construction; beyond is a boiler covered with asbestos insulation, ready for the thin sheet-steel covering.

luxurious form of sleeping accommodation available, but a great many more varieties of sleeping berths are in use today.

There are, for example, the roomettes, which are small rooms dovetailed into one another along both sides of a central corridor. In the daytime the roomette is occupied as a sort of lounge, and there is no sign of a bed. The passenger is free to remain as long as he pleases on one of the comfortable lounge seats.

At night, however, when he wishes to sleep, the bed, folded up against the wall, slides down at a touch all ready for use. More capacious than these are the single bedrooms and double bedrooms which are to be had on most of the night expresses, and on some even a complete suite can be obtained, including a private shower-bath. Such accommodation costs the equivalent of British first-class fare with the Pullman

supplement in addition, though actually the cost per mile works out at a lower figure in the United States.

For day use, there are equally luxurious parlour or lounge cars of many different kinds, including the popular observation cars which bring up the rear of most American express trains. These are a development from the early open-end cars, which had a platform on which passengers used to take a somewhat draughty seat in fine weather. Modern observation cars have the rear ends completely enclosed in a semicircular bow window of glass, which on some lines has earned them the name of solarium lounges. Occasional tables and armchairs, and the most modern furnishings, colourings and lighting effects, give them quite an exceptional beauty.

The dining cars are also magnificently decorated, many of them conveying all the

VERY COMFORTABLE, a Pullman car section turned into sleeping quarters for the night. The curtains in front can be drawn right across the berth, giving a measure of privacy. Compartments such as this form armchair seats during the day—two double seats facing each other—and are arranged on each side of a central gangway.

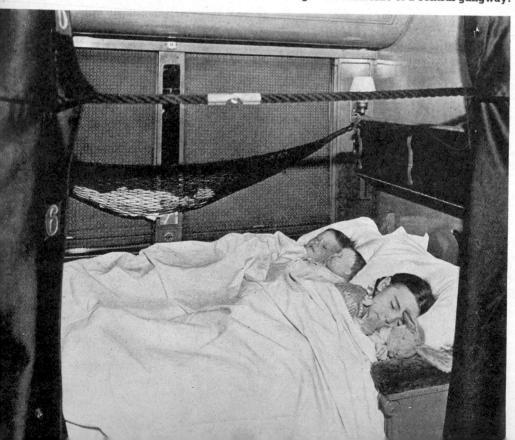

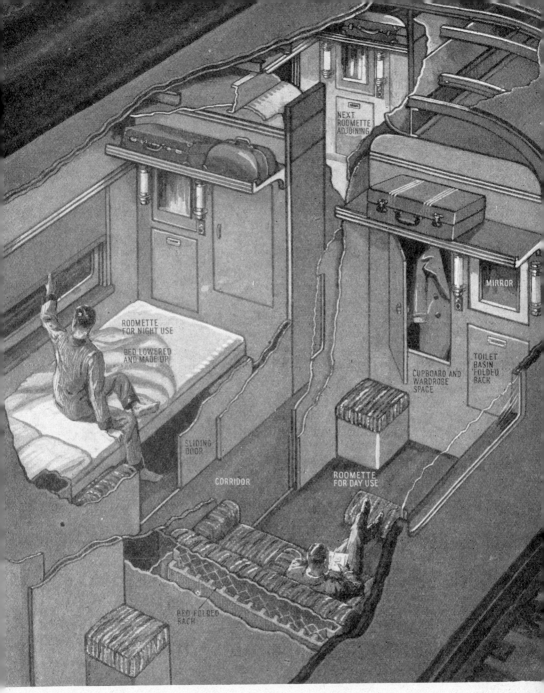

Labels within illustration:
NEXT ROOMETTE ADJOINING
MIRROR
ROOMETTE FOR NIGHT USE
BED LOWERED AND MADE UP
CUPBOARD AND WARDROBE SPACE
TOILET BASIN FOLDED BACK
SLIDING DOOR
CORRIDOR
ROOMETTE FOR DAY USE
BED FOLDED BACK

AMERICAN SLEEPING BERTH of a more luxurious type. Pullman roomette for day or night use. Like the older-type Pullman sleeping berth illustrated on the opposite page, these roomettes are arranged on each side of a central corridor, but are completely self-contained. Sliding doors shut them off from the corridor, and they are large enough to provide the luxury of a private sitting-room during the day.

illusion of a restaurant, especially at night. Part of the car may be windowless, and along the enamelled and decorated walls are seats and concealed lighting. At the ends there may be the more usual transverse tables.

Novelty appeal is the keynote of all these interior coach schemes. Nor is the passenger limited to a set meal, but has a choice of as wide a variety of courses as in a regular restaurant. Further, few long distance trains have a dining car only; on many there are buffets and light refreshment cars, and on some trains more than one.

American third-class passengers travel in what are invariably called coaches, to distinguish them from the Pullmans and first-class lounge vehicles. In the modern coach there are reclining chairs for each passenger, and each chair can be tilted to any angle its occupant desires. The chairs thus provide comfortable accommodation both by day and by night. On some important main lines it has become the practice to make up trains entirely of these reclining-chair streamlined coaches with a dining car, and often a buffet-lounge and observation car as well, and to run them at almost, if not quite, the same speeds as the first-class Pullman streamliners.

Third-Class Streamliners

The third-class passenger is as well catered for as the first-class, and most of the famous first-class flyers have their counterparts in third-class coach streamliners. Between New York and Chicago, for example, on the New York Central System, the first-class Twentieth Century Limited is run very closely by the all-coach Pacemaker, which takes only an hour longer on the journey. Similarly, on the Pennsylvania

ONE WAY OF LOADING COAL OR ORE, the conveyor belt used as a chute above the trucks. By means of a moving belt, the loading can be regulated more effectively than with a plain chute working purely by gravity. As each truck is filled, it is moved from under the mouth of the chute, and another one takes its place for loading.

Labels on image:
CARRIER LIFTS TO DISENGAGE
SHOE TRANSFERRING PART OF WEIGHT OF FRAME TO BOOSTER BOGIE
SWIVEL JOINT EXHAUST TO CHIMNEY
HYDRAULIC CONTROL PIPES
AXLE PINION
IDLER
REAR END OF BOGIE
CRANKSHAFT PINION
SLIDING PLATE
VALVE SPINDLE
CONNECTING ROD
CYLINDER BLOCK
VALVE SHAFT
AXLE-BOX OF DRIVING WHEEL
STEAM PIPE
VALVE ECCENTRIC ROD
PISTON IN CYLINDER
PART OF SUPPORTING BRACKET
EXHAUST PIPE CONNECTS WITH JOINT ABOVE
—R.B.WAY—

BOOSTER BOGIE, device used on a locomotive to give extra push at starting or on heavy gradients. Comparatively small cylinders and pistons drive the wheels of the bogie through gearing and can be cut out of action, like the free wheel of a bicycle, when the speed is sufficiently high. Boosters are usually fitted to the small diameter wheels under the locomotive cab, and provide valuable auxiliary power.

line, the first-class Broadway Limited has its counterpart in the third-class Trail Blazer, while the equally famous all-Pullman Super Chief, running between Chicago and Los Angeles, is matched by the all-coach El Capitan.

Taking tickets for these long journeys is generally a complicated business, because it includes the reservation of sleeping accommodation or a numbered seat in a chair car. The time-tables, or folders as they are called, show how each train is made up, and any accommodation available can be booked in accordance with the plan.

Nearly all long-distance trains carry a valet, a barber and a stewardess, and for the entertainment of the passengers there are radio sets, current magazines and a library. Some even carry professional entertainers, while on business trains there is usually a stenographer.

The lavishness of the service frequently results in an additional service charge being made, which is not surprising. To take one extreme example, the staff riding with the Twentieth Century Limited, on its long run from New York to Chicago, is never less than forty-four, and consists of the chief Pullman conductor, a Pullman porter or attendant for each sleeping car, the train secretary, barber, lady's-maid and dining-car and refreshment-car staffs. The latter staffs consist of two chief stewards, two chefs, six cooks and fourteen waiters, and, in addition, there is an attendant for each of the bars in the two lounges. The operating side requires a conductor, a baggageman and two brakemen.

Make-up of Train

The complete train of sixteen cars is made up as follows: first comes the baggage and mail car, and this is followed by a buffet-lounge; then comes a group of five single-

ELEVATED RAILWAY CROSSING, photographed from a Chicago sky-scraper. The "elevated" still runs in Chicago, with all its accompanying noise and nuisance, and this crossing over Lake and Wells Streets is reputed to be the busiest on any elevated railway in the world. Two hundred and twenty-four trains pass over it in one hour during the rush period, and as each train consists usually of six cars, there is a constant rattle and roar in the streets below.

room sleeping cars; the two dining cars follow this, in the centre of the train; following these is another group of five sleepers, and finally a second buffet-lounge and the observation car.

One of the most distinctive features of the working of such long-distance trains is that the cars always run in the same order. On reaching the end of the journey, the whole train is turned round a triangle for the return journey, so that the same order is maintained.

All express trains are now completely air-conditioned, a great boon both in summer and winter, and are still becoming more and more luxurious. At one time, it seemed almost as though the road and the air would take the bulk of passenger traffic, but the railway gives a comfort that can be found in neither of the other services.

Rail Travel Revolutionized

What a contrast against the old days when the pioneer track unfolded itself across the western prairies! Then the mere fact that one could be reasonably sure of reaching one's destination in safety was a tremendous step forward. The modern flyers are like moving hotels, providing all the conveniences of a first-class hotel in any large city, and a journey in them, far from being a pilgrimage of wearying monotony, is an experience worth having for the mere pleasure of the trip.

Road and air undoubtedly have a part to play in future transport over long distances, each in the manner best suited to its own sphere, but in a vast country like America, not only the heavy freight traffic, but also the great bulk of the passenger traffic, will long be carried by that most character-istic of American institutions—the railroad.

274

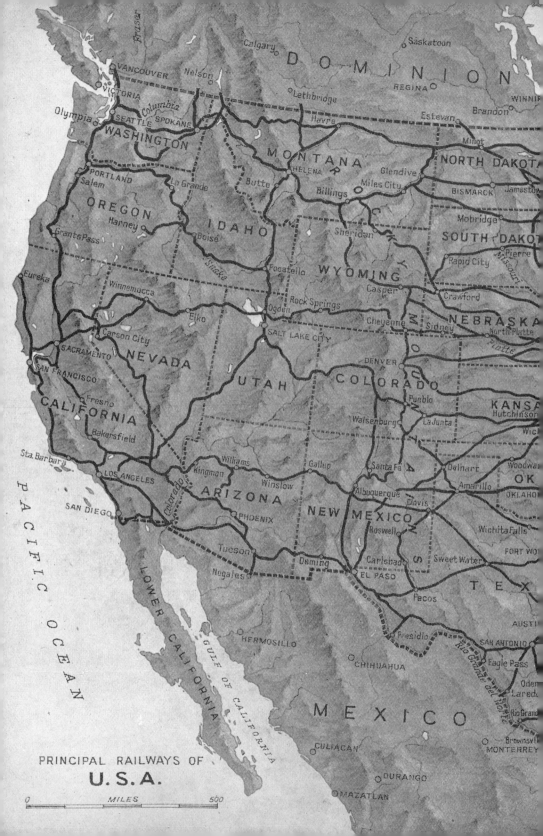

PRINCIPAL RAILWAYS OF
U.S.A.

0   MILES   500

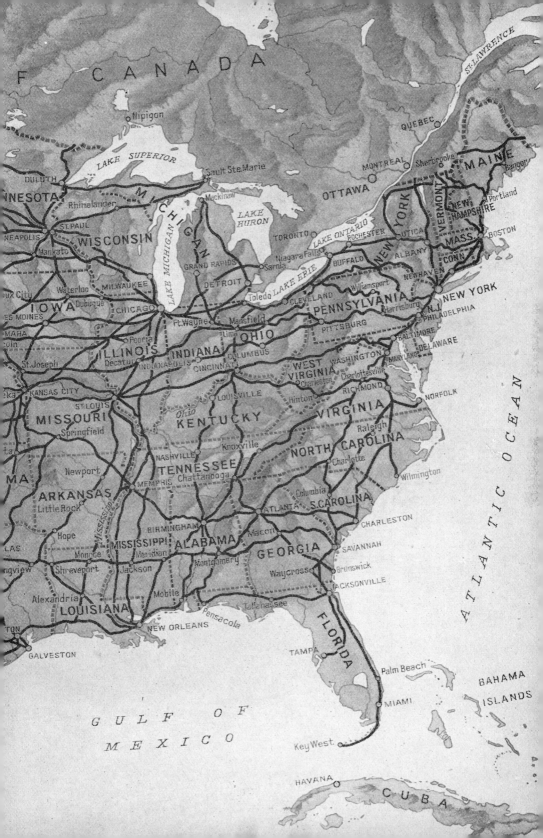

East portal of the five-mile
Connaught Tunnel, on the
Canadian Pacific Railway,
the longest tunnel in Canada

CHAPTER FOURTEEN

FROM ATLANTIC TO PACIFIC ACROSS CANADA

IN Montreal stands one of the finest and most up-to-date stations on the American continent, a magnificent building through which all trains are worked electrically, so that there is no smoke nuisance in the middle of the city.

The station is arranged so that any future buildings around it will have their ground floors on a level with the concourse, although this is actually above the level of the tracks. Massive pillars have been built into the area surrounding the station to take the weight of any such future development.

There are five floors altogether, the top two of which are offices. Below these is the concourse, with wide stairways and escalators giving access to the platforms, which are built high as in British practice, so that they are level with the carriage floors. Below these again is a sub-basement for the handling of goods and parcels.

Modern Canada

This is the new Central Station of Canadian National Railways, interesting because of the general impression, current in many parts of the world, that Canadian railways consist mainly of single tracks across snow-covered prairies. The prairies are there, of course, in the vast spaces of the west, and so, in the winter, is the snow. But this is Montreal, in the busy eastern provinces, from which trains cross the border into the still busier cities of Boston and Chicago.

Canadian lines are all of standard gauge, and there are two main railway systems, the Canadian National and the Canadian Pacific. The latter is world-famous as the first to cross the continent and find a way through the Rockies, but the Canadian National, an amalgamation of a number of smaller companies, is actually the larger. Owning altogether over twenty-three thousand route miles of line, it is the largest single railway system on the continent, nearly twice as large as the largest American company. The Canadian Pacific, however, with its magnificent line of steamers, partly encircles the world by sea as well; it also owns a chain of big hotels.

Crossing a Continent

Both companies cross the whole width of the Dominion with their own tracks, from the Atlantic to the Pacific, and provide the longest continuous railway journeys in the British Commonwealth, the longest, with one exception, in the whole world. That of the Canadian Pacific is three thousand three hundred and sixty-four miles in length, while the Canadian National route is even longer with three thousand seven hundred and seventy-one miles.

Altogether, there are three routes through the Rockies, two owned by the Canadian Pacific and one by the Canadian National. The former company finds its way through this mountain chain by way of the Kicking Horse Pass and Crow's Nest Pass, and the latter by way of the Yellowhead Pass, the route, curiously enough, originally surveyed for the Canadian Pacific. It was abandoned by the pioneers as being too long, and they chose the far more difficult Kicking Horse Pass instead.

Although the idea of a railway across Canada in the early days was slow in taking shape, it was eventually laid so rapidly, once it was begun, that the feat still remains one of the wonders of railway engineering. To appreciate it fully, however, one has to understand the difficulties that were met with after the prairies had been crossed and the track was entering the wild and lonely mountain gorges.

Through the Mountains

Here, for over six hundred miles, the line travels through range after range of mountains. Over three hundred miles of the route, in fact, had to be cut from solid rock.

In addition, fourteen rivers had to be diverted from their courses by means of tunnels, and innumerable others had to be crossed.

In spite of this, and the speed at which it was laid, the work was in no way scamped. Only over certain sections were steeper gradients than desirable tolerated as a temporary measure, and many ravines bridged by timber trestles run up with timber cut in the neighbouring forests.

Relocation Schemes

This explains why, in recent years, the Canadian Pacific has carried out a number of relocation schemes on its main line west of Calgary. In the Yoho Valley, for example, there was originally a gradient which for three miles was at the terribly severe slope of one-in-twenty-three and, as traffic increased, this proved a formidable obstacle to the working of eastbound freight. A single freight train of seven hundred tons required the services of no fewer than four one-hundred-and-fifty-ton locomotives to get it over the summit.

To overcome this Big Hill, as it became known, an improved route consisting of two spiral tunnels was opened. This lengthened the line by four and a half miles, but reduced the gradient to only one-in-forty-five.

Another steep gradient was to be found in Rogers Pass, four thousand feet above sea level, where there was an abrupt fall of nearly three thousand feet in twenty-two miles.

Not only did this section make excessive demands on motive power, but the exposed location of the line made it necessary to cover miles of it with timber snowsheds, as

APPROACH-VIADUCT AND EMBANKMENT to the new Central Terminal of Canadian National Railways in Montreal. All trains are worked in and out of the station by electricity, which accounts for the clear atmosphere and absence of smoke and soot in the city. Current is supplied to the locomotives by means of overhead conductors, and electricity also controls all signalling and records the movement of traffic.

SIGNALLING BY PUSH-BUTTON. Illuminated track diagram in control cabin of the new Central Terminal at Montreal. The diagram is over thirty-four feet in length and has over six hundred control buttons. In the foreground is a centre panel with seventy push-buttons, twenty-four telephone connexions and ten telegraph sets.

the route would otherwise have been completely blocked during the winter months.

It was, therefore, decided that the Rogers Pass section should be cut completely out of the route, and this was done by means of the Connaught Tunnel. Five miles in length, this both reduced the maximum altitude by over five hundred feet and abolished the curvature of the old route to the extent of seven complete circles.

Some revolutionary methods were adopted in the boring of this tunnel. With the help of a pioneer bore, nine feet wide and seven feet high, the piercing was accomplished in just over two years. The main tunnel was divided into short sections only fifteen hundred feet in length, and each of these was entered from the pioneer bore, thus providing a working face in each direction.

Instead of the usual two gangs working from each end towards the centre, thirty-two gangs were at work in the Connaught Tunnel simultaneously. This is the longest tunnel in Canada, and cost a million and a quarter pounds to build.

Great Viaduct

The Canadian Pacific second route through the Rockies, by way of the Crow's Nest Pass, is notable for a huge viaduct near Lethbridge, Alberta, which is one of the biggest structures of its kind in the world. Here again, the line originally consisted of some steep gradients and severe curves, which were cut out of the route when the viaduct was built.

It consists of plate girder spans carried on thirty-three trestles standing on concrete pedestals, and at its highest point carries the rails over three hundred feet above the valley floor. Its total length is five thousand

ALL-STEEL WAGON FOR IRON ORE, belonging to the Canadian National Railways. A type introduced to deal with shipments of this heavy mineral from the Steep Rock Iron Mines near Atikokan, Ontario, a hundred and fifty miles southwest of Port Arthur. Iron ore is one of the heaviest freights dealt with by the Canadian National Railway.

HOISTING A LOCOMOTIVE in the erecting shop preparatory to lowering it on to the running track. The weight is taken by two overhead cranes, travelling on rails on top of the curved girders across the roof of the workshop. These are driven and controlled by electricity, and raise the engine clear of all obstructions.

three hundred and twenty feet, or just over a mile, and twelve thousand tons of steel were used in its construction.

The route of the Canadian National, through the Yellowhead Pass, is entirely different in conception from either of those of the Canadian Pacific. Although to anyone who knows the Rockies the idea would seem absurd, the engineers of the company that built the line were enjoined to keep all gradients down to one-in-two-hundred-and-fifty.

Amazingly enough, the final result was that the line was eventually carried through the entire Rocky Mountain territory with no gradient greater than one-in-a-hundred.

For the last two hundred and fifty miles to Vancouver, at which port the rival lines terminate, nature has forced both the Canadian competitors into the same valleys,

first the Thompson River valley and then the valley of the greater Fraser River, which for some distance flows in what is more like a canyon than a river valley.

Rival Routes

The layout of the two lines here is extraordinary. Each keeps strictly to its own side of the river, until at Cisco they change places by means of great separate bridges. The Pacific, which was first in the field, chose all the best locations, and the National engineers, forced to whichever side of the river the Pacific did not want, had a far more difficult task in finding a path for their track.

In the entire two hundred and fifty miles, except at the Vancouver end, there are not more than two rail bridges across the river between the two main lines.

Such were the conditions dictated by

competition in the past. As a result, the improvement in working which might have been brought about by mutual agreement, had it been possible to operate the two single main lines as a double track, is now out of the question.

Competition in Speed

On the eastern side of the Dominion, however, the situation between the two companies is very different. Here certain agreements have been entered into for the smoother working of the train time-tables, although even these agreements were preceded by some remarkable rivalry in speed, which at one time put the Pacific in possession of the fastest railway run in the world.

This was in 1931, when the Canadian National accelerated two of its fastest trains, the International Limited and the Inter-city Limited, to cover the three hundred and thirty-four miles between Montreal and Toronto in six hours flat.

The Canadian Pacific replied with a time of six and a quarter hours over its three-hundred-and-forty-mile route between the

TWO CANADIAN SEMI-STREAMLINED LOCOMOTIVES. Above, is shown a Jubilee type Canadian Pacific locomotive, weighing with its tender four hundred and sixty-one thousand pounds. Tender capacity is seven thousand gallons of water and twelve tons of coal. The driving wheels have a diameter of six feet eight inches and the total overall length is eighty feet five inches. The Canadian National Railways locomotive (left) has a cylindrical tender, carried on twelve wheels, and the 4-8-4 wheel arrangement. Tender capacity in this case is eleven thousand seven hundred gallons of water and twenty tons of coal. In the early days there was considerable rivalry between these two great railway companies in Canada, and each tried to outdo the other in speed. However, a compromise was eventually reached on the eastern side of Canada and now there is an arrangement by which both companies pool their traffic and make use of each other's lines as well as rolling stock between Montreal and Toronto, and between Montreal, Ottawa and Quebec.

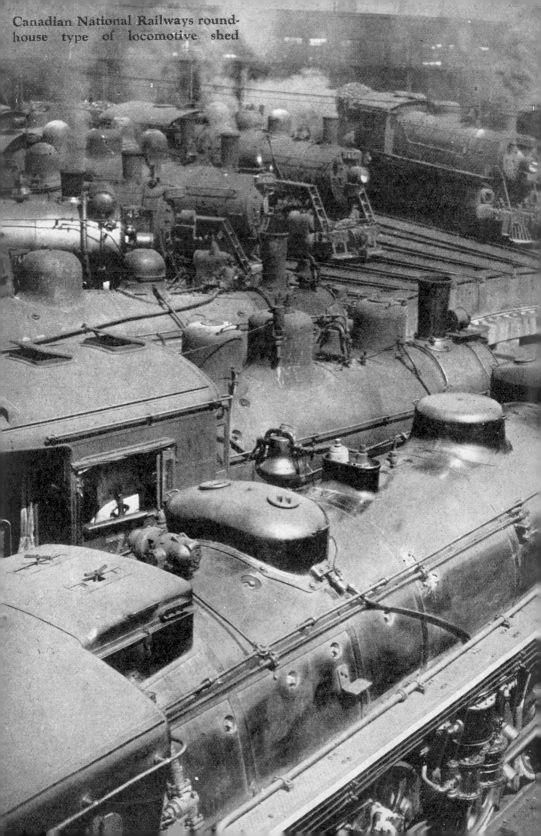

Canadian National Railways round-
house type of locomotive shed

THROUGH THE CANADIAN ROCKIES

by different routes, two pictures giving some idea of the mountainous country traversed by Canadian railways. The top photograph shows a train of the Canadian Pacific Railway, which was the first to cross the continent and the only one to do so in one continuously-planned line. The original route lies through the famous Kicking Horse Pass; it had some amazingly steep gradients, but these have since been rebuilt and reduced. There is now another to the southward, belonging to the same company, which makes its way along the Canadian-American border by way of the Crow's Nest Pass. In the lower view is the Continental Limited of Canadian National Railways, seen in the Rockies of British Columbia with the snow-capped peak of Mount Robson, thirteen thousand feet above sea-level, in the background. The Canadian National route travels north of the Canadian Pacific by way of the Yellowhead Pass, and has the distinction of having found its way through the mountainous district of the Rockies with no gradient greater than one-in-a-hundred, an amazing engineering feat.

same cities, and as a considerable length of this is single track, some particularly high speeds were needed for timekeeping. That is to say, trains using the same track in opposite directions, needed to arrive very punctually at the passing loops for smooth working.

The Pacific expresses, therefore, had to cover certain sections of line at an average of over sixty-eight miles an hour, including stops, and this meant that in places they were reaching speeds of upwards of eighty miles an hour. New 4-6-4 locomotives were built specially for the service, but the pace was too hot to last.

The result was that the two companies entered into an agreement to pool their traffic, not only between Montreal and Toronto, but also between Montreal and the other great cities of Ottawa and Quebec.

In the Pool Trains, as they are called, the stock of both companies is incorporated, and the stations of both railways are used interchangeably. For example, the International Limited of the Canadian National, complete with Canadian National loco-

motive, now starts in Montreal from the Windsor Street station of the Canadian Pacific, and crosses over to the Canadian National tracks outside the city.

Unfortunately, one result of the pooling was that in certain cases speeds were reduced, so that now the fastest time between Montreal and Ottawa is six and a half hours; but the advantages in other directions are indisputable.

The Canadian National system has some fine engineering structures, one of which is world famous. This is the enormous Quebec Bridge, which links the lines on the north and south banks of the St. Lawrence River, just to the west of the city.

Greatest Cantilever Span

The Quebec Bridge boasts the largest single cantilever span in existence, just eighteen hundred feet in length. It clears the surface of the river by a hundred and fifty feet, and contains no fewer than sixty-six thousand tons of steel.

The story of its erection is one of tragedy, and yet one of eventual triumph over early

ANCHOR SPAN 500 FT LONG

"K" TRUSSES

ANCHOR STANCHIONS

SPAN DIAGRAMMATICALLY CUT AWAY

FOOTWA

APPROACH SPAN

GRANITE FACING

COMPRESSION CHORD

CONCRETE PYLON

ST LAWRENCE RIVER

6-KNOT CURRENT

14 FT

DIFFERENCE BETWEEN HIGH AND LOW TIDE

FORE-SHORE

L. ASHWELL WOOD

QUEBEC RAILWAY BRIDGE
THE LONGEST CANTILEVER SPAN IN THE WORLD
Shortens the C.N.R. route Halifax-Winnipeg by 200 miles

SECTION OF ONE MAIN TOWER 310 FT HIGH

CANTILEVER SPAN 580 FT LONG

CENTRE SPAN 640 FT LONG HELD BY CANTILEVER SPANS

2-RAILWAY TRACKS

FOOTWAY

16 FT ROAD

SECTION OF DECK AT TOWER !

150 FT HEADROOM

BEARING PIVOT PINS

STONE PIER

BEARING SHOE

26,000 TON C.P.R. LINER

SUNKEN CAISSON FILLED WITH CONCRETE

DEPTH OF WATER 200 FT

MUD

ROCK BED

disasters. At one time, indeed, it seemed as though the building of the bridge was under some fatal spell.

The first designs were agreed upon as far back as the year 1901, and work was commenced upon it by an American firm. The bridge then under construction was a cantilever type, as at present, but considerably less substantial than the existing bridge, as only forty thousand tons of steel were allowed for, or less than two-thirds the present amount.

Six years work had gone into the erection of the south cantilever, and seventeen thousand tons of steel had been put together, when, one afternoon in August, 1907, the lower chords of the anchor arms suddenly gave way, and the whole cantilever collapsed into the river without warning.

This was the first disaster. Of eighty-six men working on the arm at the time, only eleven were saved. In addition, there followed the complex task of cutting up this mass of steelwork, and one even more complex of designing a bridge that would be beyond the reach of another collapse.

American, Canadian and British engineers were called into consultation, and finally the existing design was chosen out of thirty-five different designs submitted. To undertake the construction, two Canadian firms combined to form a separate company, and were required by the government to deposit a quarter of a million pounds before the work was allowed to proceed.

Removing the Wreckage

Nearly a year was spent in clearing away the wreckage of the collapsed cantilever, a task which was accomplished by means of explosives and oxy-acetylene torches, and the new bridge was begun in 1909. The design called for two diamond-shaped cantilevers, each consisting of an anchor arm over five hundred feet long on the shore side, and a cantilever arm five hundred and eighty feet long extending towards the centre of the river.

Linking these cantilevers, there was to be

INTERIOR VIEW OF ROYAL TRAIN. The Canadian Royal Train was specially fitted for the visit of their Majesties to Canada and the United States of America just before the outbreak of the Second World War. The photograph shows the general arrangement of the furnishings and decorative scheme of the Queen's boudoir.

AT WORK ON A CANADIAN LOCOMOTIVE, with some slight assistance from a crane. All locomotive overhaul and repair work is of a heavy nature, and even small parts, comparatively, have to be lifted and swung into position by mechanical means. Great accuracy is necessary in locomotive erection, and the various moving parts must be machined and bored to fine tolerances to ensure trouble-free working.

a central span of six hundred and forty feet, which, with the two cantilever arms, made up the main span of the bridge of eighteen hundred feet across the river. The bridge floor was to be eighty-eight feet wide, and to carry a double railway track, a roadway and two footways.

Owing to Canadian winter conditions, it was necessary to suspend work for three months out of the year, and to concentrate as much work as possible into the months that remained. The job was consequently a long one, and not till 1916 were the two cantilever arms finished and ready to receive the immense centre span of six hundred and forty feet.

This had been put together at Sillery Cove, some three and a half miles down the river, the idea being to float it into position

on pontoons, and then raise it to the necessary height by means of cranes and lifting tackle on the ends of the cantilevers.

These alone weighed four hundred and forty tons, two hundred and twenty tons on the end of each arm. The span itself weighed over five thousand tons, and it had to be raised one hundred and fifty feet.

Second Tragedy

All went well at first. The span was successfully floated to the site by seven powerful tugs, and there moored in position to be taken in hand by the special lifting tackle. This was connected, the span was lifted until it was about thirty feet above the river, and then, again without warning, a vital part of the lifting gear collapsed.

In a few seconds, the whole span had

COAL HOPPER 20 TONS

STREAMLINED TOP CASING

SAFET VALVE

REGULATOR HANDLE

INNER FIRE-BOX

AIR-BRAKE RESERVOIR

CANADIAN NATIONAL

WATER 11,700 GALLONS

OUTER FIRE-BOX

ASBESTOS BOILER LAGGING

FEED SCREW

FLEXIBLE COUPLING

MECHANICAL STOKER

6401

RUNNI BOARD

TRAILING BOGIE-TRUCK

BRAKE HANGERS

6 FT. 5 IN. COUPLED WHEELS

ASHWELL WOOD

CANADIAN NATIONAL SEMI-STREAMLINED LOCOMOTIVE used on long-distance runs with express passenger trains. The locomotive has a wide fire-box, spread across the main frames, and is fitted with screw-feed mechanical stoking similar to that used on the larger American engines. Like all American and Canadian

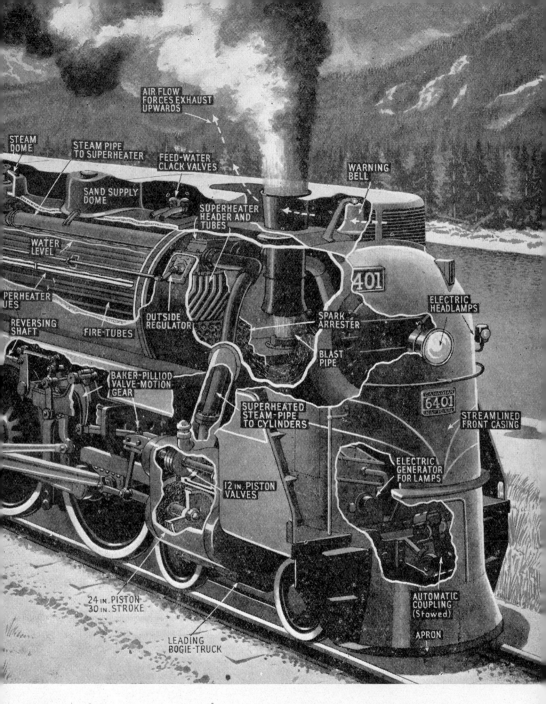

AIR FLOW FORCES EXHAUST UPWARDS

STEAM DOME

STEAM PIPE TO SUPERHEATER

FEED-WATER CLACK VALVES

WARNING BELL

SAND SUPPLY DOME

SUPERHEATER HEADER AND TUBES

WATER LEVEL

401

PERHEATER UES

ELECTRIC HEADLAMPS

REVERSING SHAFT

FIRE-TUBES

OUTSIDE REGULATOR

SPARK ARRESTER

BLAST PIPE

BAKER-PILLIOD VALVE-MOTION GEAR

CANADIAN 6401 NATIONAL

SUPERHEATED STEAM-PIPE TO CYLINDERS

STREAMLINED FRONT CASING

ELECTRIC GENERATOR FOR LAMPS

12 IN. PISTON VALVES

24 IN. PISTON 30 IN. STROKE

AUTOMATIC COUPLING (Stowed)

APRON

LEADING BOGIE-TRUCK

engines, it has a warning bell for use when running over unprotected crossings in cities and towns, and a steel apron type of cowcatcher is employed because of unfenced track. Interesting points are the Baker-Pilliod valve motion and the electric generator on the front of the engine for supplying current to the electrical apparatus.

gone to the bottom of the river, a mass of steel twisted beyond recognition, and the river here is so deep that it became a total loss. Work was begun immediately on a replacement span, and the first idea was to build it on a falsework a hundred and fifty feet above the river, and so float it on enormous pylons at the exact height at which it was needed.

But the risks of towing such a top-heavy arrangement were too great to be considered seriously. The slightest wind would have made the whole structure unmanageable, and a danger to everybody in the vicinity, so eventually the previous procedure was repeated.

Success at Last

This time there were no mishaps. The giant span was lifted in stages of two feet at a time, and fifteen minutes intervals of rest were allowed between the stages. The whole operation occupied in all three days, and though some anxiety was caused

by a high wind on the third night, the work was successfully completed on the fourth day.

The first train passed over the bridge on the seventeenth of October, 1917, and seven weeks later this monumental structure came into regular service. It is used by all the principal Canadian National trains between Montreal and Quebec, and also by those from Halifax and other points in the Maritime Provinces.

Canadian winter conditions have been responsible for some unusual engineering developments, one of which is found in the train-ferry service in the Gulf of St. Lawrence, between Cape Tormentine on the mainland, and Borden on Prince Edward Island.

In winter time the strait is a mass of ice from one side to the other, a mass made much more broken and irregular by pack-ice, which drifts in from the gulf, and rugged ice-bergs.

For this reason, the principal railway

SPERRY DETECTOR CAR, designed to detect internal flaws in the rails as it passes over them. The record is made on a roll of paper, which moves over the table in front of the operator at a speed equivalent to that of the coach. By magnetic means, all defects are detected by a shoe passing along the railhead and indicated automatically by a pen on the paper roll. Rubber stamps on the right of the table are used by the operator to mark the roll with various kinds of identifying information. When a defect is indicated, a splash of white paint is dropped on the affected rail. By the size of the mark on the roll, the relative seriousness of the defect can be gauged; if it appears to be a dangerous defect, the car is stopped so that a more accurate hand test may be carried out.

CANADIAN RAILWAYS IN WINTER, scene on the Canadian National system. Rotary and other type snow-ploughs are used for keeping the lines clear during heavy falls, but there are times when men and shovels are the only answer in an emergency. The snow on the side of this cutting appears to have caved in during a sudden thaw.

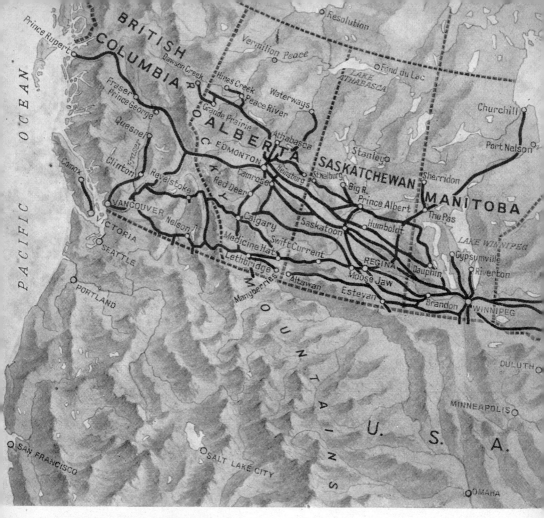

ferry steamer, the Prince Edward Island, is designed to act as an ice-breaker as well as a ferry steamer. For six feet both above and below the water line, the steel plating of the hull is of a uniform thickness of one inch, and the plates are not lapped, as is usual with steel-built ships, but are flush over the entire surface.

In addition, the frames and bulkheads are of extra large section, and the hull is of a type specially designed to offer the least possible resistance when it is being driven through ice-packs. Its length is two hundred and eighty-five feet, and there are thirty-two feet of moulded depth.

By means of this unusual ferry steamer, through sleeping cars can be run between the mainland and the island in summer and

298

winter alike, as well as through coaches and freight cars.

But it is in Newfoundland that the grim effects of winter are most noticeable. The railways here are laid on the narrow gauge of three feet six inches, and for the five-hundred-and-forty-mile journey on the main-line railway between Port Basque and St. John's, the time-table allows twenty-seven hours.

Fictional Time Schedule

This, in some of the winters known to Newfoundland, is a pure fiction, for the journey has been known to run into weeks. During the winter of 1941, one train was marooned by snow for seventeen days. A year later it became necessary to drop

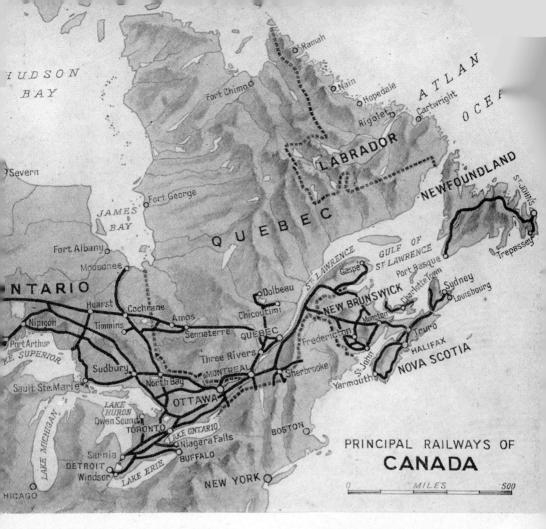

PRINCIPAL RAILWAYS OF
CANADA

food by parachute to passengers on an eastbound train which had been held up for days by a blizzard.

Rotary snow ploughs, complete with crews, are kept with steam up constantly in winter, and often precede the passenger trains over the worst sections. Reserves of coal and food also are stored at various strategic points along the line.

Once a freight train was completely lost for a week through being snow-bound, and the driver and fireman saved their lives in the arctic conditions in an astonishing manner. They drew the fire, drained all pipes on the engine that might freeze, and then crawled into the fire-box to keep themselves from freezing.

Every time the water in the boiler cooled to the point where there was danger of ice forming, they crawled out and lit a fresh fire to warm it up, after which they again drew the fire and returned to the warmth of the fire-box.

When eventually the storm abated, and the train was found by a search party, the engine had steam up, and all hands were accounted for and ready to make a fresh start.

Even in summer time, the lines may be breached by washouts, or it may be necessary in strong winds literally to chain the rolling stock to the rails. But even this is not always successful, for a freight train that was riding out a gale in this way once lost its guard's van, which was blown clean off the rails and carried right away.

ection of the cable-worked
ncline on the British-owned
Sao Paulo Railway, Brazil

CHAPTER FIFTEEN

ON THE ROOF OF THE WORLD
IN THE ANDES

A RAILWAY three miles high sounds like a fantastic dream, but in certain parts of South America, notably Peru, Bolivia and Chile, the dream becomes an astounding reality.

Here are the highest railways in the world, climbing mountains that are second only to those of Tibet. The track winds through deep gorges and along ledges cut from the wall of a sheer precipice, and a passenger can get a thrill merely by looking out at the scenery, thousands of feet below. In other places, the route lies across flat tablelands, with nothing save the rarefied atmosphere to indicate the altitude.

Surprisingly enough, most of these lines consist of normal track for smooth-tyred wheels, with no specialized mountain equipment, and at least two of the Peruvian main lines are laid on the standard gauge of four feet eight-and-a-half inches.

Famous Cable Railway

The Transandine is the only one that makes use of the rack-and-pinion principle, although there is one other with a mountain section that is worked by a wire cable. This is the famous cable railway of Sao Paulo in Brazil, one short section of which cost so much to build that it has been called the Golden Mile.

It is only a pygmy compared with the others, climbing a mountain rampart a bare half-mile in height, but the difficulties of construction were so great that many engineers despaired of ever building it at all.

The climb is achieved by means of a series of inclines, up and down which the coaches and trucks are raised and lowered by means of steel cables. From Santos to the foot, however, and again across the comparatively flat top of the tableland, ordinary locomotives are used.

There are nine inclines in all, built in sets of four and five as traffic increased.

The original inclines are each roughly a mile in length, with gradients of one-in-ten, and between each pair there is a bank-head, where the gradient flattens so that the trains can be transferred from one haulage rope to the next.

Balance Principle

They are worked on the tail-end system. That is to say, the train that is to be raised is attached to one end of the cable, and the train that is to be lowered is made fast to the other end. The principle of working, of course, is one of balance so that the descending train can help with its weight to pull up the trucks or coaches that are ascending. Three rails are laid on each slope, and these branch out into four in the passing loops in the middle of the journey. Above and below these loops, the centre rail is used by both ascending and descending trains.

When it was decided to double the route with a second set of inclines, more money was spent on the second set to ease the gradient to about one-in-twelve. Altogether, to complete these further five inclines, thirteen tunnels and sixteen bridges or viaducts were needed to carry the line through projecting spurs or across deep ravines. The old inclines are now confined to freight haulage, and all passenger trains, and any freight traffic that can be worked in, make use of the new set.

Trains Split Up

On reaching either the foot or the top of the new inclines, each train is divided into at least three parts. Passenger trains are passed on to the incline immediately on arrival, but freight stock accumulates both at the bottom and the top, so that all five inclines may be working with trains in each direction simultaneously.

The ropes on these are continuous, and at the engine-house each is passed four

GRADIENT AT BANK TOPS 1 IN 75

PASSENGER TRAIN ABOUT TO DESCEND

BOILER HOUSE

LIGHT STEAM LOCO WITH BRAKE GEAR

REVERSING SHEAVE

WINDING ENGINE BELOW TRACKS

CABLE ON PULLEYS

THREE RAILS ONLY

—R. B. WAY—

MIDWAY PASSING LOOP

EACH SECTION ABOUT 1½ MILES GRADIENT 1 IN 12½

times round a huge pulley fourteen feet in diameter. The working of the whole set is controlled from cabins on each bank-head, which are connected by telephone and electric signals with one another and with the engineer in charge of the hauling engine.

One remarkable feature of the equipment is the locomotive brake-van, the purpose of which is to grip the cable. These are quite small vehicles, but they have, in addition to the cable-gripping gear, sufficient power of their own to push any train the short distance necessary on the bank-heads to move them from one incline to the next.

One of the brakes is attached to the lower end of each set of trucks or wagons that is passed up or down the line. Each brake weighs thirty-one tons, and each individual haul, or set of wagons, is limited to a hundred and twenty tons, so that the greatest weight that can be permitted in any set of wagons or coaches is eighty-nine tons gross.

On each slope, the travelling time re-

quired is seven and a half minutes, and a further one and a half minutes is required for transferring a train from one incline to the next. Altogether, therefore, the travelling time from bottom to top, or top to bottom, works out at about forty-five minutes.

No other railway in the world conducts such an enormous volume of traffic over such gradients as the Sao Paulo Railway. On an average, six thousand tons of merchandise are moved up them daily, with sixty bogie coaches, carrying an average of three thousand passengers.

Slow but Comfortable

The rate of travel from Santos to Sao Paulo is not great, but no high average timing could be expected, with such manoeuvring of the trains. Usually, the run for the distance of fifty miles takes two hours. Very comfortable coaches are used on the passenger trains, including some three-car Diesel-electric trains with buffet accommodation, which maintain the fastest possible service between Santos and Sao

Paulo. The gauge of the railway is the wide one of five feet three inches, but most of the other lines in Brazil are on the metre gauge.

Brazil has not a great number of railways, however, owing to its dense tropical forests and the rivers which carry the bulk of the traffic. Its railways are found mainly on the coast, and although the country has over three million three hundred thousand square miles of area, its total railway mileage is under twenty thousand.

A very different state of affairs exists in Argentina. Here is to be found the ultra-modern city of Buenos Aires, with the most up-to-date railway system radiating

from it throughout the republic. From Buenos Aires, in fact, it is possible to cross the whole continent at this part by rail, in spite of the barrier of the mighty Andes.

Most of the Argentine railways, strangely enough, are British owned. The biggest system is that of the Argentine State Railways, which has nearly eight thousand route miles of line, divided between three gauges of five feet six inches, four feet eight-and-a-half inches and metre gauge. Next to this is the Buenos Aires Great Southern, with over five thousand miles of line, followed by the Central Argentine and various others. Actually, the route mileage in Argentina is roughly only twenty-four

DRAINAGE SUMP

TYPICAL BRIDGE

FREIGHT TRAIN ABOUT TO ASCEND

REVERSING SHEAVE ON RAIL TROLLEY

TENSION STATION BELOW TRACKS

TENSIONING WEIGHT IN PIT

SAO PAULO RAILWAY OF BRAZIL, cable railway that climbs a jungle cliff half a mile in height. To avoid the almost unmanageable weight of a cable five miles in length, the inclined section of track was divided into four separate lengths, one of which is shown in this explanatory drawing. Normal locomotives are uncoupled at top or bottom, and trains are passed up or down attached to cable-gripping brake-vans.

303

AERIAL RAILWAY AT RIO, suspension line to the top of the Sugar Loaf, mountain sentinel nearly fourteen hundred feet high that guards Rio de Janeiro Bay. The car is swung from twin cables and works in much the same way as Swiss lines of a similar type. It carries twenty passengers and stops at several platforms en route.

thousand, not so very much greater than that in Brazil, but the country is only a little more than a third of the size of Brazil, and the difference is the more noticeable.

It is said that the wide gauge of five feet six inches, on which most of the Argentine lines are laid, was decided more or less by accident at the time of the Crimean War. Some rolling stock and a couple of locomotives, built in Britain and intended for India, were diverted to the Crimea, and then, when the war was over, shipped on to Argentina. As these, of course, had been built for the wide Indian gauge, the Argentine track was laid accordingly. Other lines followed suit, and thus was settled for all time the main-line gauge of the Argentine Republic.

The Argentine Great Southern Railway

is one of the most enterprising in South America. It owns the magnificent Plaza Constitucion station in Buenos Aires, and handles from here over one hundred and twenty-five thousand passengers daily. In addition, it serves some of the most important ports, and at Bahia Blanca, four hundred miles south of the capital, has built the largest grain elevator in South America.

This great elevator is a monster of its type. As the grain wagons run into the dock area, they enter a shed over six hundred feet in length. Here there are six parallel tracks, and each track has eight unloading hoppers of a capacity of fifty tons each. The elevator itself has a storage capacity of eighty thousand tons, and can receive grain from the wagons at the rate of twelve hundred tons an hour. On the delivery side,

BLOWER FAN
FOR FURNACE AIR

SUPERHEATER
HEADER

REGULATOR

SAFETY
VALVES

FURNACE AIR
PRE-HEATER

BOILER
TUBES

AIR-BRAKE
PUMP

OIL-FIRED
FIRE-BOX

HOT-AIR DUCT
TO FIRE-BOX

RESERVE
WATER TANKS

FAN DRIVING
TURBINE GEARS

FUEL-OIL
BUNKER

MAIN
TURBINE

SWIVELLING
STEAM-PIPE

EXHAUST
FROM TURBINE

DRIVING
GEARS

R-S-WAY

DESERT CONDENSER OIL-FIRED LOCOMOTIVE, one of the most unusual steam
locomotives in existence. Its whole object is to use the same water again and again
on desert journeys. The smoke-box, in which there is no exhaust steam, contains a
fan instead of a blast pipe, and this draws air through the fire-box to make up for the
suction usually created by the exhaust. Further fans are provided on top of the articu-

FANS DRAW AIR THROUGH STEAM-TUBE BANKS

...ADER PIPE

STEAM TO CONDENSER TUBES

FAN-DRIVING SHAFTS

WATER IN CONDENSER DRUM

...OOLING ...IR

CONDENSER TUBES EXTENDING WHOLE LENGTH ON BOTH SIDES OF CAR

EXHAUST-STEAM COLUMN

CONDENSATE SUMP-PIPE

AIR DRAWN THROUGH CONDENSER

CONDENSER DRUM

REAR BOGIE

lated rear section, which is not a tender, to create a cooling draught through the batteries of steam pipes forming its sides. In these, the exhaust steam is cooled and condensed ready for reheating in the boiler. The method of propulsion is by a high-speed turbine which takes the place of the usual cylinders and motion, and drives the eight-coupled wheels on the rear section through gearing.

it can load as many as six ships at once at the rate of a thousand tons an hour each. Over twelve miles of conveyor and elevator belting are used, and there are in all one hundred and twenty conveyors.

The same railway also runs fast suburban trains in Buenos Aires, many of them capacious eight-car and five-car sets hauled by modern Diesel-electric locomotives. Its steam locomotives are, in the main, fitted for oil-burning, this fuel being more easily obtainable than coal.

Coal was so short, in fact, during the Second World War, that many of the Central Argentine locomotives were compelled to burn maize. Maize was plentiful,

but was not particularly successful as fuel, for at least thirteen times as much in bulk was required in comparison with coal.

This line, the Central Argentine, runs the famous Pan-Americano International express, which connects with through services to Peru and Bolivia, and is one of the few ways by which the continent may be crossed by rail. It is also the quickest route from South America to North America, for the steamer services north along the Pacific coast are much quicker than those which make their way round the Atlantic bulge of Brazil.

Forty-seven miles of the Central Argentine Railway is electrified out to Tigre from

TRESTLE BRIDGE OVER GORGE, Peruvian Central Railway. The new Carrion Bridge which was built in 1938 to replace an older type that has since been demolished. No other railway in Peru, the land of mountain lines, carries the passenger in a single day through such a variety of scenery or over so many rugged gorges. In some places the gradient is as steep as one-in-twenty-five, almost the steepest to be found on any main-line railway in the world where ordinary adhesion working is employed.

Cordoba Central station, sandwiched in between the other two, houses a metre-gauge line between two five-foot-six systems.

The most direct cross-continental journey from Buenos Aires is to Valparaiso, by way of the famous Transandine Railway. There can be no through-running of trains, however, as the Transandine is a metre-gauge railway, whereas the lines that connect with it on both sides of the Andes, both in Argentina and Chile, are of the wide five-foot-six gauge.

Land of Contrasts

The journey from coast to coast is one of strange contrasts. For hundreds of miles across the rolling pampas of the Argentine, there is not a solitary hill to be seen. Laying the track, in fact, was so simple that for a hundred and seventy-five miles the line is dead straight—the second longest straight line in the world.

Good use is made of this stretch by El Cuyano, the express which covers the six hundred and fifty miles between Buenos Aires and Mendoza in just over fifteen hours.

At Mendoza, however, the scenery changes, for the first ramparts of the mighty Andes come into view. These are the highest mountains in the world outside Tibet, although the Transandine Railway, which crosses them at this point and reaches a height of ten thousand feet, is not by any means the highest line in South America. It is at Mendoza that the change is made from broad gauge to metre gauge, and the real mountain journey begins.

Despite the gradients that the mountain train has to overcome, it is composed of

Buenos Aires, on the third-rail system, using direct current at eight hundred volts, while the Buenos Aires Western uses the same system for its twenty-three miles of electrified line. These are the only electrified sections in Argentina, although there are a number of Diesel-electric rail-cars and quite a few petrol-driven cars.

Three of the Buenos Aires terminals are side by side, those of the Central Argentine, the Buenos Aires and Pacific and the Cordoba Central. The Central Argentine station is the biggest, with a concourse nearly five hundred feet in length, and long-distance platforms as long as eleven hundred feet. Curiously enough, the

CLIMBING A MOUNTAIN WALL BY RAILWAY. Oroya line of the Peruvian Central, showing the switchback and three levels of track at El Vista. The train climbs this mountain rampart by running backwards and forwards along the zig-zag track, reversing at the end of each gradient and switching over to the one above. This railway has altogether twenty-one such reversing stations in a hundred and twenty miles of line.

STEEL GIRDERS AND SUN - BLEACHED ROCK, typical scenery through which the railways of Peru climb to their prodigious heights above the clouds. This is Sombay Bridge of the Peruvian Southern Railway. The main line starts from the port of Mollendo and runs through Puno to the famous Inca city of Cuzco. At Puno the line touches Lake Titicaca, which is two miles above sea-level and large enough to be an inland sea. Actually, the Peruvian Southern launched the first steamship on the lake. This vessel, the Inca, was first built in Hull and sailed round Cape Horn to Mollendo, where it was dismantled and taken by rail in sections to Puno, and there reassembled and relaunched on the lake, after one of the strangest journeys on record.

six coaches and includes comfortable saloon cars with a restaurant and kitchen. The motive power is a powerful tank locomotive equipped for both ordinary running and rack-and-pinion propulsion, for the Transandine line has gradients so severe that a rack is necessary, although it is the only line in all the mountain railways of South America where the rack method is employed.

The reason for the rack is that the Transandine has to make its climb in such a comparatively short distance. In a hundred miles it climbs nearly eight thousand feet, or roughly a mile and a half, and this is considerable in railway working, even although the mere figures do not sound very great.

On the other side of the range, beyond its summit, the railway has steeper gradients still, for here there is a descent of nearly eight thousand feet in less than fifty miles. This is on the stretch from Caracoles to Los Andes, down the gorge of the Aconcagua River and through some of the most wonderful scenery in the world.

On this side of the mountains, the trains are electrically hauled, and the locomotives are sufficiently powerful to mount even a gradient of one-in-twelve with a hundred-and-fifty-ton train at ten miles an hour.

At Los Andes comes the change-back on to broad-gauge track, now in the republic of Chile, and, again with electric haulage, the run to Valparaiso is finished.

The total journey is one of eight hundred and eighty-eight miles. The six hundred and fifty miles from Buenos Aires to Mendoza take a day and a night, and a whole day is spent in cutting through the Andes and running down to Valparaiso, a distance of two hundred and thirty-eight miles.

In all lofty mountain areas, there are times at which the dealings of Nature can be very violent, and the Andes are no exception to this rule. In 1934, there was such a violent disaster that for ten years the Transandine Railway ceased to operate.

The disaster was due to the bursting of a glacier, although, at the time, the burst was unnoticed. Indeed, it was only by aerial reconnaisance later that the cause was discovered. However, the glacier split and dammed up a high mountain valley, and behind the dam there accumulated an immense and undetected lake of ice-water.

In time the pressure of the water became more than the accidental dam could stand, and this in turn burst suddenly and set free a flood that roared down one of the valleys to the Mendoza River.

Mile after mile of the railway track was carried away, and massive steel girders were tossed from their bedstones as though they were corks. Some of them were found more than a mile from their original positions, and the damage was so extensive that funds were not available at the time for the necessary work of reconstruction. It was the traffic demands of the Second World War, felt even in South America, that caused the work to be put in hand, and the line was re-opened in 1944, when the Argentine section was taken over by the Argentine State Railways.

Future Plans

Various plans are now under consideration for the improvement of the line. One, which is to introduce three-car lightweight Diesel-electric trains, with comfortable seating and buffet accommodation, will probably be realized in the very near future, and is expected to cut the time of the actual mountain journey almost by a half. Another and more ambitious scheme, is to bore a thirteen-mile tunnel at a much lower level than the railway's present summit, and cut out much of the slow and grinding rack-and-pinion working.

Going north from here we come to what, in South America, are the real mountain lines. The summit of the Transandine Railway, ten thousand feet above sea-level, is considerably above that of any railway in Europe, but is dwarfed by comparison with the Antofagasta (Chili) and Bolivia, Southern Peruvian and Central Peruvian tracks. What is more, although the Transandine summit may eventually be lowered

by a tunnel, there can be no reduction in the lonely summits of these other lines, for they were built mainly to carry ore from the silver mines at these altitudes.

The record is held by the Antofagasta and Bolivia line, which reaches the prodigious height of fifteen thousand eight hundred and seventeen feet. The Peruvian Central Railway comes next with a summit only eleven feet shorter.

Altitude Effects

These altitudes are roughly equivalent to the height of Mont Blanc, the highest mountain in Europe, but the fact that they stand so much nearer the equator makes a considerable difference. Whereas the crest of Mont Blanc is above the perpetual snow-line for a great many months of the year, these altitudes in the Andes are well below it, and snow forms no obstruction to the working of the lines concerned.

There are no startling gradients. The trains climb steadily from the coast, mounting into the mist and clouds, and the climate changes gradually in a few hours from burning tropical heat to perpetual autumn.

Although it is gradual, however, the change from sea-level to twelve or fifteen thousand feet is not without its effect on passengers, and most trains carry oxygen cylinders for use in cases of mountain sickness. This is caused by the rarefied atmosphere, and can best be avoided by sitting still and breathing steadily.

Reversing Stations

By keeping to a normal track and smooth-tyred wheels, the Peruvian lines have been under the necessity in many mountain gorges of making use of the reversing station. It is only by this means that they succeed in climbing some mountain walls that look almost sheer, like the side of a house.

The reversing station is simple. When the track has been laid along a shelf cut from the wall of a canyon as far as possible, or as far as the builders desire, the lines are led back on to another shelf above it, and so on. Viewed from the opposite side of the gorge, therefore, a series of reversing stations has the appearance of a zig-zag line up the side of the mountain, and the

Carvalho Viaduct on the
Parana railroad, Argentine

trains run forward on one shelf and then back up the next. In roughly a hundred and twenty miles of line, the Peruvian Central has twenty-one such stations.

The Peruvian Central is, perhaps, the most astonishing of the high mountain railways in South America, both as an engineering achievement and as a scenic route. No other carries the passenger in a single day through such a variety of scenery, or ascends so many rugged gorges.

For long stretches, the line is at a gradient of one-in-thirty, steepening in places to one-in-twenty-five, almost the steepest in use for any locomotive working with smooth-tyred wheels. It crosses some remarkable viaducts, and is laid through tunnels at a height of more than two miles. The most notable of these is the Galera

Tunnel, driven through solid rock at a height of nearly sixteen thousand feet. The tunnel is nearly four thousand feet in length, and the difficulties of driving it in such a rarefied atmosphere were tremendous. As explained, even passengers sitting quietly in their coaches are sometimes affected by mountain sickness, and only those thoroughly acclimatized to the altitude could possibly be engaged as workers.

This line is sometimes known as the Lima-Oroya-Huancayo line, from the three main cities it serves. On leaving Lima, the capital, it runs first through a sub-tropical landscape of sugar-cane and cotton fields, but soon starts mounting the gorges by means of the reversing stations, and here the passenger is hard put to it to know whether he is going or coming.

The train is constantly backing part of

RAILWAY THREE MILES HIGH, station on the Peruvian Central line from Lima, capital of Peru, to Huancayo. This is, perhaps, the most picturesque and astonishing route of any railway in the world. Trains climb to over fifteen thousand feet above sea-level and oxygen is carried for the relief of passengers suffering from mountain sickness. The line is standard gauge and is worked by adhesion throughout.

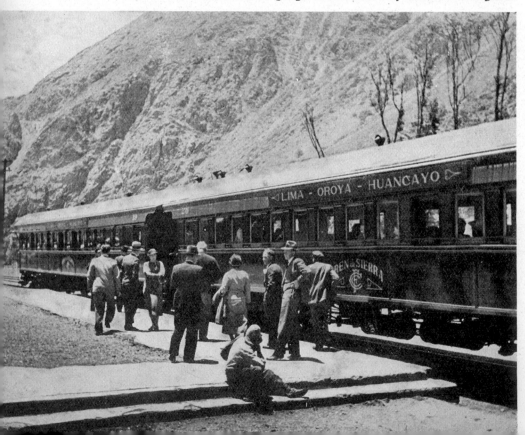

NEARING THE ROOF OF THE WORLD, train on a section of the Oroya, Peruvian Central line nearly sixteen thousand feet above sea-level, and level with the summit of Mont Blanc, highest mountain in western Europe. With the snow-clad mass of the Andes towering above it, the steam locomotive and its line of flat wagons approaches the highest mountain pass found on any railway. Owing to the nearness of the equator, even at this altitude the line is free of ice and snow in summertime.

the way up a mountain, and then running forward again, except where it crosses a viaduct and comes back on the other side of the gorge. Altogether it travels through sixty-five tunnels, totalling some five miles in length, and over sixty-one bridges or viaducts across the ravines. The viaduct at Verrugas is nearly six hundred feet in length, and two hundred and fifty feet above the bottom of the chasm it spans.

Much of the track is laid on a ledge cut from the side of a sheer cliff. In places, the Rimac River drops to a mere ribbon, thousands of feet below, yet still visible from the carriage windows.

At such altitudes, even the engine seems to suffer from the rarefied atmosphere. Its puffing becomes more like a hollow cough, echoing from the rocky walls of the canyon, and it battles its way through sudden hail-

storms and wild winds, very different from the warm sunshine it has left only a few hours before.

Most famous of all the bridges on this line is that across a deep gash known as the Infiernillo Canyon, or Gorge of the Little Hell. The train emerges suddenly from a tunnel to cross it, clattering for a moment on rails suspended high above the floor of the narrow gorge, then dives straight into another tunnel on the other side.

The highest station on the line is Ticlio, at fifteen thousand six hundred feet. This is the highest station in the world on a standard-gauge track, but is not the highest to be found. The record is held by Condor, a branch-line station on the line from Antofagasta to Bolivia, at an altitude of fifteen thousand seven hundred feet.

The Antofagasta and Bolivia line has the

315

distinction of running for five hundred miles across a vast tableland at a continuous altitude of not less than twelve thousand feet, truly on the roof of the world. It carries ore from the copper mines, and also serves the great nitrate area owned by Chile, handling as much as a million tons of nitrate in a single year.

Changing the Gauge

Part of this company's line—then owned by an independent railway—was formerly built to the narrow gauge of two feet six inches, but the difference in gauge was so troublesome that the company undertook the herculean task of converting both track and rolling stock to metre gauge. In their workshops at Mejillones, over sixty locomotives, a hundred coaches and two thousand wagons were reconstructed. For the gauge change itself, the hundred and eighty miles of narrow track were temporarily closed down, and, despite the immense difficulties of climate and altitude, the entire conversion was completed in six days.

Another of these amazing railways of the Andes is the Peruvian Southern, which begins its course from the port of Mollendo, and runs through Puno to the famous Inca city of Cuzco. At Puno, it touches the most extraordinary lake in the world, Lake Titicaca, which, although two miles above the sea, is large enough to provide a steamer trip of a hundred and twenty miles.

Steamer's Rail Trip

The railway itself was instrumental in getting at least one of the steamers to the lake, for the Inca, a craft over two hundred feet in length and driven by triple-expansion steam engines, was first of all built in Hull and then sailed round Cape Horn to Mollendo. Here she was taken to pieces, the various parts were loaded on trucks, and eventually put together again, high up in the mountains, and launched as a complete ship on the lake, one of the strangest journeys on record.

The mighty chain of the Andes extends northward through Panama to Mexico, and even beyond, and in Mexico, in addition to the railways and lines over flat country, there are more mountain railways, some of

them reaching summits as high as eight and nine thousand feet.

One of these is the Mexican Railway, which in the two-hundred-and-sixty-mile stretch from Vera Cruz to Mexico City, provides one of the most spectacular rail trips in America, sometimes known as the "rail trip of a thousand wonders."

For the first fifty miles from Vera Cruz, there is nothing more spectacular than plantations of bananas, tobacco and sugar-canes, but at Paso del Macho the oil-burning steam locomotive is replaced by an electric locomotive for the sixty-mile mountain journey that lies ahead. Gradients of one-in-twenty-five have to be surmounted, and with electric haulage it has been found possible to take trains weighing as much as nine hundred tons up these awe-inspiring grades.

Before the line was electrified, Fairlie articulated engines were employed on the mountain section, and even now, when the worst of the climbing is over, an oil-burning locomotive again takes charge.

Amazing Engineering

The greatest engineering feats on this line are found between Paso del Macho and Esperanza. In the Metlac Ravine, where the track is cut into the side of a cliff, there is a plate-girder bridge which is not only built to a sharp curve, but also slopes at a gradient of one-in-thirty-three. Trains are accompanied across it by a flagman on foot to ensure that speed is reduced to a walking pace.

Beyond Orizaba the track twists and turns in all directions, and at one point, from the rear observation platform, it is possible to see no fewer than six different sections of the track at once, far away in the valley below. The summit is reached at Acocotla, eight thousand three hundred odd feet above the sea, and for most of the journey it is possible to see the snow-mantled peak of Orizaba, at more than eighteen thousand feet, one of the highest peaks in the whole of North America.

There are higher railway summits in Mexico, however, than that at Acocotla. Another famous scenic line from Mexico City is that which passes over a summit level at Cima not far short of ten thousand feet,

PRINCIPAL RAILWAYS OF
**MEXICO AND
CENTRAL AMERICA**

0   MILES   500

also with gradients of one-in-thirty-three. Originally, the approach to Mexico City from the north was over another Cima summit, but this was by way of a line that was narrow gauge, and when it was altered to standard gauge the summit was cut out by the construction of a new and longer line which did away with some of the steepest gradients of the old route.

Modelled on United States

Mexican lines in general are worked in much the same kind of way as those of the United States. Their locomotives and rolling stock are very similar in appearance, and at least one important Mexican line, the Southern Pacific Railroad of Mexico, is a subsidiary of the great Southern Pacific of the U.S.A.

It enters Mexico at Nogales and runs down the Pacific coast for a considerable distance, turning inland finally to Mexico City. Through sleeping cars are run to Mexico City over this route from the famous Californian city of Los Angeles.

The largest railway system in Mexico is that of the National Railways of Mexico, which has nearly seven thousand miles of

line on standard gauge, and another twelve hundred odd miles on a gauge of three feet. Most Mexican railways, too, like those of South America, were built originally with British capital and experience.

At some distant date, perhaps, there will be complete rail communication down the whole length of the Americas, from the far north to the farthest south. Such communication is, of course, long since complete from Canada down to the south of Mexico, for the Pan-American Railway has been taken right down to the borders of Guatemala.

Here the Suchiate River has been bridged, and the Guatemalan railways linked with those of Mexico. Unfortunately, Guatemalan lines are built on narrow gauge, so at the moment transhipment is necessary.

Only a small beginning, therefore, has been made towards the Pan-American railway dream. In Central America railways are scarce, and below Panama, in Colombia and Ecuador, almost non-existent. But it is not impossible, even so, that through coaches will one day be running, not only from Panama, but even from New York to the lonely summits of the mighty Andes.

INDEX

PAGE NUMBERS IN ITALICS REFER TO ILLUSTRATIONS

318